PSYCHOANALYTIC TREATMENT OF SCHIZOPHRENIC AND CHARACTEROLOGICAL DISORDERS

PSYCHOANALYTIC TREATMENT OF SCHIZOPHRENIC AND CHARACTEROLOGICAL DISORDERS

by

L. Bryce Boyer, M.D.

and

Peter L. Giovacchini, M.D.

With a Contribution by

Edward D. Hoedemaker, M.D.

SCIENCE HOUSE, INC., NEW YORK

Library of Congress Catalog Card No. 66-29486
Manufactured in the United States of America

CONTENTS

Preface No. 1

In 1911 and 1914, Freud presented his formulations concerning the psychopathology of the psychoses. He stated that in psychosis there was a break with reality which consisted of a total decathexis of libido from objects of the external world and their mental representations. The libido then became attached to the self. Freud conceptualized that after the psychotic person had regressed to such a narcissistic phase, he gradually recathected mental representations of external objects in a distorted manner, usually through hallucinations and/or delusions. He believed the psychotic was unsuitable for psychoanalytic therapy because of an assumed incapacity to develop transference relations. Since then, clinical observations have indicated that the development of the schizophrenic state is not precipitous in at least a significant minority of cases, and that psychotic individuals develop intense transference relationships.

Freud was aware of a continuum of disorders ranging from psychoneuroses through characterological disorders and borderline conditions to unmistakable psychoses. After 1914, his own use of psychoanalysis as a method of treatment included patients who suffered from severe characterological disorders, and in at least one instance, overt psychosis. The literature of the past thirty-five years reveals that an ever-increasing number of psychoanalysts have used analytic techniques for the treatment of a broadening range of psychopathological conditions, including schizophrenic states, and have reported satisfactory results. Yet the majority of psychoanalysts have continued to abide by Freud's interdiction against the use of psychoanalysis as a method of treatment for people who suffer from borderline and schizophrenic disorders. Their conservatism has been reflected in training programs for psychoanalytic candidates. Some institutes in the United States fail to present varying viewpoints concerning the psychopathology and treatment of the psychoses. In consequence, psychoanalysts and candidates who are interested in exploring various methods of therapy for psychotic patients have had to study alone or in extracurricular groups.

In 1964, the Program Committee for the Biannual Meeting of the West Coast Psychoanalytic Societies, the Chairman of which was Dr. Sydney L. Pomer, arranged for a panel discussion entitled "Psychoanalytic Therapy of Schizophrenic Patients" and invited one member from each of the participating societies to take part, with Boyer acting as Chairman, and Giovacchini an invited panel member. Sufficient interest was evinced in the discussion before the meeting took place so that time allotted for the panel was extended to a full day, although the total congress lasted but a day and a half. The panel members, in addition to the contributors to this volume, were Doctors Bernard S. Brandschaft of the Los Angeles Psychoanalytic Society and Alfredo Namnum of the Asociación Psicoanalítica Mexicana. Dr. Steven Schwartz of the Southern California Psychoanalytic Society was to have contributed but was prevented because of illness. Brandschaft presented a thoughtful and most interesting account of his attempts to understand the psychopathology of the psychoses through application of Fairbairn's viewpoint and of his own experience in treating schizophrenics psychoanalytically. Namnum offered a scholarly review of the role of countertransference in the treatment of individuals who have schizophrenic disorders. Boyer presented a brief historical survey and spoke of his efforts in psychoanalyzing schizophrenics. Giovacchini spoke of the structuralizing effects of interpretation in the treatment of serious characterological disorders and borderline conditions. Hoedemaker gave the paper which is included in this volume. There ensued a lively discussion which included contributions from many psychoanalysts in the audience in addition to the panel members.

During the ensuing weeks, I (Boyer) received a number of requests from audience members to serve as editor of a book which would present the proceedings of the panel, requests which produced mixed reactions of pleasure and reluctance: pleasure because of the interest elicited in this approach to the understanding and treatment of these disorders, and reluctance because I was involved deeply in studying and reporting the data obtained from research in another area and because a larger work than merely an editorial task might be required.

Because of the aforementioned continuum of psychopathological disorders, it seemed advisable to include in a single volume remarks pertaining to the pathology and therapy of the entire range of conditions for which psychoanalysis has been considered to be inapplicable as a treatment method. Because I had limited my research to the application of psychoanalysis to the borderline states and the schizophrenias, I asked Giovacchini to join me in editorship of the proposed volume, because he had had a large experience in working with serious characterological states, some of whose victims belonged clinically to the borderline states. We soon decided that the panel contributions had dealt deeply with too few areas to delineate adequately the historical, theoretical, and clinical issues. At the same time, if we were to include all of the panel presentations, there would be unnecessary duplication of discussion of some issues. We decided to write a book together, and, most reluctantly, to include in it only the contribution of Hoedemaker, since his particular approach to the therapy of schizophrenia emphasized elements which were not included in our own work and writings.

We are deeply indebted to Brandschaft and Nammum, and trust we have done justice to their contributions in this volume, although we have not specifically spelled out the areas in which their stimulating ideas have enriched our own thinking.

L. BRYCE BOYER, M.D.

May, 1966

Preface No. 2

The recollection of my own and my colleagues' reactions shortly after beginning psychoanalytic practice brings to mind the confusion we had about the applicability of the psychoanalytic method. True, we had learned from our courses at psychoanalytic institutes, and the pedagogic value of our personal analyses could not be overestimated.

Since the limitations of psychoanalysis had been so clearly spelled out, we eagerly awaited the "analyzable" patient. How often did this type of patient present himself? And, if we were to discuss him at a postgraduate seminar, it was usually decided that his "classical" neurosis was only a superstructure for a basically psychotic core. These nosologic decisions were not rare even when control cases were presented in the classroom.

As the years went by, some of us became convinced that many patients could be treated psychoanalytically; the whole question of what is analyzable and the conceptual basis of the analytic process had to be scrutinized further. I can recall innumerable private conversations with colleagues who "confessed" that they were analyzing patients who traditionally would be considered too sick or not sufficiently motivated. Gradually, some of us became bolder and voiced our opinions at workshops and seminars. Although there was often considerable opposition, it usually led to clarification, and it was gratifying that there were many common meeting grounds.

Therefore, I was especially pleased to have been invited to present my views to the District Meetings of the Western Psychoanalytic Societies. I was astonished how well received the ideas emphasized at the panel were. It was both reassuring and exciting to know that there were analysts in other parts of the country asking similar questions and groping with identical problems.

The purpose of this book is to record systematically what has been discussed in the innumerable private conversations mentioned above. In many instances it is difficult to ascertain where a particular idea came from. So many of our opinions were impressionistic. The panel compelled us to organize our thinking and to recall the clinical data that led to our impressions. This can be a tedious task, but it has its compensations, for not only does this work clarify, but it stimulates further ideas. The stimulating effects of the panel were obvious to everyone, and, in turn, led to many more private conversations which, in time, will have to be put in an orderly form.

Our book begins with Dr. Boyer's introduction and review of the literature. The latter was a prodigious task, as is evidenced by the length of his bibliography. However, even here there were gratifications, since one was able to reach some conclusions from the study of

Freud's writings in particular, about why there was a reluctance to treat schizophrenia. A more extended view of object relations and a concept of libido that always includes an object, in terms of a developmental spectrum, might have made the absolute distinctions between the transference neuroses and the narcissistic neuroses superfluous.

Dr. Boyer then continues in essentially a clinical fashion and presents the results of his work with schizophrenic patients. He began treating these patients because he believed that the psychoanalytic method would be applicable. As yet there had not been much theoretical understanding of the various facets of the therapeutic process as it related to the treatment of psychotic patients. As mentioned above, the concept of transference as it occurs or does not occur in these patients was, and to a large measure still is, imperfectly understood. Most analysts were aware of countertransference elements, but how they might be utilized was not so much emphasized as their deleterious effects.

Dr. Hoedemaker next explores some of these countertransference elements, his presentation also being mainly clinical, but he begins, as does Boyer, to establish a theoretical rationale for his therapeutic technique. To recognize how to be comfortable as countertransference is stimulated and to utilize the patient-analyst interaction for the achievement of therapeutic benefit is, in my mind, the most interesting aspect of Hoedemaker's chapter.

One can discern a natural continuum from Boyer's observations to Hoedemaker's formulations. I wrote the next three chapters with the intention of maintaining this continuum. In Chapter Six, I am concerned with some of the theoretical features of the therapeutic process in order to distinguish what has been referred to as classical analysis from other types of therapy which are usually designated as supportive. In dealing with cases suffering from severe psychopathology, not necessarily schizophrenia, I attempt to review the applicability of the psychoanalytic method from a theoretical viewpoint. This, of course, is also pragmatic. In so doing, the various concepts that we have crystallized from our focus on ego processes are helpful to our understanding of the therapeutic action of psychoanalysis. We believe that the helpful supportive aspects of therapy are intrinsic to analysis and do not require any (or, as Boyer states, only a minimum of) extra-analytic maneuvers. The mechanism of interpretation and its synthesizing features as part of the intrinsic help analysis offers is also discussed from a conceptual frame of reference.

In the next chapter, this exploration is pursued further, and many of the criteria for analyzability are reviewed from an ego-psychological perspective. Many reactions that were once considered contraindications to analysis, such as the negative transference, are now reviewed in terms of their value to the therapeutic interaction.

Finally, and this is an area which has received very little attention, the psychic processes occurring within the analyst as he is analyzing are focused upon. The limitations of analysis have been stressed, but one also discovers that the analytic attitude is often unwarily abandoned. Concentrating on external realities, for example, may shift the therapeutic focus so that the spontaneous elaboration of fantasy is hindered and the unfolding of the transference is so contaminated that further analytic activity becomes impossible. The role of the analyst's primary and secondary processes is also stressed in his understanding of the patient's intrapsychic state and the communication of insight (interpretation).

Naturally, in undertaking a project where the applicability of therapeutic technique is explored from a clinical and theoretical perspective, one cannot expect universal agreement. The reader will note occasional criticism by one author of some of his colleagues' ideas. During the panel discussion, the format was purposely set up so there would be discussion and criticism. Here it was felt that each discussion had a theme of its own which should be explicitly stated rather than being merely a point of departure from a critique of the previous paper. However, disagreement is to be expected and eventually the therapist will choose the conceptual system that offers the best clinical advantages.

It is impossible to thank everyone who was instrumental in writing this book. We have received considerable support and encouragement from our colleagues around the United States. The private conversations the authors found so helpful were held mainly in our home areas, the West and Midwest, but our Eastern colleagues' interest at conventions and workshops was also stimulating and reassuring. We wish especially to thank Dr. Gene Borowitz and Dr. Alfred Flarsheim for their painstaking reading of our manuscripts and their innumerable suggestions, both conceptual and editorial, which we did our best to incorporate into the text.

PETER L. GIOVACCHINI, M.D.

May, 1966

CHAPTER ONE

Introduction

L. Bryce Boyer, M.D.

The orientation of modern clinicians generally is that the technical procedures developed by psychoanalysts for the treatment of the transference neuroses are not applicable to the narcissistic neuroses, including the group of schizophrenias. We hope to demonstrate, on the basis of a review of clinical and theoretical data, that the psychoanalytic model, one designed for the transference neuroses, may be the psychotherapeutic method of choice for a large number of individuals whose diagnoses fall within the continuum of states which are included in the group of schizophrenias.

In this first chapter, a number of related subjects will be discussed conjointly: (1) the importance of the schizophrenias from the standpoint of social waste and personal suffering; (2) the historical development of attitudes concerning the genesis of these disorders; (3) the difficulties involved in diagnosis; and (4) an introductory statement about the psychoanalysis of the schizophrenias.

Throughout history, perhaps the most bewildering

and challenging of all the abnormal behavioral syndromes have been those which are now included in the group of schizophrenias. The social significance of such disorders is vast. Today, in the United States, schizophrenia is considered to be the most important of the major psychoses. Individuals who are diagnosed to be schizophrenic constitute 20 percent to 25 percent of first admissions to hospitals for the treatment of mental disorders. Because of the relative youth of patients when first hospitalized and the length of their hospital stay, the group makes up some 55 percent of the residual population in such institutions (Arieti 1964; Fein 1958; Goldhammer and Marshall 1949; Gorman 1956; Hoch and Zubin 1961; Landis and Page 1938; Malzberger 1940). It is well known that psychosomatic disturbances sometimes mask psychotic conditions and probable that a significant minority of patients who are treated in public institutions for chronic physical and psychosomatic illnesses are afflicted with schizoid conditions.

Numerous observers have held that psychotic illnesses increase as cultural conditions become more complex. Thus, Carothers (1948, 1953), Devereux (1939), E. Faris (1937), R. Faris and Dunham (1939), Opler (1956, 1959), Rose (1955), Seligman (1929), and Sachs (1947), believing that fewer serious mental disturbances were found among isolated nonliterate and nonindustrialized societies than among those which had experienced continuous contact with European civilizations, concluded that cultural homogeneity and intimate social contacts protect against the development of schizophrenias. However, other students have noted that valid epidemiological surveys have yet to be conducted among primitive cultures, and Beaglehole (1940) remarked that structural social complexity is not necessarily related to subjective complexity. Winston (1935), using data collected by Mead (1939), found a high incidence of psychosis among some nonliterate peoples. Malzberger (1940) believed there has been an actual increase in the incidence of psychoses in the United States, but Elkind and Taylor (1936), Goldhammer and Marshall (1949), and Winston (1935) stated there was insufficient evidence to indicate that mental disorders rise in incidence with increased complexity of civilization. More recently, Rin, Chu, and Lin (1965) have demonstrated in one Taiwanese area that the severity of psychophysiological changes parallels certain stresses of socioenvironmental milieux and rapid culture alterations. However, schizophrenic disturbances appear to have approximately equal prevalence in those areas of the world in which reliable epidemiological surveys have been conducted. (See Cawte 1964, 1964a; Cawte and Kidson 1964; Rin and Lin 1962).

Although adequate diagnostic surveys have yet to be done, clinicians and social workers estimate in private conversations that perhaps 10 percent of the population of the United States and Western Europe suffer from schizoid states or from apparently neurotic disabilities which deteriorate periodically into overt schizophreniform episodes, most of which do not require hospitalization. Anthropological descriptions of the characteristics of individuals in various culture areas the world over suggest that among some groups schizoid personalities are typical (Bateson and Mead 1942; Fortune 1932).

Numerous clinicians have found the current methods

used in establishing diagnoses to be deficient (Astrup, Fossum, and Holmboe 1962; Hoch and Zubin 1961; Schumacher 1963). They stress especially the difficulties in determining whether individual patients suffer from schizophrenic states. Partly as a result of confusions to be found in present classification standards, there has been a tendency toward diagnostic nihilism. As a consequence, various psychiatrists have recommended complete revisions of nosological philosophies and criteria (Pokorny 1965). Some psychoanalysts have suggested that the use of the word "schizophrenia" be discarded and that regressive reactions be described in terms of which ego and superego functions are pathologically distorted and to what degree (see Chapter Seven).

The responses of military and civilian populations to the varying stress conditions produced by World Wars I and II demonstrated that many people who previously had functioned adequately underwent regressive responses which included "schizophrenic" symptoms. When the manifestations of such states responded quickly to combinations of altered environment, rest, medicine, and physical treatments such as electroplexy and insulin shock therapy, they were given nonspecific labels. Thus words like "battle fatigue" found their way into the charts of military personnel, whereas a variety of names were ascribed to the regressive responses of civilians. We now have many diagnostic terms with poorly defined meanings such as pseudoschizophrenic neurosis, pseudoneurotic schizophrenia, ambulatory schizophrenia, borderline schizophrenia, borderline states, latent psychosis, schizoid personality disorder, and psychotic character. *Frequently the label depends upon the theoretical orientation of the diagnostician and sometimes a name is applied which reflects social or economic requirements, rather than the psychopathological state involved.* Although few articles in the literature deal specifically with such reactions, patients who have been diagnosed to be neurotic undergo transient psychotic episodes during psychoanalysis (Reider 1957; Romm 1957; Wallerstein 1965). When such states respond favorably to further analytic or nonanalytic treatment, they are sometimes called "transference psychosis," but if they persist, it is usual for the analyst to decide he made a faulty diagnosis and to apply one or another of the labels mentioned above.

The difficulties involved in the diagnosis of mental disorders in general and the schizophrenias in particular lie in three general areas: (1) the underlying causes of psychopathology have not been defined clearly; (2) no unanimity exists concerning the differentiation between normal and abnormal behavior (Devereux 1956), and (3) there is a continuum of psychopathological states, at one end of which lie the transference neuroses and at the other, the narcissistic neuroses. Such areas of complexity can be separated arbitrarily for purposes of exposition. We shall deal first with the lack of agreement concerning the basic causes of psychopathology.

From time immemorial, mankind has been concerned profoundly with aberrant human behavior and particularly with the manifestations of psychosis. Men have sought to understand its origins and striven to develop rational therapeutic measures. The ancients, as do members of today's nonliterate and nonindustrialized societies, ascribed abnormal conditions to a variety of agents, both natural and supernatural (Cameron 1964;

Frank 1964; Zilboorg 1931; Zilboorg and Henry 1941). Such causes include noxious environmental influences, hereditary taint, organic disease, demoniacal possession, and loss of mind or soul. The treatments employed to cure illnesses which were thought to result from natural causes have included medical and surgical procedures, purging, bleeding, cold-water shocks, and removal of supposedly offending organs. Therapy for abnormal behavior which was ascribed to supernatural causes has included exhortation, incantation and religious ritual, the use of medicines with allegedly magical effects, and various operative procedures, such as craniotomies which were designed to permit the egress of evil spirits. During various periods and among widely differing cultures, capital punishment has been used, as in the killing of psychotic people who were called witches (Zilboorg 1935; Boyer 1964).

The predominant viewpoint of nineteenth-century psychiatrists was that all of the disorders manifesting psychological aberrations resulted from neuropathological conditions which were the products of inherited, constitutional, and/or degenerative states. The majority of modern psychologists divide psychotic states into two large groups. In the first are those psychoses which are attributable to toxic states or conditions in which neurological abnormalities can be demonstrated. In the second, severe psychopathological disorders are thought to result from the influences of unfavorable environmental milieux which combine with hereditary or otherwise acquired organic abnormalities. The influences of nonsalutary interpersonal relations on the growing human are held to be of paramount importance in the genesis of psychoses of the second group. A minority of psychologists believe that the role of organic states is exclusively determinant. Arduous and continuous investigations have attempted to evince toxic or other organic origins for the schizophrenias. Thus far, no convincing evidence indicates such causes to be present or particularly relevant to our understanding of the psychotic process.

In regard to genetic factors, too, the issues are clouded. Kallmann (1950) stated that schizophrenia appears to be genetically specific, but Gregory (1960) averred that the extent and nature of possible genetic elements remains uncertain. Malis (1959:6) wrote, "The only conclusion that may be deduced from the work dealing with the role of heredity in the development is thus that an endogenous predisposition . . . is by no means an essential factor in its causation." Recently, Smith (1965) postulated a "genetic error" as an etiological factor in the causation of "nuclear schizophrenia." He hypothesized the "error" to be at the thalamic level and to interact with psychological and sociological factors to produce the clinical illness. Lidz *et al.* (1962) and Rosenthal (1963) and his co-workers demonstrated environmental complexities which cause one to question seriously the stand of those who believe that genetic factors are predominantly causative.

According to Heath (Arieti 1964), schizophrenia is a disorder of metabolism and hinges on the formation of a substance he and his collaborators have isolated and named taraxein. Many chemical compounds have been thought to engender symptoms similar to those of schizophrenia. Examples are bulbocapnine, which brings about in experimental animals a state like catatonia, and mescaline and lysergic acid which cause thought and perception disorders in humans, similar to those observed in schizophrenia.

As was noted earlier, psychoses were ascribed to both organic and psychological causes from the earliest times. Although in recorded history the importance of emotions and interpersonal relations has been acknowledged implicitly and explicitly in the development of syndromes of aberrant human behavior, no comprehensive psychological theories were developed. Modern abnormal psychology can be said to have its origin in the eighteenth century, when Mesmer demonstrated that aberrant behavior can be intentionally induced and removed through the influence of one person on another. His concept of animal magnetism stirred much interest, but his new technique resulted in general hostility toward himself and his method (Goldsmith 1964). In the middle of the nineteenth century, mesmerism was reintroduced under the term hypnosis and its effects were studied especially by Charcot, Bernheim, and Janet. However, principally because of the limited scope of the theoretical originality of those investigators, their influence on the development of psychology has declined steadily. As will be discussed in Chapter Two, Freud's first interest in purely psychological explanations of behavior probably stemmed from his contacts with hypnotists. As is commonly known, no other person has influenced the development of psychology so profoundly as Freud, and psychological theories concerning the genesis of schizophrenia probably stem more from his contributions than those of any other investigator. Although Freud concluded eventually that the theory of behavior is best understandable in terms of psychology, he never gave up the belief that the link between psychoanalysis and physico-chemico-biological processes would be found ultimately. Nevertheless, Freud's studies were extended beyond his intentions by a group of investigators who eventually disregarded the biological elements of human behavior (see Chapter Three). The nineteenth-century viewpoint that the group of schizophrenias was attributable to genetic, constitutional, and/or degenerative factors was followed in the twentieth century by the antithetical viewpoint that it was the product solely of faulty socialization processes.

Today, the argument concerning the relative importance of organismal and behavioral development is considered to be essentially irrelevant by most observers (Bateson 1960; Ham 1963; Hinde 1954; Jores and Freyberger 1960; Lorenz 1952; Money 1963; Will 1961). Research in schizophrenia proceeds at a variety of levels: chemical, genetic, neurological, psychological, and sociological (Astrup, Fossum, and Holmboe 1962; Handlon 1960; Hoskins 1946; Kline 1957; Malis 1959; Malamud and Overholzer 1958; McKnight 1958; Smythies 1963).

It was stated earlier that one of the major areas of difficulty in establishing diagnoses was that no unanimity exists concerning the differentiation between normal and abnormal behavior. Let us now consider this problem.

The approaches to defining normal and abnormal behavior and thinking range between polar opposites. Cultural relativists define normality strictly within the context of cultural functionalism, a position which states that conformation with the average expectable behavior of the group is judged as normal (Ackerknecht

1943). The following data illustrate some difficulties which are inherent in this viewpoint.

Among the Balinese, the tendency of the average person to be withdrawn and to undergo trancelike states is well known (Bateson and Mead 1942; Belo 1960; Gill and Brenman 1959; Montagu 1951; Van Wulfften Palthe 1940; Boyer 1964a). Presumably due to Balinese social structure and socialization processes, the typical culture member has a personality pattern which could be considered to fit within the group of schizophrenias in other cultures, but the Balinese are fully functioning members of their society.

The Apache of the Mescalero Indian Reservation who would be considered to be most representative of his group by his culture mates has personality traits which, viewed from the standpoint of Western psychiatry, warrant the diagnosis of character disorder with attributes of the hysterical personality and the impulse neuroses (Boyer 1964a). Psychotic manifestations of these Apaches almost always portray schizophrenic characteristics. According to the cultural relativists, the typical Apache would be considered normal.

At the opposite pole is the orientation of the adherents of Freudian thinking who consider mental health and illness rather than normality and abnormality. Mental health is defined as mature personality development, and depends upon the degree of development of ego functions and of differentiation of ego from the id.

The following clinical example illustrates exquisitely the difference between the two viewpoints. For some eight years, which included almost two years of actual field work, Boyer (1964a) cooperated with anthropologists and psychologists in a study of the interactions among social structure, socialization patterns, and personality organization of the Apaches. His principal research method was to conduct investigative interviews in a psychoanalytically oriented psychotherapeutic situation. It was learned that culturally determined fears and phobias are universal among these Indians. An astute Chiricahua man suffered from nightmares and phobias and requested treatment. During some 165 interviews, interpretations related to dependency and unresolved oedipal problems led to his being freed of his presenting symptoms. Thereafter, he was unafraid of ghosts, witches, the dead, and various cultural bogies. Viewed from the standpoint of the cultural relativists, he had become abnormal, although he had become healthier from the viewpoint of those who follow the psychoanalytic orientation.

Whether an individual administrator or clinician subscribes to the orientation of the cultural relativists or that of the followers of Freud may be of great importance to his decision regarding the diagnosis and care of a suffering person, but when it comes to the practical disposition of a single case, the theoretical stand taken by the administrator or clinician may have little practical relevance. Every major society contains a number of differing although usually overlapping cultural groups, most of which include members of varying ages. In the United States, there is a multiplicity of ethnic and religious subcultures, each of which has, in addition to elements which share attributes with the general society, individual patterns as regards social structure and socialization. The characteristics of behavior and the patternings of mental illness within cultural groups are well known (Durkheim 1897; Montagu 1961). Additionally, the economic group from which the person derives influences heavily his *Weltanschauung* and the nature of his emotional and/or mental disorders (Hollingshead and Redlich 1958). Furthermore, varying culture groups have instituted differing methods for handling their disturbed members. Montagu (1961:19) wrote, "In some cultures mental illness is institutionalized, by which is not meant that the individual is put into an institution as a sick man, but rather that he and his behavior are incorporated into the society as a normal part of it."

The Apache culture, now a subculture of the major society of the United States, is characteristic. The typical member, as has been noted, is disturbed, but he functions within the framework of his group's expectations. The individual Apache whose behavior is sufficiently deviant from the norm of the group in a manner which disturbs others is treated, at least initially, by a shaman, whose main purpose is to remove transiently the individual symptoms which have distressed the suffering person or other culture members. To the Apache, further treatment of an "insight" nature is thought to be irrational. Eaton and Weill (1953) have demonstrated that the Hutterites have relatively few schizophrenics and many manic-depressives. Depression among them appears to be an intensification of a culturally supported normative trend. The Hutterites internalize their problems and, under stress, are more apt to be antiself than antisocial. The individual submits to community expectations of personal guilt and pacifism. The Hutterites provide within their social framework functional roles for their mentally ill and look askance at treatment from outsiders. Persons from low economic groups generally view insight therapy as nonhelpful. The attitude of the suffering individual and his relatives from such cultural and economic groups is that of the cultural relativists. Whatever the viewpoint of the administrator or clinician, people from such subcultures and economic strata would usually be loath to undertake prolonged treatment, even were it available.

The age of the suffering person also plays an important part in influencing diagnosis and recommended therapy. Treatment is seldom sought among some groups for children and adolescents whom most psychiatrists would judge to be severely ill but whose behavior does not unduly disturb their parents or others. The same can be said for deviant behavior which is associated with stress states, such as childbirth and terminal illness.

As stated previously, the third major difficulty involved in establishing a diagnosis of schizophrenia exists because there is a continuum of psychopathological states lying between the transference and the narcissistic neuroses. Freud conceptualized the psyche as an organ of the body and used the word "neurosis" to indicate a disorder of the psyche, although the use of the word "psychosis" would appear to have been more consistent. He subdivided neuroses into: (1) transference neuroses, by which he meant those in which there is a capacity to transfer feelings or affects to another person; transference neurosis is an alternate word for psychoneurosis, and such a state constitutes a psychopathological syndrome, characterized in the main by special combinations of anxiety, compulsions, conversion symptoms, obsessions, and phobias; (2) narcissistic neuroses, in which libido is bound to the self and is not subject to "natural displacement" to another person. The "psychogenic psychoses" are narcissistic neuroses.

Some clinicians, particularly certain neo-Freudian psychoanalysts and their enthusiastic cross-disciplinary followers, have included all of the schizophrenias among the psychogenic psychoses. Others divide the schizophrenias on the basis of their usual clinical courses into two major categories: (1) those which prove refractory to treatment and have a progressive, chronically deteriorating course are named process or nuclear schizophrenia; in general, this group are thought to be of exclusively organic origin; (2) those which lose their overt manifestations with or without treatment, although symptoms may recur episodically, are called psychogenic schizophrenia. Those who so divide the schizophrenias have considerable difficulty in classifying certain chronic, barely progressive or nonprogressive schizoid states and severe, recurrent conditions from which patients apparently recover their prepsychotic personalities. Implicit in the earlier discussion is the modern consensus that there may be no exclusively psychogenic psychoses but instead only psychopathological disorders in which the psychological causes are probably more important than contributory organic tendencies.

Psychoanalysts have long been aware of the difficulty in distinguishing the psychoneuroses from the schizophrenias. Freud's ideas and those of his followers will be outlined in the second and third chapters. Concerning Freud, suffice it to note here that although he considered the use of the classical technique for the treatment of the schizophrenias to be contraindicated, he used it in the treatment of a number of patients who have been rediagnosed as schizophrenic by several later investigators. The literature contains fragments of case histories which reveal that psychoanalysts have unwittingly undertaken the analyses of individuals whom they have diagnosed as neurotic but subsequently discovered schizophrenic symptomatology; some such analyses were continued with or without technical modifications and reached apparently successful conclusions.

The point of view of psychoanalysts has been that psychoneuroses are products of regressive operations which defend individuals from anxieties stemming from unresolved oedipal conflicts. The hysterias have been considered to exemplify most graphically this hypothesis and treatment was directed in the past specifically toward the analysis of neurotic symptoms in terms of genital sexual components. Freud (1909) considered the hysterical attack to be the equivalent of coitus. However, apparently accurate interpretations of the sexual components of hysterical symptoms unmasked intense unresolved oral conflicts (Marmor 1953) and psychotic regression sometimes took place during the analysis of a "classical" hysteric. Some few therapists continued to use the standard technique and learned that, subsequent to the analysis of the psychotic episode, reexamination of the oedipal conflicts led to cure. Today, analysts are more reluctant to make a diagnosis of hysteria than was formerly true, having become more acutely aware of the continuum between the hysterias and the schizophrenias.

The 24th International Psycho-Analytical Congress in 1965 was devoted to a reevaluation of the obsessional neurosis. With few exceptions, each presentation which depicted some phase of the analysis of a diagnosed obsessional patient was followed by a discussion of the intermixture of neurotic and schizoid components which were combined in his psychopathology. Not infrequently, a debate ensued concerning whether the patient should be called neurotic or psychotic. The same problem is found in making a clear diagnosis of patients who in past years would have been labeled unhesitatingly psychoneurotic of any of the usual types.

Whereas in the early days of psychoanalysis, the disorders of patients were separated into transference and narcissistic neuroses, this classification was gradually found to be inadequate. In part, this was because it was discovered that, contrary to Freud's early judgment, schizophrenic patients were found to be extremely capable of developing transference relationships, although their manifestations are often quite different from those of neurotic patients (Searles 1963). Additionally, it was gradually discovered that underlying the neurotic symptoms lay a personality substratum in which pathological traits were built into the character (Adler 1917; Jones 1938). Frequently the patient was found to be unaware of having a personality distortion; his pathological character traits were largely egosyntonic. Progressively over the years, the term *character neurosis* has come to have a nosological value. Today, many analysts use the term *neurotic*, which stresses the egodystonic symptomatology, less and less frequently, and the term *character neurotic*, which emphasizes the personality structure, more and more often. At first, the term *neurotic character* was used to describe a position between the healthy and the clear-cut neurotic personality, although Alexander (1929) stressed the impulsive and compulsive components. Then the character neuroses were differentiated according to their dominant characteristics and such terms as *hysterical, impulsive, obsessive, paranoid,* and *psychotic character* (or *personality*) *disorder* have become progressively more popular as nosological terms (see Chapter Seven).

Whereas psychoanalysis in the past was aimed primarily at symptom removal, it has become more generally employed for character modification. Such alteration is thought to result from interpretation and working through of the transference neurosis, which has a different nature in each of the types of character disorder. With the growing emphasis on character analysis, psychoanalyses have gradually become longer and the personality structures of patients are found to regress in the transference relationship to a point where some of their thinking patterns, object relations, and defensive manifestations are not confined to the analytic situation; in such instances, most analysts are inclined to alter the original diagnosis from neurosis or character disorder to one or another of the psychogenic psychoses, usually one of the group of schizophrenias. To judge from case fragments in the literature and from informal discussions, some analysts change the diagnosis when the patient manifests some indefinite quantity of primitive thinking. It may be argued that such instances of apparent psychotic regression are not genuine but are artificially induced and therefore spurious. With the present state of nosological confusion, such a position is difficult to maintain. The classification of patients as transference or narcissistic neurotics appears to be untenable in a large number of instances, perhaps in all cases.

It would appear, then, that although formal teaching of psychoanalysis continues to recommend psychotherapy of a "supportive" or covering nature for the narcissistic neuroses and classical analysis for the transference neuroses, operationally these technical recommendations are followed irregularly. This is inevitable, since the concepts of transference and narcissistic neurosis are so hazy. It seems also that the lack of uniformity of treatment procedures depends upon a growing judgment that the classical technique of psychoanalysis has broader application than is generally recognized publicly. One of the most interesting phenomena to be observed in discussions at psychoanalytic meetings is that the critics who are most adamant in their stand that psychoanalysis is not applicable without gross modifications for the treatment of patients suffering from one of the group of schizophrenias are those who either (1) have never attempted knowingly to treat such patients by the classical method, or (2) have altered their therapeutic procedures by introducing extensive parameters or abandoning psychoanalysis altogether when patients originally diagnosed to have neuroses or character disorders have begun to regress seriously in treatment.

SUMMARY AND COMMENT

The schizophrenias probably cause more social waste and personal suffering than any other group of psychopathological conditions. They comprise a wide range of psychical disorders, including acute and chronic psychotic states which are easily diagnosed and a continuum of conditions which are scarcely distinguishable from severe psychoneuroses, characterological disorders, and psychosomatic illnesses. Although physical and chemical treatments have been devised which are used with some success in restoring the acutely psychotic individual to his previous psychosocial level of adjustment, such therapeutic methods have proved to be ineffectual in reconstituting the personality structure of the schizophrenic and ensuring his psychical maturation.

There is no unanimity among students of the schizophrenias concerning their causation. Some observers believe that hereditary and/or other organic abnormalities are involved. They can be successfully treated only through the use of chemical or physical agents which have yet to be discovered; psychotherapeutic methods at best are palliative. Another group of observers consider the schizophrenias to result from unfavorable interpersonal and social influences and consider whatever pathological organic states may be found to result from as yet undelineated psychosomatic mechanisms. They think that psychotherapeutic methods alone can be used to alter the personality of the schizophrenic in such a manner that he can learn to be pleased with himself and live successfully and productively within the social group. The majority of students, including the present authors, deem an interplay among the myriad potential influences of heredity and socialization to be causative. Some who hold this view, however, believe that such an interplay has led to a psychosomatic state which is irreversible. They agree with the organicists that psychotherapeutic methods can be employed to alleviate some of the symptomatology but not the underlying, ill-defined, so-called schizophrenic process which is part of the psychosomatic disruption. They believe that the patient's environment must be altered so that he will have a minimum of external conflictual, anxiety-provoking stimuli and that psychotherapeutic measures should be limited to vaguely defined supportive and suppressive measures. Others of the third group are more optimistic. They hold that psychotherapeutic steps can be used to reverse the schizophrenic process.

To date, psychotherapeutic methods which are based on psychoanalytic principles are the only ones which have shown promise in reconstituting personality structure. The psychoanalytic method was devised by Freud and his followers to treat individuals through analysis of transference relations. Interpretation is the ultimate technical procedure which is effective in such analysis. Freud stated that some people are incapable of developing a transference relationship and, therefore, refractory to psychoanalysis. He categorized psychopathologies into two large groups, the transference neuroses, comprising illnesses in which transference can develop, and the narcissistic neuroses, constituting those states in which transference relationships do not develop or are so tenuous that their analysis is impossible. Freud was aware of the continuum of psychopathological states which range between the transference neuroses and the narcissistic neuroses, but he took the conservative position that the psychoanalytic method is applicable solely to patients whose illnesses were clearly definable as transference neuroses.

Freud's classification system was based on clinical observations made during the theoretical period preceding introduction of the revised anxiety theory and the formulation of the structural hypothesis. It has long since been learned that individuals who are incapable of developing transference relationships must be very rare, and recently Freud's original theoretical position concerning the narcissistic neuroses has been questioned by an increasing number of analysts (Arlow and Brenner 1964). The transference relationships of hypothetically simple neuroses are relatively easily understood and are characterized largely by manifestations of thinking and behavior which are to be found in individuals who have traversed the oral stage of psychosexual development with only minor psychical injury. The psychoses reflect the effects of severe psychical traumata during narcissistic and oral phases and are characterized by a predominance of primary process mentation, primitive defenses, and immature handling of affects. In the continuum of states lying between the neuroses and the psychoses, there are all gradations and combinations of the capacity to use secondary process thinking, the maturity of defenses, and the stability of affective attachments.

A variety of psychotherapeutic procedures appear to alleviate psychopathological symptoms and there are a sufficient number of so-called spontaneous recoveries of both obvious psychotic and psychoneurotic symptomatologies that some observers have developed a nihilistic viewpoint concerning the value of psychotherapy (Eysenck 1965). Psychoanalysts use a different yardstick concerning the value of psychotherapy. In general, they aim at more than mere symptom alleviation and believe that personality modification is necessary for lasting benefit. While some continue to favor the use of the diagnostic term *psychoneurosis* for most of their patients, they know that in the main they are treating personality disorders underlying the neurotic symptoms.

As has been stressed, the personality disorders make

up the continuum of states which lie between Freud's transference and narcissistic neuroses. Consequently, psychoanalysts face an enigma which has been discussed frequently, namely the determination of the limits of applicability of the psychoanalytic method. For many years, some analysts have continued to use the classical method or have added minor modifications when patients who were diagnosed as neurotic regressed during their treatment; an increasing number of reports in the literature reflect this trend. A few analysts have intentionally used the classical technique with very few alterations for the treatment of psychotic patients or patients with severe characterological problems. Their results have been encouraging.

While it is important that research continue into the causes and treatment of the schizophrenias, the standpoint of this book is that psychoanalysis has more to offer for this group of disorders than has been recognized. We believe that more parameters have been employed in treatment than are necessary and even suspect that sometimes it has been the introduction of parameters which has resulted in some of the severe regressions seen during psychoanalysis. We have reached our bias as a result of our clinical experience which has suggested that even patients who are commonly diagnosed to suffer from borderline or frankly psychotic disturbances are susceptible to treatment with psychoanalysis which includes few parameters.

We think that a review of the psychoanalytic literature combined with our own work supports the hypotheses that: (1) the so-called schizophrenic process probably is reversible in some instances and its reversibility depends upon the possibility of reconstitution of the character structure; (2) such reconstitution can result from psychoanalytic treatment; and (3) Freud's formulations concerning the psychological aspects of the genesis of the group of schizophrenias needs revision. We think that all of the characterological disorders are understandable within the framework of the structural theory, and that Freud's objections to the psychoanalytic treatment of psychoses is no longer theoretically valid within the framework of the structural hypothesis. This statement does not preclude the possibility that further research will produce better theoretical formulations and therapeutic procedures. It simply presents the viewpoint that for the present there exists no treatment method which offers as much hope as psychoanalysis.

CHAPTER TWO

Historical Development of Psychoanalytic Psychotherapy of the Schizophrenias: Freud's Contributions. Background Information

L. BRYCE BOYER, M.D.

Freud was taught that psychopathological states were the products of neuropathological conditions which, in turn, were attributable to hereditary, constitutional and/or degenerative states. His early scientific interests were in the fields of biology, histology, and neurology. He obtained a medical degree with the hope that he might have a better chance to obtain a university appointment which would enable him to continue his studies in those fields. After Freud received his doctorate of medicine in 1881, he continued his researches in Brücke's physiological laboratory (Jones 1953:58–77). Despairing of becoming Brücke's successor and pressed for money, Freud reluctantly prepared for the practice of medicine. He devoted himself to neurology, and in 1884 was appointed *Privatdocent* in neuropathology, as the result of his having written six monographs in the fields of histology, pharmacology, and medicine (Kris 1954:16).

Despite his primary interests, Freud evinced curiosity about psychological conditions per se. As a medical student he observed an exhibition given by the magnetist Hansen and "from noticing that a hypnotized person had been made deathly pale, became convinced that hypnotic phenomena were genuine" (Jones 1953: 235). He met Breuer while still a student and, in the early eighties, the great physician told his young friend of his therapy of Miss Anna O. (Kris 1954:12), a celebrated case which constituted one of the starting points that led to psychoanalysis (Breuer and Freud 1895).

Between 1880 and 1882, Breuer treated a girl who has been considered generally to have suffered from a classical hysteria, although Reichard (1956) and others have rediagnosed her as schizophrenic. Breuer hypnotized Anna O. when she was in states of altered personality with confusion and found that when she related fantasies and simultaneously released affect, her conversion symptoms disappeared one by one. Breuer called her states hypnoid and he and Freud attributed them to dammed-up, intracerebral excitation, a concept that both may have learned from Brücke.[1]

Perhaps because of his contacts with Breuer, Freud's interest in hypnosis and its effects and implications led him to use a grant to study under Charcot during four months of 1885–1886. Upon his return to Vienna, he lectured about hysteria in the male (Freud 1886), but his psychological explanation fell on deaf ears. He continued to do laboratory research, but also undertook the private care of "nervous" patients, primarily neurotics. His first attempts at treatment were with the application of Erb's electrotherapy, a fact which Jones (1953: 235) attributed to Freud's remaining under the influence

[1] Freud's later extrapolations from this idea led him to ideas about regulatory mechanisms of the psyche which belong today to the fundamental assumptions of psychoanalysis (Bernfeld 1944).

of Charcot's derogatory attitude toward the cathartic method of Breuer. Freud confined himself to electrotherapy for some months, although he used various adjuvants as well, such as baths and massage. Jones wrote (1953:235), "elsewhere he made the caustic remark that the only reason he could not agree with Moebius in ascribing the results of electrical treatment to suggestion was that he did not find any results to explain."

Despite his discouragement with the results of the therapeutic methods he was using and his contact with Breuer's work, Freud did not use hypnosis in his psychiatric practice until the autumn of 1887 (Freud 1887–1902:53), with Frau Emmy von N. (Breuer and Freud 1895). Hypnosis excited him because he saw in its use the possibility of "arriving at a purely psychological theory of hysteria, with affective processes in the front rank" (Freud 1914a:18). However, he was unable to alter the mental state of most of his patients. In 1889 he observed Bernheim's demonstration that patients who were in a state of hypnotically induced somnambulism only appeared to have forgotten their somnambulistic experiences. Freud used hypnosis for some eighteen months, but then changed his procedure in order to work with patients in their "normal state." At first he declared they would remember when he put his hand on their foreheads and, although he found the procedure laborious and "unsuited to serve as a permanent technique," he continued to use it until he was certain that forgotten memories are not lost (Freud 1914a:23). Freud looked upon psychical splitting itself as an effect of a process of repelling which he first called defense and later repression. He gradually developed the relatively noninterfering techniques of psychoanalysis, becoming aware of the roles of regression, infantile sexuality and, later, transference.

THE DEVELOPMENT OF FREUD'S THINKING CONCERNING THE SCHIZOPHRENIAS

It is not easy to follow the development of Freud's thought in regard to the schizophrenias, partly because his utilization of the words *neurosis* and *psychosis* was not clearly defined. Zilboorg (1954) has suggested that Freud's apparent "nosological laxity and even confusion" resulted from an essential indifference to diagnostic entities. An early example is to be found in Freud's first letter to Wilhelm Fliess, in which, without amplification, he wrote, "In neurasthenia, a hypochondriacal element, an anxiety psychosis, is never absent . . ." (Freud 1887–1902:51). Freud (1911:75–76) also spoke directly to the point with his remark, "it is not on the whole of very great importance what names we give to clinical pictures." In his last work (Freud 1940: 195), he wrote, "it is not scientifically feasible to draw a line of demarcation between what is psychologically normal and abnormal."

In an 1893 draft of the paper "On the Grounds for Detaching a Particular Syndrome from Neurasthenia under the Description Anxiety Neurosis," Freud (1895) divided hysterias into hereditary and traumatic and asserted that all cases of "acquired" hysteria had a genital sexual origin. He distinguished between periodic depression, which he regarded as a third form of anxiety neurosis, and melancholia proper, implying that the latter is of an hereditary nature. In Freud's remaining letters to Fliess, his use of the word *melancholia* leaves the reader in doubt as to whether it signified neurotic or psychotic depression. The same looseness of utilization of the term is to be found frequently in the German psychiatric literature of that time.

Freud distinguished between psychopathological states of hereditary and acquired origins, and his early attempts to understand the bases of acquired neuroses and psychoses included organic explanations. By 1893, he had abandoned hypnotherapy and the tedious technique of placing his hand on the patient's head while demanding the production of associations. He was, however, still convinced that acquired psychopathological states were attributable to sexual *noxae*. Nevertheless, in that year he introduced the then revolutionary theory that the symptoms of psychotic patients were understandable in the same way as were the dreams and actions of normal persons and the symptoms of neurotic individuals. In "The Neuro-Psychoses of Defence" Freud (1894) conceptualized acquired hysteria, phobias, obsessions, and certain hallucinatory psychoses to constitute defensive states which served the purpose of keeping unacceptable sexual ideas from consciousness. One of his obsessional patients suffered from (p. 55) an *Überwältigungpsychose* (a psychosis in which the ego is overwhelmed); another from hallucinatory confusion. In this paper Freud designated his treatment method as "psychical analysis" (p. 47), "clinicopsychological analysis" (p. 53), and "hypnotic analysis" (p. 59), and stated that it could be used to remove conversion, displacement, and splitting of consciousness through counteracting the effects of repression.[2] He was clearly aware of current combinations of neurotic and psychotic symptoms in the same patient. In this first article he presented an hypothetical mechanism of psychosis to which he returned thirty years later in his last papers concerning the same subject. Contrasting two cases with obsessions, in which the defense against an intolerable idea was effected by detachment of the affect, with a case of hallucinatory confusion, in which a "more energetic and successful kind of defence existed," Freud (1894:58) wrote concerning the latter: "Here, the ego rejects the incompatible idea together with its affect and behaves as if the idea had never occurred to the ego at all. *But from the moment at which this has been successfully done the subject is in a psychosis, which can only be classified as 'hallucinatory confusion.'* " He continued (p. 49), "the ego has fended off the incompatible idea through a flight into psychosis," and added, "The ego breaks away from the incompatible idea; but the latter is inseparably connected with a piece of reality, so that, in so far as the ego achieves this result, it, too, has detached itself wholly or in part from reality."

In 1894, Freud (1887–1902:86–88) included melancholia and mania among the neuroses, although in 1895 he wrote (p. 103), "the typical and extreme case of melancholia appears to be the periodic or cyclical form."

In a draft of a paper written in 1895 entitled "Paranoia," Freud wrote (p. 109), "delusional ideas stand alongside obsessional ideas as purely intellectual disorders, and paranoia stands alongside obsessional

[2] Later in the same year, he (Freud 1894a:75) used the term *psychological analysis*. *Psycho-analysis* first appeared in the French paper on the etiology of the neuroses (Freud 1896a:151).

insanity as an intellectual psychosis" and "chronic paranoia is a pathological mode of defence." At a later time, in his thirty-ninth letter to Fliess, he repeated that theme, as though to reassure himself of its validity (Freud 1887–1902:141), "paranoia is really a defence neurosis," and in a draft of a paper written the same year, "The Neuroses of Defence," we find (p. 146): "There are four types of these, and many forms. . . . They are pathological aberrations of normal psychical states of affect: of *conflict* (hysteria), or *self-reproach* in obsessional neurosis, of *mortification* (in paranoia) and of *grief* (in acute hallucinatory dementia.)" Freud (1896) published both drafts as "Further Remarks on the Neuro-Psychoses of Defence," and in that elaboration, he presented the case history of a woman who suffered from chronic paranoia or dementia paranoides whom he had treated psychoanalytically. He wrote (p. 175), "This is a psychosis of defence." Freud's laxity in distinguishing neuroses and psychoses remains apparent. Without having in the meantime defined those states with any more clarity he soon (Freud 1898) stated that psychoanalysis was a method of treatment designed only for psychoneurotics, but later in the same year Freud (1898a) included paranoia among the psychoneuroses.

In 1904, Freud wrote of the limitations of the psychoanalytic method. In his words (Freud 1904:257), it "was created through and for the treatment of patients permanently unfitted for life." Patients were to be accepted for treatment only if they possessed a "reasonable degree of education and a fairly reliable character." Analytic psychotherapy was considered unsuitable (p. 258) for the treatment of "neuropathic degeneration" and "psychoses, states of confusion and deeply-rooted (I might say toxic) depression." He suggested that "by suitable changes in the method we may succeed in advancing beyond these hindrances—and so be able to initiate a psychotherapy of the psychoses," and added (p. 259) that from analytic therapy "no injury to the patient is to be feared when the treatment is conducted with real comprehension." He did not suggest what technical modifications might make the method suitable for the treatment of the psychoses. He supplemented these remarks later, commenting (Freud 1904a) that persons with "deep-rooted malformations of character, traits of an actually degenerative constitution" are also unsuitable for psychoanalysis.

It is to be noted that Freud had yet to define what he meant by neurosis or psychosis. Although he had not written directly of acquired versus hereditary psychoneuroses for some years, a picture of his conceptualizations gradually emerged. He believed that psychoanalysis was to be recommended for illnesses which were predominantly, if not totally, caused by traumatic life situations and that psychoanalysis was contraindicated for states which stemmed from hereditary or constitutional origins. This would seem to indicate that when Freud judged a condition to have been caused by the latter, he included it among the psychoses or severe character malformations. Five years later, Freud (1909) offered a criterion for making such a differentiation, stating "Psychoanalytical research into the neuroses (the various forms of nervous illness with mental causation) has endeavored to trace their connections with instinctual life and the restrictions imposed on it by the claims of civilization." His inference was that other "forms of nervous illness" have hereditary, constitutional, or degenerative causations, but he did not amplify this point or indicate methods to differentiate between illnesses caused by socialization or by organic factors. There is another implication to be found in his remarks, namely that if a "nervous illness" is predominantly due to the claims of civilization, it should be amenable to psychoanalytic therapy.

Soon thereafter, Freud (1911) turned his attention to an amplification of his libido theory and to the development of a theory of narcissism, to which he had alluded at a meeting of the Vienna Psycho-Analytical Society in 1909 (Freud 1914:69). He chose as a point of departure a study of the autobiographical account of a paranoic. Freud developed his argument in four steps. He sought (1) to understand the origins of paranoia by an analysis of the phenomenology which characterized Schreber's illness, (2) to separate paranoia from the schizophrenias, (3) to develop a theory of the psychoses, and (4) to exploit his ideas concerning the psychopathology of the psychoses to clarify his theory of narcissism.

From an interpretive analysis of Schreber's recorded symptomatology and the development of his delusional system, Freud (1911:429) concluded, "the basis of Schreber's illness was an outburst of homosexual feeling" toward his physician, Flechsig, a father surrogate. After stating that the "father complex" was the dominant element in Schreber's case, Freud noted (p. 59), "But in all of this there is nothing characteristic of the form of the disease known as paranoia, nothing that might not be found (and that has not been found) *in other kinds of neuroses.*" (Italics added.) He maintained his earlier position (Freud 1894, 1896) that the symptomatology of the neuroses and psychoses was the result of defensive mechanisms, and defined the protective nature of Schreber's paranoid symptoms by adding (Freud 1911:59), "The distinctive character of paranoia (or of dementia praecox) must be sought for elsewhere—namely in the particular form assumed by the symptoms; and we shall expect to find that this is determined, not by the nature of the complexes themselves, but by the mechanism by which the symptoms are formed or by which repression is brought about" and "what was characteristically paranoid about the illness was the fact that the patient, as a means of warding off a homosexual wishful phantasy, reacted precisely with delusions of persecution of this kind." He added (p. 62), "paranoics *endeavor to protect themselves against any such sexualization of their social instinctual cathexes.*" He then reviewed the roles of fixation, repression, and irruption of the repressed in the formation of symptoms, and wrote (p. 71), "*The delusion formation, which we take to be a pathological product, is in reality an attempt at recovery, a process of reconstruction*" and "the process of repression proper consists in a detachment of the libido from people—and things—that were previously loved."

In his exposition of the significance of such conclusions, Freud then exploited the data to develop a theory of the psychopathology of the psychoses. He noted that the process of repression happens silently and can be inferred only from later events. He stated (p. 71): "What forces itself so noisily upon our attention is the process of recovery, which undoes the work of repression and brings back the libido again onto the people it had abandoned. In paranoia, this process is carried out by the method of projection. . . . Such libido detachment occurs in other conditions. . . . It is possible that a detachment of libido is the essential and regular mechanism of every repression." He found that (p. 72) "paranoics have brought along with them a *fixation at the stage of narcissism,* and we can assert that the length of *the step back from sublimated homosexuality to narcissism* is a measure of the amount of *regression* characteristic of paranoia." Such libidinal detachment may be partial, or (p. 73) "it may spread to a general one, which will loudly proclaim its presence in the symptoms of megalomania," and (p. 75) "It cannot be asserted that a paranoic, even at the height of the repression, withdraws his interest from the external world completely—as must be considered to occur in certain other kinds of hallucinatory psychosis (such as Meynert's amentia [an acute hallucinatory confusion])."

Here, then, we have the core of Freud's theory of the psychoses. Whereas Kahlbaum (1863) emphasized the motor phenomena in schizophrenia, Kraepelin (1903) the progressive course leading to dementia, and Bleuler (1911) the thought disorder and affective disturbance, Freud considered the patient's changed relationships with people and other objects to be of primary importance. He was particularly impressed by the generally verifiable observation that there is a gross withdrawal of interest from the environment which is reflected in varying behavioral and subjective changes in different forms of psychic disorders. Normal people, when subjected to object loss, do not become ill but find some other objects onto whom or which they can transfer the interest that was attached to the previous love object. Individuals who suffer from hysteria, anxiety hysteria, or the obsessional neurosis—Freud (1911) now refers to this group as transference neuroses—repress the mental representations of the lost libidinal objects and the cathexis of object-libido to those unconscious mental representations is maintained, revealing itself in the symptoms which are characteristic of those disorders. In psychotics, the situation is quite different. They have the notion that the world about them and the people in it have somehow changed and sometimes the world appears to them to have been destroyed. Freud later (1924, 1932) referred to this group of symptoms as the patient's break with reality.

In 1911 and 1914, Freud attempted to explain the psychopathology of the break with reality on the basis of a quantitative or economic factor: the distribution of the patient's libidinal cathexes. He deemed it to be the consequence of the patient's having withdrawn *totally* his libidinal cathexes from the mental representations of his love-objects and having attached the detached object-libido to his self.

Freud then sought to answer the question: What happens to the object-libido which has been detached from love-objects and invested in the self? He noted the presence in the paranoic and the schizophrenic of megalomanic symptoms and a period of hypochondriasis, a state which ushered in Schreber's paranoia. At the same time, Freud knew of the important part played by regression in psychosis; he had written of the significance of the similarities among sleep, dreams, and psychosis (Freud 1900). He had perceived the profound similarities between the psychotic patient and the infant, and he assumed that, in both, cathexes of object representations are either absent or insignificant compared with the quantity of libido invested in the self. He reasoned that the psychotic patient regressed to the stage of narcissism through which every normal child was thought to traverse early in life.

How did Freud attempt to explain megalomania? He wrote (Freud 1914:74–75), "What happens to the libido which has been withdrawn from external objects in schizophrenia? The megalomania characteristic of these states points the way. This megalomania has no doubt come into being at the expense of the object-libido. The libido that has been withdrawn from the external world has been directed to the ego and thus gives rise to an attitude that may be called narcissism. But the megalomania itself is no new creation; on the contrary, it is, as we know, a magnification and plainer manifestation of a condition which has already existed previously. This leads us to look upon narcissism which arises through the drawing in of object-cathexes as a secondary one, superimposed upon a primary narcissism that is obscured by a number of different influences."

Let us now follow Freud's argument concerning hypochondriasis. He wrote (Freud 1914:82), "a person who is tormented by organic pain and discomfort gives up his interest in the things of the external world, in so far as they do not concern his suffering. Closer observation teaches us that he also withdraws *libidinal* interest from his love-objects." He "withdraws his libidinal cathexes back onto his own ego, and sends them out again when he recovers." (It should be remembered that in German the word *Ego* has the dual connotation of self and ego.) Freud continued, "Here libido and ego-interest are once more indistinguishable from each other. The familiar egoism of the sick person covers both." He went on (p. 83): "Hypochondriasis . . . has the same effect as organic disease on the distribution of the libido. The hypochondriac withdraws both interest and libido—the latter specially markedly—from the objects of the external world and concentrates both of them upon the organ that is engaging his attention," and (p. 84), "the familiar prototype of an organ that is painfully tender . . . is the genital organ in its states of excitation." Freud, referring to his "Three Essays on the Theory of Sexuality" (Freud 1905), suggested that cathected organs become erotogenic organs and wrote (Freud 1914:84–85), "For every such change in the erotogenicity of the organs there might then be a parallel change of libidinal cathexis in the ego." He noted, "If we follow up this line of thought, we come up against not only the problem of hypochondria, but of the other 'actual' neuroses—neurasthenia and anxiety neurosis" and "we may suspect that the relation of hypochondria to paraphrenia is similar to that of the other 'actual' neuroses to hysteria and obsessional neurosis: we may suspect, that is, that it is dependent on ego-libido just as the others are on object-libido, and that hypochondriacal anxiety is the counterpart, as coming from ego-libido, to neurotic anxiety. Further, since we are already familiar with the idea that the mechanism of falling ill and of the formation of symptoms in the transference neuroses—the path from introversion to regression—is to be linked to a damming-up of object-libido, we may come to closer quarters with the idea of a damming-up of ego-libido as well and may bring this idea into relation with the phenomena of hypochondria and paraphrenia." Noting that damming-up of libido is perceived as unpleasurable and the degree of unpleasure is dependent upon the quantity of dammed-up libido, Freud continued, "Here we even venture to touch on the question of what makes it necessary at all for our mental life to pass beyond the limits of narcissism and to attach libido to objects."

Let us now return to Freud's theory of psychosis during this period when his orientation was that of the libido theory within the framework of the topographical hypothesis. The repression of the neurotic and the psychotic is silent. Evidence of its existence can be obtained only through an analysis of symptoms which show themselves during the period of improvement. Such symptoms are compromise formations which result from the psyche's attempt to relieve the unpleasure which has resulted from dammed-up ego-libido. With improvement, the psychotic's withdrawn libido becomes gradually reinvested in the outer world and its objects in a pathological manner, that is, delusions and hallucinations. This attempt at reinvestment Freud called the restitutive phase of the psychosis.

The decathexis of object representations which characterizes the first stage of a psychosis is the analogue of a neurotic repression, but in the case of the psychotic, repression is a deeper and further-reaching process. It does not simply prevent ideas and memories from reaching consciousness, but results in a profound change in the mental representations themselves. The repressed contents of the neurotic's unconscious remain cathected, but the mental representations of the psychotic become truly decathected and no longer exist for him. Freud wrote (1914:74): "Paraphrenics display two fundamental characteristics: megalomania and diversion of their interest from the external world—from people and things. In consequence of the latter change, they become inaccessible to the influence of psychoanalysis and cannot be cured by our efforts." Freud (1915:124) first used the term *narcissistic neurosis* to designate schizophrenia. To paraphrase his view, we can say, *the schizophrenic cannot reinvest actual external objects; he suffers from a narcissistic neurosis and is incapable of transference. Thus, he cannot be treated by psychoanalysis.*

Let me summarize the argument. The break with reality, or complete withdrawal of cathexis from the environment, is the most characteristic single feature of the psychoses. The repression employed by the psychotic is more profound than that of the neurotic and consists of a total decathexis of libido from mental representations. The self-centeredness of the psychotic results from the turning of the decathected libido onto the self, resulting in megalomania when it is attached to the ego and hypochondriasis when it is attached to the body. Following regression to such a narcissistic stage, the psychotic gradually recathects mental representations of external objects in a distorted manner, usually via hallucinations and delusions, in a restitutive phase.

It will be recalled that in the analysis of the Schreber case, Freud sought also to distinguish paranoia from the schizophrenias into which group it had been included by Kraepelin and Bleuler. Freud, however, believed (1911:76) "paranoia should be maintained as an independent clinical type, however frequently the picture it offers may be complicated by the presence of schizophrenic features" as it had been in the Schreber case. He gave as his reason, "For, from the standpoint of the libido theory, while it would resemble dementia praecox in so far as the repression proper would in both disorders have the same principal feature—detachment of the libido, together with its regression onto the ego—it would be distinguished from dementia praecox by having its dispositional fixation differently located and by having a different mechanism for the return of the repressed (that is, for the formation of symptoms)," namely, projection. He stated that the attempt at recovery employed in dementia praecox (paraphrenia), in contrast to that used in paranoia, is hallucinatory. Freud stated that the hallucinatory mechanism is hysterical and continued (p. 77), "this is one of the two major respects in which dementia praecox differs from paranoia."[3] A second distinction lies in the natural history of the disorders. It "is shown by the outcome of the disease in those cases where the process has not remained too restricted. The prognosis is on the whole more unfavorable than in paranoia. The victory lies with repression and not, as in the former, with reconstruction. The regression extends not merely to narcissism (manifesting itself in the shape of megalomania) but to a complete abandonment of object-love and a return to infantile autoerotism. The dispositional fixation must therefore be situated further back than in paranoia, and must lie somewhere at the beginning of the course of development from autoerotism to object-love. Moreover, it is not at all likely that homosexual impulsions, which are so frequently—perhaps invariably—to be found in paranoia, play an equally important part in the aetiology of that far more comprehensive disorder, dementia praecox."

[3] Today we would not consider this argument to be valid, since projection is clearly involved in the process of hallucinating.

Freud ended his analysis of the Schreber case by stating (p. 79): "Lastly, I cannot conclude the present work . . . without foreshadowing the two chief theses towards the establishment of which the libido theory of the neuroses and psychoses is advancing: namely, that the neuroses arise in the main from a conflict between the ego and the sexual instinct, and that the forms which the neuroses assume retain the imprint of the course of development followed by the libido—and by the ego." That he considered the same to be true for the psychoses is apparent from what follows.

The onset of Schreber's illness consisted of a state which was labeled hypochondria. Freud considered that during the hypochondriacal phase, Schreber had not "overstepped the limits" of a neurosis. However, he also included paranoia among the neuroses (p. 59). During the unfolding of Freud's argument which sought to differentiate paranoia from schizophrenia, he indicated his cognizance of another nosological difficulty, writing (p. 77), "Our hypotheses as to the dispositional fixations in paranoia and paraphrenia make it easy to see that a case may begin with paranoic symptoms and may yet develop into a dementia praecox, and that paranoid and schizophrenic phenomena may be combined in any proportion." Freud, then, implied that there is a continuum of states which lie between normality and psychosis, various degrees of neurotic and psychotic mechanisms are employed in the different psychopathological states, and the diagnostic terms which are to be applied to different abnormal states depend upon quantitative or economic assessments. In other words, as Freud had indicated before (1896) and would again later (1924), the psychic processes in neurosis and psychosis display a fundamental unity. In 1911 and 1914, reasoning from the libido theory, he sought to establish that paranoia lay between neurosis and psychosis, between the transference and the narcissistic neuroses.

Although Freud maintained his position regarding the fundamental unity, he apparently altered another judgment. In the libido theory, derivatives of instinctual drives are inaccessible to consciousness and the removal of symptoms depends upon making that which has been repressed available to the system *Cs.* In Freud's early letters to Fliess, he held the vastly optimistic viewpoint that all of the acquired psychopathologies could be cured through the removal of repression, the only defense he then recognized. He had generally included paranoia among the neuroses and apparently thought some cases to be acquired, that is psychogenic. By 1896, he had become less optimistic regarding the efficacy of psychoanalysis in the treatment of paranoia and he remarked at the beginning of his analysis of the Schreber case (1911:9) that "paranoics cannot be compelled to overcome their internal resistances."

At this point, let us summarize the development of Freud's thinking up to 1914, pertaining to the psychoses and the applicability of psychoanalysis to their treatment.

In 1893, Freud (1895) divided psychological illnesses into those of organic and psychological origin, although neither then nor at any subsequent time did he present clearly his criteria for deciding which patients suffered from organically or psychologically caused psychopathological states. In 1894, he (1887–1902:86–88) included melancholia and mania among the neuroses and in 1895 (1895:141), paranoia. He soon

(1896:175) hinted that identical symptom complexes could result from either predominantly organic or mental causes, placing paranoia among the psychoses. In "Further Remarks on the Neuro-Psychoses of Defence" Freud (1896) designated as chronic paranoia the illness of a woman whose case material served as the basis for his discussion of paranoia, but in 1924 he added a footnote, naming the condition *dementia paranoides*. Perhaps his early diagnostic label implied that he considered her condition to have been psychogenic and subsequently, on the basis of material which was omitted from the case presentation, had decided the causes of her psychopathology to have been organic in nature. Two years later, Freud (1898) concluded that psychoanalysis was suitable only for the treatment of neuroses, but he did not state his reasons. Soon (1898a), he included paranoia anew among the neuroses. A few years later, Freud (1904:258) believed psychoanalysis to be contraindicated for "neuropathic degeneration," psychosis, states of confusion, and toxic or "deeply-rooted" depression, implying that it was to be used for the treatment of illnesses which were not of organic origin. By 1909, Freud (1909) made this judgment explicit, stating that psychoanalysis was to be used to treat illnesses which had mental causation and implied that such pathological conditions resulted from the claims of civilization. He then (1911) implied that paranoia is not amenable to psychoanalysis when he said that paranoics cannot be compelled to give up their resistances, but he (1911, 1914) also placed paranoia between the transference neuroses and the psychoses, represented by paraphrenia. In schizophrenia the break with reality constitutes complete withdrawal of libidinal cathexis from the environmental and turning it onto the self. If the decathected libido becomes attached to the ego, megalomania results, and if to the body, hypochondriasis. Such libido withdrawal recreates the early narcissistic state of the infant and following such regression, the psychotic gradually recathects mental representations of external objects in a highly primitive manner, through hallucinations and delusions.

A number of questions are obvious.

How is one to distinguish between psychopathological states of organic and psychogenic origin? If Freud is correct that at least some psychopathologies of mental origin, that is, resultant from socialization, are amenable to psychoanalysis, the answer to this query is crucial. Freud implied that such a differentiation could be made retrospectively by the clinical course of the illness, which in organically caused conditions was gradually deteriorating, but that an early differentiation might have to be devised by scientists of other disciplines. It seems that the implication would be that psychoanalytic therapy should be attempted for some unstated period of time, regardless of the patient's state when first interviewed, but this is not stated overtly.

During what period is a patient to be considered psychotic? Apparently some degree of decathexis short of total withdrawal of libido is to be found in all other conditions; in them the previous cathexis of persons and things is replaced by cathexis of fantasized objects. But the same phenomenon occurs with the psychotic during the restitutive phase. Megalomania and hypochondriasis are also conditions which can be observed in states other than paraphrenia, as in paranoia.

Why is the psychotic not amenable to psychoanalysis? Freud felt there was insufficient libidinal cathexis available for investment in external objects and, therefore, transference would not occur. But what quantity of cathexis has to be available for transference to exist? How can that be determined without an attempt at psychoanalysis? Freud did not say. He implied that psychoanalytic therapy could not be done while the patient was hallucinating and deluded, but this judgment was inconsistent, because some of his "hysterical" patients hallucinated and some of his "obsessional" patients were deluded. Before 1911 and again in "On Narcissism: An Introduction" in 1914, paranoia had been included among the conditions which were possibly amenable to psychoanalysis. But then, even though the paranoic was not psychotic within the framework of the orientation of the libido theory, he was not subject to psychoanalysis; nevertheless, persons who suffered from acquired melancholia and mania presumably were. Freud also made amply clear his awareness that the symptoms of paraphrenia and paranoia were frequently intermixed and he remained dissatisfied with his formulations. These and other vexing problems pertaining to a theory of the psychoses, as we shall see below, continued to trouble him throughout his life. We shall now continue to present the unfolding of his thinking concerning the psychoses.

In 1910, Freud (1918) undertook the psychoanalysis of the Wolf Man, who had been hospitalized for various periods with a diagnosis of manic-depressive insanity; the initial period of treatment lasted until 1914, when Freud regarded the case as completed. He considered the Wolf Man's condition to represent a severe case of obsessional neurosis.[4] Freud set an arbitrary date for

[4] Jones (1955:273) wrote: "The patient suffered from an extremely severe neurosis." Zetzel (1965) stated it to be probable that whenever Freud diagnosed a patient to have been a severe neurotic, that patient was either a borderline psychotic or frankly psychotic.

termination of the analysis because it seemed that this passive patient had become too comfortable in his relationships with Freud and it appeared unlikely that further movement would take place without his taking an unusually active step. Following the completion of the four-year psychoanalysis, the Wolf Man appeared to be symptom-free during a period of five years; then he returned for another four-month period of analysis, afflicted with a severe case of "hysterical constipation." By that time he had lost his wealth and Freud not only treated him without charge, but even arranged to support him and his invalid wife through solicited contributions. Freud continued to present him with money for the next six years.

In 1923, the Wolf Man learned that Freud had undergone an operation on his mouth. Apparently this news caused the Wolf Man to masturbate compulsively. Subsequently he learned that Freud suffered from cancer. In the same year, the Wolf Man's mother developed a wart on her nose and became hypochondriacal. During the next three years, he developed a hypochondriacal type of paranoia. He became convinced that his nose had been deformed by a physician whom he equated with Freud. In 1926 he returned to Freud for further treatment and was referred to Brunswick (1928) who analyzed him without fee for four or five months. She found his hypochondriacal ideas to mask persecutory delusions. The Wolf Man had identified both with his mother and a castrated image of his father. Brunswick wrote (p. 440): "The source of the new illness was an unresolved remnant of the transference, which, after fourteen years, under the stress of peculiar circumstances, became the basis for a new form of an old illness." During his treatment by Brunswick, the

Wolf Man overcame his fear of castration and lost his paranoid psychosis. She saw him for a second period of analysis two years later and had occasional interviews with him during the next fourteen years. In 1940, she reported him to be in excellent health, as did both Gardiner (1953) and Jones (1955:273–278) some fifteen years later.

The implications of Freud's having accepted the Wolf Man in psychoanalysis are interesting. Despite his use of the label "severe obsessional neurosis," he could scarcely have been unaware of the man's being what we would today call a borderline schizophrenic. The past history was available to Freud, and during the first interview, the Wolf Man offered to submit to anal intercourse with Freud and then to defecate on his head. This gives credence to the supposition that Freud probably felt that a trial period of psychoanalysis was indicated for many patients who presented mixed symptomatology, so long as there was evidence that transference could develop. However, we can only infer what constituted such evidence to Freud. He considered psychotic patients to be incapable of transference, at least theoretically. *It would appear that when Freud used the word* transference *in this context, he meant transference reactions which he could trace obviously to oedipal traumata and which did not shift rapidly during the course of the treatment.*[5]

Let us now retrace our steps and consider another

[5] Today we know that psychotic patients are indeed capable of the most intense of transference relationships, except possibly during the brief moment when the silent pathological process of schizophrenia is in operation (Pious 1949; Pichon Rivière 1961; Searles 1963). Glover (Hinsie and Shatzky 1940: 532–533) said a transference neurosis is "a new artificial neurosis" which "occurs only during psychoanalytic treatment. It is the reappearance of the early Oedipal situation." Possible implications of Freud's having terminated the analysis arbitrarily and his providing money for the Wolf Man will be discussed later.

facet of Freud's thinking. As we have seen, he did not initially occupy himself with problems of definition of psychopathological states. He was more interested in creating an operational model of psychical structure, one which would account for the observations he made of his patients' productions. In 1895, in "Project for a Scientific Psychology," Freud (1887–1902:347–445) sought to represent the psychical apparatus in terms of neurophysiology, but became dissatisfied with his formulations and never completed and published the fruits of his efforts. From the early nineties, he developed his hydrodynamic libido theory, which, as illustrated above, formed the basis of his theory of the psychoses. However, his thinking went further and in Chapter VII of *The Interpretation of Dreams,* Freud (1900) systematically proposed the topographical theory.[6] His formulations concerning the psychoses have been understood generally by psychoanalysts principally in terms of the libido theory within the framework of the topographical hypothesis and not within that of the structural theory. As we shall see below, Freud at-

6 The following synopsis of the topographical theory is taken from Chapter VII (Freud 1900) and "The Unconscious" (Freud 1915). See also Arlow and Brenner (1964). In the topographical theory, the psychical apparatus is divided into the systems *Ucs., Pcs.,* and *Cs.* on the basis of their relationships to consciousness. The elements of the system *Ucs.* are unavailable to consciousness and are governed by the primary process. The elements of the system *Pcs.* are more readily accessible to consciousness. Both the systems *Pcs.* and *Cs.* are governed by the secondary process. The repressing agency which keeps forbidden memories and wishes in the *Ucs.* is the censor of the *Pcs.* The crucial factor in neurotic symptoms formation consists of the accessibility to consciousness of mental elements, those elements being unconscious sexual wishes which are in conflict with the individual's conscious moral standards and practical life goals. Repressed wishes threaten to overcome the repressive forces of the censor; compromise formations result in the production of neurotic symptoms. Only an unconscious wish can be pathogenic. The task of therapy is the removal of repression to make relevant contents of the *Ucs.* accessible to the *Cs.*

tempted, albeit unsuccessfully, to reconcile his theory of the psychoses with the structural hypothesis.

In "The Unconscious," Freud (1915) began to express dissatisfaction with the topographical theory, because he had discovered the existence of unconscious fantasies and found they could not be placed rationally in any of the systems provided by his model. Inaccessibility to consciousness was the cardinal criterion for distinguishing between the systems *Ucs.* and *Pcs.* Unconscious fantasies belong by definition to the system *Ucs.*, but such fantasies are composed of definite word and object representations and their formal aspects reveal influences of the secondary process; thus they should be assigned to the system *Pcs.* In "On Narcissism: An Introduction," Freud (1914) had postulated a differentiating grade within the ego, which he called the ego-ideal and later the superego. By the time he contributed "Beyond the Pleasure Principle," Freud (1920) had become certain that both unconscious libidinal and aggressive drive derivatives could result in psychical conflict when they threatened to irrupt into consciousness. The topographical theory had made provisions only for repressed sexual drives. Freud's growing dissatisfactions with the topographical theory led him to revise fundamentally his concept of psychical structure and to create a new hypothetical view of psychical systems which was incompatible with the topographical hypothesis. This led to his publication of *The Ego and The Id* (Freud 1923).

In *The Ego and The Id,* Freud postulated a psychical structure with two parts. The id was the repository for the instinctual drives, which included aggressive as well as libidinal drives. The ego, more coherent and organized, mediated between drive-derivatives and the demands of the external world; it contained the anti-instinctual forces of the mind, some of which were unconscious. The ego itself came to have a second division, the superego; this consisted of the moral functions of the ego.

Freud was particularly struck with two sets of clinical observations: (1) in neurotic conflicts, repressive forces are *not* always readily available to consciousness, and (2) a need for punishment may be inaccessible to consciousness. The significance of the first observation was that accessibility to consciousness cannot be used as the basis for dividing the mental apparatus into systems. The second had further meaning. When Freud found an unconscious need for punishment in some patients, he concluded that conflicts existed not only between the demands of id and ego, but also between those of ego and superego.

In "Mourning and Melancholia," Freud (1917) determined that an object which had been lost was reinstated within the ego, that is, that an object cathexis had been replaced by an identification. In *The Ego and The Id*, he (1923:35) concluded, "this kind of substitution has a great share in determining the form taken on by the ego and that it contributed materially towards building up what is called its 'character.'" He added, "In the primitive oral phase of the individual's existence, object-cathexis and identification are hardly to be distinguished from each other." He suggested (p. 36) that such identification might be the sole condition under which the id can give up its objects, and that "the ego is a precipitate of abandoned object cathexes and . . . maintains a record of past object choices." In the dissolution of the Oedipus complex, the object cathexis of the mother must be given up and its place could be filled either with an identification with the mother or an intensified identification with the father. The dissolution of the Oedipus complex resulted in the formation of the superego; the identifications were those of the parents' ethical and moral aspects, as they had been perceived by the child.

Thus Freud developed the structural model to account for mental phenomena which are not explained by the topographical theory. The fundamental changes of hypotheses implied the need of a vast change in the aims of psychoanalytic treatment and, in fact, the effect of the change on psychoanalytic technique has, in my opinion, been enormous. (See Alexander 1930; Arlow and Brenner 1964; A. Freud 1936; Freud 1932, 1940; Hartmann 1951; Kris 1951; Loewenstein 1951.)

In the topographical theory, the therapeutic task is to make the contents of the system *Ucs.* conscious. Symptom formation results from the failure of repression; the irruption of unconscious instinctual wishes into consciousness threatens. Their derivatives are excluded from consciousness through the substitute expression of wishes in the form of symptoms. Therapy aims at the abrogation of repression, to recover forgotten data, especially those pertaining to childhood traumata.

In the structural theory, intrapsychic conflict is viewed as much more than a problem of inaccessibility to consciousness. Since the defenses themselves are frequently unconscious, their analysis is part of the therapeutic task; their automatic actions must be resolved and the integration of instinctual derivatives and their memories which were previously defended against should be permitted into the normal parts of the ego. In addition to the analysis of id derivatives and ego defenses, it is of great importance to analyze whatever superego manifestations are part of the pathogenic conflict.

Freud was aware of a lack of consonance between his theory of the psychoses and the structural hypothesis. In 1911, when he had not formulated clearly the system ego, he had postulated a complete withdrawal of libido from objects of the external world and a regression to the stage of narcissism, in the psychosis. By 1923, he thought that lost objects were reinstated within the ego, or that object cathexes were replaced by identifications. The ego was conceptualized as a precipitate of past object cathexes. In the topographical hypothesis, libido is both withdrawn and detached from objects, whereas in the structural theory libido is conceptualized as being attached *always* to *some* object representation, no matter how primitive and archaic. Insofar as the building blocks of the ego consist of precipitates of internal objects, ego-libido must, of necessity, be attached to such objects. Within the framework of the structural hypothesis libido cannot exist in a vacuum, that is, without an object component. Theoretically, therefore, some degree of transference is possible whenever *any* ego structure persists, insofar as that structure has been developed from object precipitates. Freud's formulations concerning the treatment of the psychoses can be seriously questioned, since they rest on the premise that transference is impossible.

Soon after the appearance of *The Ego and The Id*, Waelder (1924) discussed a schizoid mathematician whom he believed had made a reasonably successful adjustment by sublimating his narcissistic libido. Waelder reached the practical conclusion that there can be a "union" of narcissistic and object libido and, therefore, transference is possible. Freud read Waelder's manuscript in the spring of 1924 and was stimulated to reconsider his position about the psychoanalytic treatment of the psychoses. A few weeks later he published "Neurosis and Psychosis." In the second paragraph he wrote (Freud 1924a: 149): "In connection with a train of thought raised in other quarters which was concerned with the origin and prevention of the psychoses," which was a reference to Waelder's manuscript (Waelder 1965).

Freud made two brief attempts to apply the structural hypothesis to the theory of the psychopathology of the psychoses, "Neurosis and Psychosis" and "The Loss of Reality in Neurosis and Psychosis" (1924). They were his last papers which dealt specifically with this subject, although he continued to occupy himself with the dissonance between the formulations he had propounded in 1911 and the structural theory. Nevertheless, he did not totally relinquish his original position concerning the psychoses.

In "Neurosis and Psychosis," Freud considered the role of the superego in the psychoses. In the topographical theory, moral trends were thought to be conscious and governed by the secondary process. He noted that the role of the superego must be taken into account in every form of psychical illness and wrote (1924b: 152), "There must also be illnesses which are based on a conflict between the ego and the superego," such as melancholia. He used the term *narcissistic neurosis* for such illnesses and continued, "Transference neuroses correspond to a conflict between the ego and the id; narcissistic neuroses to a conflict between the ego and the super-ego; and psychoses to one between the ego and the outer world." Freud (1915:124; 1915a:196) had previously used the words *narcissistic neurosis* in connection with his idea of libido withdrawal in the psychoses.

In "The Loss of Reality in Neurosis and Psychosis" Freud stated (1924:185): "Both neurosis and psychosis are . . . the result of a rebellion on the part of the id against the external world." In both conditions there is a disturbance of the patient's relations with reality due to a failure of repression. In the development of a psychosis, however, a second step is involved. In "The Neuro-Psychoses of Defence" Freud (1894:58) had written, "The ego rejects the incompatible idea together with the affect and behaves as though the idea had never occurred to the ego at all." Now (1924:184–185) he wrote, "The second step of the psychosis is indeed intended to make good the loss of reality, not, however, at the expense of restriction of the id . . . but by the creation of a new reality." Although he used his new concept of the id, he retained the old theory of anxiety, that of the libido theory within the framework of the topographical hypothesis; he continued: "In a psychosis, the transforming of reality is carried out upon the psychical precipitations of former relations to it . . . this relation was never a closed one; it was continually being enriched and altered by fresh perceptions. Thus, the psychosis is also faced with the task of procuring for itself perceptions of a kind which shall correspond to the new reality; and this is radically effected by means of hallucinations." "Probably in a psychosis the rejected piece of reality constantly forces itself upon the mind, just as the repressed instinct does in a neurosis." He determined the role of fantasy to be important in both neurosis and psychosis. In the former condition, disagreeable reality is compensated for by a world of fantasy, but in psychosis, too (p. 187), "phantasy plays the same part . . . it is the storehouse from which materials of the pattern for building the new reality are derived." Thus, "both in neurosis and psychosis there comes into consideration the question not only of a loss of reality but also of a substitute for reality."

In this attempt to integrate his formulations concerning the psychopathology of the psychoses with the structural theory, Freud appears to have begun to consider the possibility that *the fantasies of the psychotic are tied to those elements of ego structure which have resulted from identifications.* However, he did not amplify this theme or carry it to its logical conclusion regarding transference.

In "Fetishism," Freud (1927) discussed two patients who refused to believe in the deaths of their fathers, but neither had become psychotic. This clinical datum contradicted his thesis that only psychoses are detached from reality. He then wrote (p. 156): "It is true that there is one way out of the difficulty. My formula only needed to hold good where there was a higher degree of differentiation in the psychical apparatus (than in childhood); things might be permissible to a child which would entail severe injury to an adult." However, the patients had not merely "scotomized" their fathers' deaths. They had a split attitude; the attitude of the wish and that of the reality existed side by side. He added, "in a psychosis the one current—that which fitted with reality—would in fact have been absent."

In *An Outline of Psychoanalysis,* Freud's last publication on this subject, he noted (1940:114) that either an intolerably painful reality situation or "extraordinarily intensified" instincts could precipitate the outbreak of a psychosis. Then he reversed his original hypothesis of complete withdrawal of cathexis from mental representations, writing (pp. 114–115): "The problem of psychoses would be simple and intelligible if the withdrawal of the ego from reality could be carried through completely. But that seems rarely if ever to happen. Even so far removed from the reality of the external world as hallucinatory confusional states, one learns . . . that at the time in some corner of their mind, there was a normal person hidden, who watched the hubbub of the illness go past, like a disinterested spectator." He continued (pp. 115–116), "what occurs in all such cases is a split in the mind. Two mental attitudes have been formed instead of a single one—one, the normal one, which takes account of reality, and another which under the influence of the instincts detaches the ego from reality." "If the second is or becomes the stronger, the necessary condition for a psychosis is present. If the relation is reversed, then there is an apparent cure of the delusional disorder. Actually, it has only retreated into the unconscious." Freud, then, suggested once again the existence of a continuum of psychical illnesses, which were to be differentiated from one another largely on the basis of quantitative factors. Additionally, he suggested but did not adumbrate a major revision of the first part of his original formulations concerning the development of the schizophrenias, namely that there is a total decathexis of the objects followed by a restitutional phase. In this final monograph, he suggested that complete withdrawal of cathexis did *not* take place.

Through the courtesy of Dr. Dieter Eicke, we are able to reproduce a translation of a letter written by Freud in 1935.[7] It concerns a patient whom Freud treated psychoanalytically, presumably in the late 1920's and early 1930's. Although the patient was not schizophrenic, according to Freud, he was nevertheless psychotic. From the symptomatology which is listed, either the diagnosis of schizophrenia or of schizo-affective psychosis seems possible.

Wien 30.6.1935

Sehrgeehrter Herr Doktor,

I was most touched by your news of the death of Mr. X., since he occupied my highest professional interest for many years. I was not much concerned about his typical constitution or about classifying him psychiatrically. Like you, I am not satisfied with the diagnosis of schizophrenia in his case. I shall impart to you here what I feel that I understood about the psychic mechanism of his illness.

He complained of a total loss of capacity to work and a decrease of interest in professional and business matters. I was able to bring him back to conducting his business but he was unable to resume his theoretical work. I never made him quite normal. The way he treated symbols in his mind, confused identifications, falsified memories and kept to his delusional superstitions made him always psychotic; his mood was always hypomanic. As for the aetiology, one had certainly to think of constitutional factors, but there was the question of an individual cause of his illness which I

[7] This letter has been published in its original form by Binswanger (1956). In a personal communication which was received after this chapter was written, Dr. Binswanger stated that the patient later had an acute "schizophrenic-manic outburst" and subsequently died of "catatonic fever." The patient had had other "attacks" before he was treated by Freud and after his treatment by Freud he had periods of remission and his "mental state was almost good" but from time to time hospital treatment was required.

was unable to answer. Nevertheless, one day I had the opportunity to observe him more clearly. He was left alone in my room and accused himself of an act of indecent behavior, a fact which he could easily have kept secret. (He had read private notes on my desk.) This confession impressed me deeply. I felt seduced to analyze it. He was then oppressed by something he had done and he was troubled to keep it secret. I recalled then that he habitually spoke vividly of all of the phases and instances of his life, but omitted a great technical invention and its implications. I got the impression there had been something amiss concerning the history of this invention, that he accused himself of something pertaining to it, which he tried to deny. I had no idea what it could be. However, I doubted the advisability of continuing to attempt to lift this denial. With a neurotic this would have been the only correct way and would have promised the end of the illness, but I was probably right in doubting the influence of analysis on a psychotic. In making conscious the conflict I had to fear a new psychotic breakdown which I would then be unable to manage. Therefore I decided to leave the theme and to be satisfied with an imperfect and temporary success.

Soon afterwards the patient left me, pretending that he could no longer stay away from his business. Fortunately for my own future I had refused his invitation to move with him to Berlin. A short time later I heard from a reliable person that the partner of my patient, with whom he had worked on his invention and who was now working in a firm in Czechoslovakia, had accused him of having cheated him out of his right of possession to the patent. He had proposed to my patient an arrangement which he rejected violently. This had happened during the period of his analysis with me, but the patient had never mentioned it and I did not even know of the existence of a partner. My patient instituted and lost a lawsuit. I do not know what happened later. Nevertheless, I felt this material confirmed my suspicion. My patient was a neurotic criminal, that is a swindler with a sensitive conscience. He could not resist the temptation to take more of the rights of the invention than were due to him but he had to pay with useless humiliations for the guilt instigated by his silence. Even his working had the characteristics of self-punishment. All his unconscious attempts to avoid hearing his hatred of himself while he defended himself against his unconscious conscience were fruitless. He then unfortunately got known with such an unscrupulous swindler and exploiter as (name).

With kind regards,

Freud

At least two points relating to Freud's having undertaken the analysis of this patient whom he considered to have "always been psychotic" and to the technique he used are significant. It may be that Mr. X. was the only psychotic patient with whom Freud attempted psychoanalysis, subsequent to his presentation in 1911 and 1914 of his formulations concerning the psychoses. We must wonder why Freud never published this case history, since to have done so would have indicated that his viewpoint was changing concerning the applicability of psychoanalysis to the psychoses and perhaps have encouraged other analysts to engage in such treatment.

Despite Freud's having undertaken this psychoanalysis, he apparently had from the beginning a pessimistic viewpoint, since he wrote, "I was probably right in doubting the influence of analysis on a psychotic." It would seem that the treatment went well until Freud abandoned the classical technique and failed to pursue the unresolved conflict because of his fear of "a new psychotic breakdown." Just what Freud meant by this statement is obscure, when we recall he said the patient was "always psychotic" and that Freud had begun the analysis while, presumably, Mr. X. was in a state of psychotic decompensation. At any event, Freud believed that the lifting of a denial would have been detrimental to the patient, producing a clinical state "which I would have been unable to manage." Why he would have been unable to manage that breakdown is unstated. By implication, he seems to have consigned the patient to permanent psychosis, by failing to analyze the defensive nature of the denial and uncovering the unconscious delusions which it no doubt held in check. It seems probable that the patient sensed Freud's pessimism and fear, because soon after the investigation of the denial was abandoned, Mr. X. found reasons to discontinue therapy. It seems reasonable to suspect that this analysis failed *because* Freud abandoned the classical technique.

We have to wonder, in view of Freud's actions with this psychotic patient, whether his analysis of the Wolf Man may also have remained incomplete because of his behavior. To be sure, Brunswick's case presentation and her recounting of Freud's technique during the first analysis of the Wolf Man give no such indication. However, it seems unlikely that she would have openly criticized her esteemed mentor. Her explanations for Freud's failure to complete the Wolf Man's analysis seem unconvincing. Concerning the first period of analysis, she attributed it both to Freud's arbitrary setting of a termination date and to a supposed impossibility that the Wolf Man could have been analyzed by a man. Many patients who suffered from deep-seated problems related to latent homosexuality have been analyzed successfully by men. We have scant factual data concerning Freud's ongoing technique during that period of treatment. However, we know that during the second analysis with Freud, the Wolf Man was seen without fee and that Freud even supported him and his wife. Further, we know that during the six-year period when Freud continued to supply him with money the Wolf Man was in possession of family jewels and consciously defrauded Freud. We can surmise that Freud's parameter of paying the patient to come to see him and to continue to have contacts with Freud was not satisfactorily analyzed. When the Wolf Man later said he considered himself to be Freud's favorite son, surely his judgment was not determined entirely by fantasies based on transference. The similarities between the fraudulence of the Wolf Man and the deception of Mr. X. of the 1935 letter are obvious. It seems reasonable to suspect that a combination of countertransference involvement combined with Freud's viewpoint concerning the impossibility of cure of psychosis by psychoanalysis may have caused him to abandon classical analytical technique with the Wolf Man as well as with Mr. X. and to raise the question of whether such abandonment was responsible for the incompleteness of both analyses.

SUMMARY

This chapter has outlined the development of Freud's thinking concerning the psychopathology of the psychoses, epitomized by the schizophrenias. That development can be divided into three phases: (1) During the period when Freud was groping with the problem of whether psychopathological states were rationally attributable solely to organic etiologies or their origins could be traced purely to psychogenic causes, he apparently concluded, although he never stated specifically, that some psychical disturbances had their causes in hereditary, constitutional and/or degenerative factors and the genesis of others could be ascribed to conflicts between instinctual forces and socialization agents. Psychoanalytic therapy was considered to be potentially beneficial to disorders of the second group. (2) Freud then developed the libido theory within the framework of the topographical hypothesis. In the constellation of those postulations, he devised his formulations concerning the psychoses: in psychosis there is a total decathexis of libidinal investment from mental representations of the objects of the external world and an attachment of the detached object-libido onto the self. If the erstwhile object-libido becomes invested in the subject's ego, he becomes megalomanic and if it be attached to the body, hypochondriasis results. Following regression to such a narcissistic phase, the psychotic gradually recathects mental representations of external objects in a distorted manner, usually via hallucinations and delusions, in a restitutive phase. The implications of this formulation were that psychoanalytic therapy of the psychoses was contraindicated, because, as a result of total withdrawal of libidinal cathexis, the development of transference was either impossible or too tenuous to permit lasting relationships with a therapist. (3) After Freud's clinical observations led him to revise his ideas concerning the nature of the mental apparatus and to devise the structural hypothesis with its attendant alterations in instinct and anxiety theories, he sought to bring his theory concerning the psychoses into consonance with his new and profoundly altered position. Although in his last writings he indicated awareness that in the schizophrenias total withdrawal of instinctual cathexis does not take place, he never totally abandoned his theory of the psychoses.

The following chapter will be concerned with the historical development of the thinking of other psychoanalysts concerning the genesis and therapy of the schizophrenias. Arguments will be presented which are intended to indicate that the psychoses are better understood within the framework of the structural theory and that psychoanalytic therapy is logically applicable to the psychoses.

Chapter Three

Historical Development of Psychoanalytic Therapy of the Schizophrenias: Contributions of the Followers of Freud

L. Bryce Boyer, M.D.

As outlined in Chapter Two, the development of Freud's thinking concerning the psychopathology of the schizophrenias can be divided somewhat arbitrarily into three phases.[1]

Between 1893 and 1910, Freud viewed the psychoses from the aspect of libido development and laid stress on fixation points, defense mechanisms, the aims of the sexual instinct, and object cathexis. During this first period, he groped with the problem of whether psychopathological states could be attributed solely either to organic or psychological causes and apparently concluded that some psychical disturbances had their origins predominantly in hereditary, constitutional, and/or degenerative phenomena but the genesis of others could be ascribed mainly to conflicts between libidinal forces and socialization agents. Psychoanalytic therapy was considered to be useful in the treatment of the second group and to be operative by means of making elements

[1] See also Rickman (1926, 1927), who divided Freud's contributions into three slightly different phases. Rickman listed 500 references.

of the system *Ucs.* available to the systems *Pcs.* and *Cs.* through removing repressions.

Between 1911 and 1923, Freud's views concerning the structure of the psychical apparatus changed fundamentally. As he became dissatisfied with the topographical theory, he presented the dual instinct theory (1920) and introduced the structural hypothesis (1923). Concerning the psychoses, he presented a formulation which used the libido theory within the framework of the topographical hypothesis (1911, 1914a). Freud concluded that in psychosis there was a break with reality which consisted of a total decathexis of libido from objects of the external world and an attachment of the detached object-libido onto the self. If the libido which had been detached from objects were invested in the subject's ego, he became megalomanic; if it were attached to his body, hypochrondriac. Following regression to such a narcissistic phase, the psychotic person gradually recathected mental representations of external objects in a distorted manner, usually via hallucinations and delusions, in a restitutional phase. Psychoanalytic treatment of psychotics was considered to be contraindicated because, with total withdrawal of libidinal cathexis, the development of transference was either impossible or too attenuated to permit lasting relationships with a therapist.

In 1924, following his revision of the instinct theory and the introduction of the structural hypothesis, Freud (1924, 1924a) wrote his last papers which dealt specifically with the psychoses. In them, he began to bring his formulations concerning the psychoses into consonance with his new and basically altered position. He then knew that serious disturbance of ego functions occurs regularly in the neuroses and the psychoses, although he stressed that in the latter conditions they have more serious consequences. When he presented his revised theory of anxiety, Freud (1926) clearly recognized that the disturbances which occur in ego functions are primarily defensive in nature, and knew much of their relations to anxiety and the aggressive drive. Nevertheless, he never rejected completely the theory of the psychoses which had been propounded within the framework of the topographical theory, despite the fact that in his latest writings Freud (1940) indicated his awareness that total withdrawal of instinctual cathexis does not take place regularly in the schizophrenias.

In order to maintain his original formulations regarding the genesis of the schizophrenias, Freud had to ignore the fact that the course of development of at least a significant minority of patients does not follow the pattern he had outlined, that is, severe disruption of relations with the environment followed by a restitutive phase.[2] As far as his writings indicate, he did not come to the conclusion that in both neuroses and psychoses, various ego functions are disturbed as part of the defensive struggle against instinctual derivatives, self-punitive trends, or both. This is especially interesting, since Freud was well aware of the existence of psychoses which continued from childhood and developed insidiously and gradually; he knew, too, that psychotic persons had various degrees of ego maturity. Tausk, who wrote before the introduction of the structural theory and used the language then in vogue, seemed to understand to a degree which was advanced for his pe-

[2] In one recent population study, it was found that schizophrenia "had an acute onset in approximately 40% of the cases and a periodical course in as many cases." (Hallgren and Sjögren 1959:59.)

riod the contributions of derivatives of libidinal and aggressive drive energies to the development of normal, neurotic, and psychotic components within the same person. He rediagnosed Freud's "hysterical" patient, "Miss Emma A.," as a case of "paranoia somatica." Freud attended Tausk's (1919) presentation of his classical paper before the Vienna Psychoanalytic Society and raised no objection to Tausk's stand on these matters.

This chapter will be devoted to tracing the historical development of the thinking of Freud's followers concerning the therapy of the schizophrenias. The treatment of schizophrenia involving psychoanalytic principles has developed concurrently in Europe and the Americas. Nevertheless, its course has varied on the three continents. For convenience, this survey will be divided into two parts: (1) The first will deal with the growth of interest and the alterations of technique which have been employed in Europe and Latin America. (2) The second will concern itself with the attitudes of psychoanalysts of the United States. Because psychoanalysts have moved from one continent to another during their productive years, a strict division on the basis of geography is impossible.

THE CONTRIBUTIONS OF PSYCHOANALYSTS OF EUROPE AND LATIN AMERICA

The Pre-Kleinian Period

This section will trace the development of the thinking of psychoanalysts pertaining to the schizophrenias before the introduction of the Kleinian system of thought and its application to the treatment of this group of disorders.

Reading the pre-Freudian psychiatric literature and subsequently the writings of investigators of even the first decade of this century provides an exciting adventure—the contrast between the nihilistic attitude toward treatment of patients with psychopathological disorders which existed during the nineteenth century, and the initially exaggerated optimism reflected in the literature of the early twentieth century is remarkable. The difference between the sterility of theories concerning psychiatric illnesses before Freud introduced the results of his studies and the freshness of various subsequent approaches as reflected in the reports of clinicians who sought to test his ideas reminds one of the contrasting experiences of first viewing a still, arid desert in which but a few bedraggled, gray-green scrubby bushes dot the landscape, and then a verdant, semicultivated valley in which a shining stream provides sustenance for the growth of a number of species of varicolored plants.

The first group, stimulated by Freud's ideas, that sought to study the psychoses from a fresh viewpoint was headed by Bleuler at Burgholzli. His early thinking was influenced by Wundt. He sought to reconcile the differences between the opposing viewpoints of Wundt and Freud and to determine whether mental disorders could be explained best on an organic or a psychological basis. Bleuler (1911) introduced the term *schizophrenia* as a substitute for dementia praecox. He demonstrated the part that autistic thinking plays in the development of paranoia. He studied the language of schizophrenia, and explored regressive behavior. He believed the discrepancy between the aspirational level and moderate ability of the individual sets the stage for the development of delusions (Dorcus 1964). Bleuler (1911:1) wrote, "An important aspect of the attempt to advance and enlarge the concepts of psychopathology is nothing less than the application of Freud's ideas to dementia praecox." He also credited Abraham, Jung, and Riklin as having contributed greatly to the development of his ideas.[3]

Jung found so many similarities between hysteria and dementia praecox that one must wonder whether he clearly differentiated these conditions. Although he considered dementia praecox to be rooted more deeply in organic predisposition, he also considered hysteria to contain (1907:97) "in its innermost essence a complex which could never be totally overcome." His principal therapeutic tool for both seems to have been interpretations aimed at the removal of repressions. He eventually considered schizophrenia to be caused by an unusual strength of unconscious urges, so that an abnormal number of atavistic tendencies resulted in faulty adjustment to modern life.

Jung, although initially influenced heavily by Freud's ideas, deviated sharply later (Freud 1914; Glover 1950). His viewpoint was essentially biological, and, while he paid some attention to the effects of the past life of the individual, he conceptualized the existence of a collective unconscious in which primordial images or archetypes had been deposited as a result of countless recurrences of identical situations in previous generations. Whereas Freud wrote of inherited maturational

[3] See also Bleuler 1906, 1920; Jung 1906, 1907, 1908, 1911, 1914, 1939; Riklin 1906, 1907, 1910.

trends, Jung believed there to be inheritance of thought content.

Abraham (1907) believed that the symptoms of hysteria and schizophrenia were elaborations of sexual fantasies of an infantile character. He (1908) found that dementia praecox destroys the capacity for sexual transference and object-love, a condition that explained indifference to the outer world, but not other symptoms of the disorder. Nevertheless, Abraham mentioned gradations of schizophrenic involvement in different individuals and used interpretations aimed at the removal of repression with at least some patients. He considered the schizophrenic to be "ripe for delusions of persecution," because the patient who has withdrawn libido from objects to himself has set up an antithesis between the outer world and himself; then he loves only himself and his hostilities are projected onto persons who were previously loved. Abraham explained delusions of grandeur and overvaluation of the self on the basis of the attachment to the self of libido after its decathexis from love-objects. Thus the sexual overestimation which had returned to the ego was the source of the delusion of grandeur. He differentiated between hysteria and schizophrenia as follows: in the autoerotism of dementia praecox there is a return of the libido to the self, but in hysteria, object cathexis is exaggerated; in the former there is a loss of the capacity to sublimate, and in the latter there is increased sublimation. Although both conditions have an innate psychosexual constitution, that of schizophrenia depends on an inhibition of development. Abraham thus anticipated parts of Freud's (1911, 1914a) formulation concerning the psychoses.

In his 1908 presentation, Abraham did not consider

the psychotic to be incapable of hostile transference. Within a few years, he discussed a schizophrenic male. The patient had identified his father with the sun (as had Schreber). He wrote (1913:175): "The patient had also transferred to the sun his ambivalent attitude toward his father in a remarkable way. He disliked the light of the sun but loved its warmth." Thus, by 1913, Abraham no longer considered schizophrenics to have totally decathected libido from love-objects, and thought them to be capable of transference of libido as well as hostility.

Maeder (1910, 1911, 1923) found delusions of persecution to reflect projection and unresolved homosexuality; he thought delusions of grandeur to result from an introversion of libido which coincided with regression to a state in which all wishes could be satisfied in a world of fantasy, following removal of the inhibitions imposed by reality. He (1910) wrote (Payne 1913–1914:202): In psychosis "the content is strongly determined by individual thought elements [and] the motives for actions are relatively few and . . . most of them belong to the instinctive life of the infantile period."

Bertschinger (1911, 1911a) found that the schizophrenic patient can (1911:176) "regain control of his subconscious sphere by correction, resymbolization and evasion," and considered the outbreak of psychosis to constitute "the eruption of the subconscious into the conscious." He did not report actual treatment of schizophrenics.

Ferenczi (1911, 1914) supported Freud's position regarding homosexuality, as had Maeder, but he also wrote (Payne 1913–1914:89): "It turns out that the paranoic mechanism is not set up as a defence against all possible investment of the libido but according to present observations is directed only against the homosexual object choice." He thought paranoia in general to be "nothing else than distorted homosexuality."

Bjerre (1911) reported the intensive treatment during forty interviews of a patient who suffered from chronic paranoia. He detailed his method of therapy and was enthusiastic about its results. He wrote (Payne 1915:94): "[I worked] through the details of the patient's whole life from earliest childhood to the present, pointing out the proper value of everything false therein, sowing thousands of seeds of doubt concerning the delusions and then gradually bringing the unconscious complexes to light and setting them free." Initially, Bjerre was careful to avoid becoming the target of the patient's hostility. He was "sympathetic" and showed "not the slightest doubt" that the patient was persecuted. After the paranoic considered Bjerre to be his ally, he began to interpose explanations during the patient's recitals. Transference interpretations were made indirectly if at all. Bjerre felt the patient's feeling of security with him was a great factor in the eventual improvement. He considered interpretation to have been the principal effective tool of therapy but added (Payne 1915:100) that in the treatment of psychotics "One must also, and this in particular, take account of the immediate influences which the physician, often unconsciously, exercises by his person." Despite the tone of optimism which was so obvious in his presentation, Bjerre's forty-three subsequent articles and books do not include contributions which deal specifically with the treatment of psychotics.

Prior to Tausk's (1919) contribution, the writings of

other analysts offered but minor amplifications of Freud's views. They supported his position that the symptoms of the psychoses can be understood in the same way as those of the neuroses and that paranoia is either the product of, or closely related to, unresolved homosexuality. Fantasies and behavior were interpretated in terms of unconscious sexual meanings. Occasional analysts concerned themselves with the characteristics of schizophrenic language. Few articles demonstrated actual technical procedures employed in treatment. Most analysts who spoke directly of having treated schizophrenics wrote a single article; it usually presented an optimistic viewpoint concerning the usefulness of the procedure in producing improvement. However, since they contributed but one article, it would seem that their optimism waned.[4]

From 1919 onward, there seems to have been a renewed interest by psychoanalysts in the study of various aspects of the schizophrenias.

Boven (1921) appears to have been the first psychoanalyst to study in a systematic manner the home environments of patients who became psychotic. Storch wrote extensively of the archaic forms of inner experience and thought in the schizophrenias.[5] Hoop (1924, 1925) attributed the archaic elements of projections to the effects of the collective unconscious. Ophuijsen (1920) and Stärcke (1920) wrote of the origin of the feeling of persecution. They found the presumed attack

[4] The following contributions are representative: L. Binswanger 1910, 1917; Birnbaum 1909; Chijs 1919; Delgado 1919; Grebelskaya 1912; Hitschmann 1912, 1913; Jones 1909; Markus 1911; Morichau-Beaumont 1912; Nelken 1911, 1912, 1912a; Oppenheim 1912; Simmel 1909; Stärcke 1904; Ter-Ogannessien 1912; Wanke 1919, 1922; Wulff 1909.

[5] Storch 1922, 1923, 1927, 1930, 1947, 1948, 1951, 1957; Storch and Kulenkampf 1950.

by a homosexual love-object to be a later development of an earlier fear of attack by the skybalum. The persecutor became the personification of the fecal mass and the sensations it produced. Few psychoanalysts wrote in detail of their treatment methods.[6] Nunberg (1921) was an exception.

Nunberg wrote at length of the treatment of a schizophrenic patient. He considered the active fostering of a "positive transference" to be mandatory, a position which was widely supported later (Alexander 1931; Federn 1933).[7]

As discussed in Chapter Two, Waelder (1924) suggested that certain schizophrenic patients might be benefited by psychoanalysis without gross modifications, and Brunswick (1928) tacitly supported his stand. Landauer (1924) wrote of his procedure in treating schizophrenics, stressing the beneficial results of relatively "passive techniques." He recommended gradual education of the patient concerning his uses of projective mechanisms and active interpretation of hostile transference reactions. Positive transference manifestations were to be ignored. Landauer discovered that in dealing with auditory hallucinations, asking questions about them as though they originated from a third person resulted in improved reality testing, the patient identifying with the therapist's attitude and feeling pleasure by "overcoming" the analyst.[8]

Laforgue (1926) outlined a complex defensive sys-

6 Bumke 1924; Caravedo 1924; Delgado 1922, 1937; Delgado and Valdigan 1923; Hartmann 1925; Hartmann and Stumpfl 1930; Minkowski 1925, 1927, 1929; Saussure 1924; Stärcke 1921, 1928; Wilmanns 1922.

7 Nunberg's treatment methods had much in common with those of Federn (1933, 1952), to be outlined later.

8 Landauer's publications dealing with the psychoses reached over a 17-year period (1914, 1926, 1927, 1927–1928, 1928, 1930).

tem which he considered to be of great importance in the development of schizophrenia. His argument was the following: During the stage of psychological weaning, if the child in times of stress is refused refuge by the mother, he responds by attempting to create a narcissistic substitute for her. He introjects two images of his mother and scotomizes the real mother, from whom he withdraws and whose care he denies he needs. One introjected image is that of the caretaker, and the other is of the idealized mother who demands perfection of behavior and achievement, the mother-ideal. The development of the narcissistic substitute enables the child to avoid the sufferings of the process of psychological weaning and to neutralize the feelings of inferiority which are inevitable during that process. However, the child is unable to tolerate future frustrations and remains fixated at the anal-sadistic phase. He develops a personality split which Laforgue called schizonoia. He remains an individual who is easily traumatized by frustrations and yet attempts to live up to the self-demands imposed by the introjected mother-ideal; he cannot do so and feels guilt and worthlessness. The child also identifies one aspect of the introjected mother with excrement. In order to kill the frustrating parents, he withdraws from life; in order to castrate them, he thus castrates himself. He depersonalizes people, makes them into feces and then chooses feces as his libidinal objects. He becomes receptive to all that has to do with destruction and scotomizes that which is constructive. He chooses his own ego as a love object, but he dissects every thought until nothing remains. While he indulges in this sort of mental digestion, he projects the persecutor.

Laforgue, then, was among the first to stress the role of the sadistic and archaic superego in schizophrenia, although he did not mention that part of the psychical structure by name. At a later time (1935) he presented a case history which outlined his treatment method.[9]

Odile was a schizophrenic girl who made repeated attempts at suicide and was eventually hospitalized after she shot herself in the head, producing a superficial wound. Her illness had begun with an obsession about germs. She urinated in public, drank her urine, and ate slugs; she raged with incoherent words and suffered obstinate constipation. She was awkward and slow physically. She was brought to Laforgue's office by force and was mute. She was seen four times weekly.

Odile lived with a sister who cared for her. During the first weeks of treatment, she was panicky in Laforgue's presence and frequently ran into the waiting room to be with her sister. Since she was mute, he judged her emotional state by her pulse rate, posture, and actions. During the first months, Laforgue made his interpretations in the presence of the sister. At first he said only that she feared being alone with him. Later he said she feared love and equated it with excrement; that her constipation was connected with her disgust about sexual things. He said her guilt was great and that she hated herself for having bodily needs. He also told her that she could not collect within herself forever her physical and mental excrement.

After some months, Odile remained in the office with him but she maintained almost complete silence. She continued to make suicidal attempts, but in such a way

[9] See also Laforgue 1926a, 1929; Laforgue and Claude 1925; Laforgue and Hesnard 1930–1931.

as to be prevented by her sister. She began to talk and to lose her constipation. She developed severe insomnia; Laforgue said she remained awake lest a man enter her room. Eventually, references to sexual things did not make her pulse race. The analyst strove to lessen her guilt about sexual thoughts and about her hostile, controlling behavior toward her family. After a year, she slept well, was sociable with her family, and went regularly and spontaneously to the toilet. Suicidal behavior continued.

During a vacation period, she tried to throw herself under a train; there were no further attempts to take her life. She then began to lie on the couch and to report her dreams. Progress in locomotion was noticeable; she began to skate and to sew deftly. Nevertheless, she seemed not to exist as a feeling person; sensibility was interdicted. Her verbal productions were memories; there was no thought synthesis. Irrational fears were replaced by "rational" ones, such as being near high windows and skating on thin ice.

As she improved, her sister became glum, so Laforgue treated her as well. After he interpreted to the sister her resentment of loss of authority over the patient and said she had used her relationships with Odile to avoid men, the relationships between the sisters changed. Odile went into a rage at her sister; it was determined that the rage was at all women who couldn't have children and were thus inferior. Soon thereafter Odile became interested in the analyst and asked for personal information. Laforgue did not state whether he answered her questions, but he did give her mouth wash upon her request. The subject matter then went to her germ phobia; thence to her compulsory adolescent masturbation.

Guilt concerning masturbation had led first to the phobia and then to the schizophrenic regression. Except for the giving of the mouth wash and perhaps some personal information, the treatment technique apparently changed to orthodox analysis after the understanding of the rage at the sister.

Bychowski (1929) suggested that psychoanalytic principles be employed in the treatment of the schizophrenias, although he considered the introduction of varying modifications of the "passive technique" (Landauer 1924) to be essential. Bychowski has continued to be actively engaged in the treatment of the schizophrenias. Although his earlier writings appear to have been oriented within the framework of the topographical theory, he progressively shifted his viewpoint to the structural hypothesis. He has contributed valuable information concerning the roles of the introjects in the ego of the preschizophrenic and the schizophrenic.[10] Nevertheless, he believes that the introduction of technical modifications is necessary in the treatment of both borderline and psychotic patients.

Garma (1931) thought psychoanalysis could be used successfully without gross modification of technique. He has been using psychoanalysis in the treatment of psychotics for the past thirty-five years, employing the couch and using interpretations as his principal therapeutic tool. As with psychoneurotics, he seeks to systematically analyze the transference relationships and the defenses. He was one of the first to introduce the idea that in schizophrenia the superego is extremely punitive and archaic; he postulated that the severity of

[10] Bychowski 1923, 1932, 1943, 1945, 1947, 1951, 1952, 1952a, 1953, 1954, 1963, 1965.

the superego was in large part responsible for the repression of libidinal and aggressive drive derivatives. He became influenced strongly by Kleinian thinking and joined Rascovsky (1960) in his extension of her system into a study of fetal psychology.[11]

Federn was also a psychoanalyst who consistently treated schizophrenics over a long period.[12] He (1933) presented specific recommendations for the therapeusis of the schizophrenias and many of the technical procedures he recommended have been accepted by numerous therapists.

According to Federn, if the patient is to be helped, the family or some substitute individual must give active cooperation to the therapy. If the schizophrenic is hospitalized, the nurses and attendants should have been schooled in psychoanalytic principles. Treatment must be directed toward the patient's reason insofar as he maintains it. The transference situation of the schizophrenic is even more important than that of the neurotic, and every possible step must be taken to have the patient's attitudes toward the therapist remain positive. If the doctor-patient relationship becomes hostile, the therapist cannot be effective. Without defining just what he meant by transference or countertransference, Federn wrote (p. 210): "Psychotic patients are accessible to psychoanalysis at all, first, because and in so far as they are still capable of transference; secondly, because and in so far as one part of their ego has insight into their abnormal state, and thirdly, because and in so

[11] Garma 1935, 1945, 1962, 1965.

[12] Federn (1952) developed a theory of ego psychology which is at variance with Freud's. It will not be outlined here because it seems to have had little influence on the theoretical position of very many analysts (Weiss 1952), although some of his technical procedures have been widely imitated.

far as a part of their personality is directed towards reality." The second part of this statement depends on whether the patient has temporary remissions. The chief precaution is to avoid regression wherever possible. Free associations and the use of the couch are contraindicated and the "countertransference" must not be withheld. After the patient has learned what is wrong with his causal behavior and can dissimulate normal behavior, the analyst may cautiously investigate deeper material.

The dependency of the litigious psychotic can be exploited in the therapy. The analyst should help him in the actual affairs of his life. He should seek the connections between the patient's psychotic utterances and his symptoms and between the actual occurrences of his life and his symptoms. After these phenomena and the "actual occurrences of transference situations in his life" are determined, the analyst can explain to the patient the real motives which actuate his behavior and thinking.

While the patient who is not in analysis is benefited by the opportunity for a normal sexual life, Federn considered sterilization by ligature of the oviducts or vas deferens to be indicated in the treatment of some patients. Consistent attempts must be made to avoid flight into introversion. At the same time, "we must suffer" the affect-charged conflicts of rage; after explosions have occurred, they can be anaylzed. Only then "we can aim at substituting abreaction according to the analytic method." The psychotic must never be depreciated or treated as a child. We must fully respect the patient's right to his own personality. At the same time, the analyst should gratify the patient's oral cravings and show him hospitality. (Federn sometimes had patients live with him.) He recommended the use of a female helper and lasting postpsychotic contact and help.

The aim of Federn's treatment was to encapsulate "permanent psychotic reactions," to accomplish what occurs in "spontaneous" recovery. That he considered the psychosis itself to be incurable is implicit. Although he called his treatment "The Analysis of Psychotics," he employed very wide deviations from psychoanalysis as it is practiced with neurotics. He conducted psychotherapy in a psychoanalytical framework. Some of his technical modifications were obviously not analyzable, as is consistent with his orientation and treatment goal.

Some remarks concerning the influence of Ferenczi's technical deviations from classical psychoanalysis are in order. No systematic presentation of his ideas pertaining directly to the treatment of the psychoses has come to my attention.[13] Nevertheless, his modifications are evident in the work of analysts both in Europe and the United States, especially Melanie Klein and Harry Stack Sullivan and their followers.

Ferenczi (1929, 1931), Rank (1926, 1929), and W. Reich (1933) were dissatisfied with the efficacy of the psychoanalytical treatment of the neuroses. They considered Freud to have understressed the significance of the emotional relationship of the patient and the analyst in the therapeutic situation. Ferenczi emphasized above all that the psychoanalytic situation involved the interaction of two personalities and that its outcome depends upon resolution of both transference and countertransference phenomena. He felt the dynamic train of

[13] Ferenczi 1911, 1911a, 1913, 1914, 1922.

analytic experience to be dependent upon three precepts (de Forest 1942; Thompson 1943, 1950): (1) An emotional relationship between patient and therapist must be fostered and maintained, in part by overt "befriending" of the patient by the use of open reassurances given by the therapist, and by the use of a dramatic dialogue, including "forced fantasies," rather than the usual explanations and interpretations of the analyst-teacher. (2) The analyst must make himself the center of each association and action of the patient. At the same time, he is at liberty to validate the patient's notions about him and to disclose his own feelings. (3) To bring the critical dramatic moments of the analysis to the surface, care must be taken to avoid alleviating emotional tension. Technical terms are to be avoided and interpretive explanations are to be used most sparingly.

Thompson (1943, 1955) felt that Ferenczi's entering into the transference mood of the patient and his dramatizing interpersonal relationships may have precipitated psychotic episodes when used with borderline patients, and she doubted the value of open reassurance. It is obvious that his departures from ordinary analytic technique were gross and that some of the interventions he employed were not analyzable. Klein was heavily influenced by the thinking of Ferenczi and many of her followers seem to frame every intervention or interpretation given to the psychotic patient within the context of the transference relationship.

The Kleinian System

The development of child analysis as a specialized branch of psychoanalysis began in the 1920's. With its growth, investigators divided into two major groups whose divergent theoretical and technical orientations have significantly influenced psychoanalytic thinking regarding the genesis and treatment of the schizophrenias. The work of Anna Freud and her colleagues has contributed substantially to the unfolding of ego psychology and amplification of the structural hypothesis; they have been accepted by one group of European analysts and the vast majority of clinicians in the United States. The studies of Melanie Klein and her supporters have taken a different direction; they have shaped the philosophies of a second major group of European analysts and most of those of Latin America. Kleinian ideas have stimulated more clinicians to work psychoanalytically with psychotics without the use of extra-analytic procedures than have those of Anna Freud.

According to Glover (1945), the findings of the early child analysts were more corroborative of Freud's (1909) analysis of Little Hans than original in scope. He wrote (p. 76):

> Child analysis was in the first instance a branch of applied psychoanalysis, a behavioristic study. . . . As far as infancy is concerned it must remain an observational study, for until the child's mind has reached the stage of development at which it can understand the meanings of interpretations, the psychic system between the child and the analyst remains one of spontaneous or, at the most, of developed rapport only.

Before the 1920's, Freud had delineated positive and negative aspects of the Oedipus situation and outlined the structure of the mind during that phase. His analysis of the obsessional neurosis (1909a, 1913, 1917) had enabled him to understand the stage immediately preceding the Oedipus phase. However, between the anal phase and the earliest stages of infantile psychosexual activity, a gap remained in the understanding of psychical structure; it was but tenuously outlined by the adumbration of various steps in the development of the libido, conceptions related to the development of object relations and etiological formulations pertaining to paranoia and melancholia (Freud 1905, 1911, 1914a, 1917a). Those steps were expressed principally in terms of libidinal development although such terms as oral-sadism, anal-sadism, and ambivalence indicated some understanding of the role played by aggression. To repeat, there were in essence no clearly depicted cross-sections of the mind of children of less than three years of age which were comparable with those which had been constructed for the child of three to five years. Concepts of id, ego, and superego were first described in terms of the classical oedipal phase. Hypotheses concerning preoedipal regulatory systems were undelineated. Ferenczi (1925:267) had combined the idea of the anal-sadistic stage of the libido with that of the superego by describing "sphincter morality" but this concept was not well correlated with ego structure.

Melanie Klein, a highly intuitive pioneer child analyst who had great clinical acumen, set herself the important task of filling the gap left unexplored by Freud (between birth and the second or third year of life), to elucidate the preoedipal phases of psychical development.[14] She (1920, 1930, 1948) became aware earlier

[14] In this inadequate review of her thinking, only a few aspects are considered. The comments regarding her theories which are presented here lean especially on the evaluations presented by Bibring (1947), Glover (1945), Waelder (1937), and Zetzel (1953, 1956). See also Alexander 1933; Bergman 1962; Blum 1953; Brierley 1942; Ekstein 1949; Fine 1962; Geleerd 1963; Guntrip 1961; Pasche and Renard 1956; Rosenfeld 1959; Scott 1949; Strachey 1941; Wisdom 1962.

than most analysts of the importance of aggression and depression in psychical development. Whereas Freud (1905) had attributed the sources of sexual excitement in the young child to physiological sources, Klein sought to explain them on purely psychological grounds. In his discussion of the metapsychology of psychotic depression, Abraham (1924) had indicated clearly the important role of objects which had been introjected in an ambivalent or hostile manner in the genesis of depressive states. Klein found evidence of animistic fantasies which involved the uses of introjection and projection in her treatment of both children and borderline and psychotic adults (1930a). She wrote of her conceptualization of the development of the psychology of the preoedipal child in *The Psycho-Analysis of Children* (1932).

Applying the concepts of projection and introjection and becoming ever more convinced of the importance of the role of aggression in the development of anxiety which occurred with oral frustration, Klein concluded that the infant's life is dominated by alternating processes of introjection and projection. These mechanisms overcome the baby's anxiety with regard to his aggressive fantasies, chiefly through the development of libido and its fusion with aggression. Simultaneously, she hypothesized that these fantasies had specific contents; that they contained elements of an oedipal conflict at a period which far antedated the classical oedipal period. Then she suggested that the depression which she attributed to the early months of life could be compared in all essential aspects with the structure of depression in the postoedipal period as described by Abraham (1924).

Klein's point of departure was the effect of early anxiety situations on the development of the child. The infant's reactions to painful experiences were thought to be highly significant. Repeated and extreme oral frustrations intensified reactive feelings of sadness, anger, and rage. In the functioning of the primitive ego, intensified oral-libidinal needs merge with oral sadism, leading to internal as well as external frustration; the infant reacts with anxiety to both and considers its own destructive impulses to threaten its existence (1932:184). The resultant tension prematurely mobilizes defense mechanisms, especially projection. Consequently, the external frustrating object becomes a destructive agent and fears are focused on it. However, ejection and projection of aggression are inadequate defenses, and the panic-stricken ego seeks to protect itself from the dangerous objects through destroying them. In the oral stage, this attempt is expressed by the sadistic need to devour the breast and its contents. In this conceptualization, oral-libidinal, oral-aggressive, and self-preservative tendencies are blended into a functional whole. Since the infant is thought to hallucinate gratifications of its needs, and the hallucinations are assumed to have the value of reality, the infant believes it has truly destroyed the object. However, the fact remains that the motor discharge of the infant's tensions is limited and that hallucinated gratification is even more limited, the destructive defense is illusory. At this point, another defense mechanism sets in: the accumulated aggressive-libidinal trends spread to all bodily functions, which become vehicles of sadism. This spreading of tension, as Bibring (1947:73) notes, constitutes a theoretical conception of the first order in Klein's reconstruction of development. Its taking place can be conceptualized as a mechanical spreading from a point of high tension to that of a lower one, or it is actively distributed by the ego. Klein gives preference to the latter method.

The spreading of oral-sadistic tensions takes place in two directions: in cross-section onto a variety of existing functions and in longitudinal section along developmental lines. Abraham (1924) explained the relationship between the oral-libidinal and oral-sadistic phases by assuming that frustration at the sucking stage increased the need for gratification in the biting stage which followed; the biting stage supplanted the frustrated energies of the sucking stage and was intensified by them. The cannibalistic phase made up for the frustrations of the sucking stage. According to Klein, sensations or impulses which appeared at the beginning of dentition are not only immediately intensified by and fused with the oral tension complex, but are also forced to unfold.

The hypothesis of spreading, however, includes spreading to genital sensations and ideas at this very early age. Klein wrote (1932:188): "In the early analyses we find . . . that oral frustration arouses in the child an unconscious knowledge of sexual pleasure." The orally frustrated infant girl withdraws from the disappointing part object, the nipple, and hallucinates a completely satisfying huge nipple, capable of filling the whole mouth. This fantasy forms a transitional link between the nipple and the phallus. The infant is fully capable of the "unconscious understanding" of symbols. Klein wrote (p. 271): "This equation of penis and breast, accompanied as it is by a displacement from above downwards, activates the oral, receptive qualities of the female at a very early age." The nipple-penis is desired simultaneously in the mouth and vagina, the existence of which has been conceptualized from the extension of oral tension to the vaginal area. The concept of developmental spreading opposes the Freudian idea of development in steps or stages. In his view, the various psychosexual stages develop constitutionally in more or less typical succession. In the Kleinian hypothesis, there are no stages but a continuous development from one "position" to another. There is a genetic continuity which is a kind of chain reaction along an uninterrupted line of transitional links.

The activation process differs in girls and boys. The girl is forced to know of the vagina by her symbolic equation of nipple and phallus and her desires to have her mouth and vagina filled. In the boy, the biting impulses arouse penetration impulses of the penis. Secondary process logic is ascribed to the infant boy who, since he has the impulse to penetrate with his penis, conceptualizes the vagina as a receptor organ. Thus internal data such as obscure reference sensations and impulses lead to knowledge of such external facts as complementary sex organs. Bibring (1947:79) called such "knowledge" "sensation or impulse knowledge."

Klein assumed this sensation knowledge to play an important role in further development of boys and girls. According to her, oral frustration arouses in the child an "unconscious knowledge" that its parents enjoy sexual pleasures, originally conceived to be of an oral sort. She wrote (1932:188): "It appears that an unconscious knowledge . . . about sexual intercourse between the parents, together with fantasies concerning it, already emerge at this very early stage of development." With this new-found "knowledge" the infant enters the painful period of the early oedipal conflicts. The girl's fellatic idea is associated with the knowledge that sucking gets milk (or semen) and, from the child's alimentary experience, reaches the concepts also of excrement and baby. The nipple-penis or milk-semen are taken in and a feces-baby are made of it. Jones (1933:22–23) later wrote "the girl's wish to have a child . . . is a direct continuance of her autoerotic desire for the penis. She wants to enjoy taking the penis into the body and to make a child from it." "The insertion of the nipple into the mouth is followed by the anal-erotic pleasure at the passage of feces." He did not suggest that such mentation exists during the first year of life. The child, with the assistance of sensations and symbolic equations, comes to know of procreation, parenthood, and children, of the roles of the parents in procreation, of elimination and birth processes, etc. All of this information becomes available to the child of six to twelve months of life.

In this formulation, infantile development is precipitous. The ego develops in advance of the libido. The impetus of development is the tension resultant from oral frustration; it is an intrapsychic process when once set in motion and not the result of further interplay of growth and environment. The development of drives and some ego functions can be accelerated far beyond the total development of the child as a nearly completely independent unit. An implicit assumption in this system of thinking is that maturation, the principle of growth, does not apply to the unconscious.

Bibring (1947) has taken issue with these concepts. He noted that factors such as frustration, accumulation and intensification of tension, and anxiety which strongly influence the development of the ego and the drives are familiar to psychoanalysis. Succeeding instinctual interests can be modified by preceding stages, and such factors can have a formative influence on even infants of a few months of age. However (pp. 84–85), "it is difficult to accept the proposition that such emergency factors represent all or the most important 'motors' of development. Development is more than a defense mechanism, and the 'motors' of development something more than tensions and anxieties." Bibring also found the exclusive role ascribed by Klein to the importance of endopsychic development which is largely independent of any external simulation to be deficient, pointing to experimental observations of the development of instincts in animals which show that phylogenetically determined instincts are predominantly directed toward external stimuli. Such stimuli are, as a rule, typical and specific, producing phylogenetically determined responses; their absence during a particular stage of development may result in the nonappearance or loss of certain instinctual functions.[15]

[15] According to Hess (1964), two types of learning have been differentiated: imprinting and associational learning. The evidence summarized by Hess has established that such different learning processes and characteristics exist in birds. Washburn (1965) states that studies of anthropoids indicate the existence also of imprinting and associational learning although the time periods involved are longer for mammals than avians. The brain of birds is almost mature at birth and includes scant cortical structuration. Learning of the imprinting type appears to take place during the period which precedes the expansion and myelinization of the cortex. Associational learning takes place in the presence of a more highly developed cortex.

It may be that Bowlby's (1958) concepts of primary object-seeking and primary object-clinging, as parts of the id, may be understood within a conceptualization of human imprinting. (See also Rollman-Branch 1960.) Klein (1932) clearly ascribed associational thinking to the infant. However, Piaget's (1924, 1927) observations indicate that associational learning depends upon a physical development of the nervous system beyond that of the infant of the first few months of life.

Zetzel (1956) believed that Klein or her followers should indicate how true reality testing and secondary process thinking can be understood in terms of the basic Kleinian premises, and how maturation plays a role in the different stages of development. Without such elaboration, Klein's work cannot be correlated within the main body of analytic theory. Zetzel noted the confusion which results when concept and content are not clearly distinguished.

In the opinion of the majority of psychoanalysts whose theoretical orientation has followed the mainstream of analytic thought, those who have followed Klein have extrapolated backward from observations made during the treatment of children who can verbalize and of borderline and psychotic patients and developed a psychology which is incompatible with the structural theory. They believe that while hypothetical reconstructions of the mind in early infancy can increase the plausibility of clinical interpretations, thus giving the therapist a feeling of confidence which may be exceedingly important in his establishment of contact with his psychotic patient, such interpretations are not subject to validation from observational studies or from the memories of the patients; they may lead to confusion which frequently follows from the blending of fantasy and fact. Hartmann and Kris (1945) noted that the retrospective method was in the past in a position to direct attention to new areas in the child's life and that there is no reason to believe that this function of pointing to the essential is exhausted. However, the retrospective method can do no more than to establish interconnections between experiences that are bound to escape observers who have less intimate insight. Some followers of Klein have extrapolated her hypotheses even further backward and held that determinate fantasies and perhaps even psychic structuralization exist *in utero* and perhaps in the ovum (Rascovsky *et al.* 1960; personal communication). However, few analysts who do not follow the so-called English School believe that the existence of such fantasies in infants can be validated. Glover (1945) was especially harshly critical of this retrospective extrapolation. In his judgment, the Kleinian group have reduced to confusion Freudian concepts of the mental apparatus and have undermined basic distinctions between unconscious and conscious systems and the primary and secondary processes of mentation. With Bibring (1947), Glover considered them to have departed from the Freudian theory of nosogenesis. He suggested that the Kleinian theory of a central depressive position which develops between the third and fifth months of life is a "closed system" which, if it were generally accepted, would arrest all possibility of correlating normal and abnormal manifestations of adult life with stages of development in infancy; he also thought that such a stand subverts all standardly accepted concepts of development from the unorganized to the organized. Many analysts agree (Zetzel 1953) that while the superego of the classical Oedipus phase has forerunners and that Klein performed a valuable service with her focusing attention on that neglected area, her formulations depend on dogmatic assumptions.

In 1932, Klein had stated that the phase of maximum sadism occurs toward the end of the first year of life, and she spoke of the importance of introjection and projection of good or bad part objects and of the denial of reality. Soon thereafter, Klein (1935) stated that a depressive position develops at the stage of passing from "part object" to "whole object" relations, between the third and fifth months, at which time there is an increase in projective processes which have the purpose of preserving the love-object inside the self. Rivière (1936) then stated that all neuroses are different varieties of defense against the fundamental anxiety of the depressive position. This position appears to have been accepted generally by the Kleinians. Segal (1954) considered infantile neuroses to constitute means of working through earlier psychotic anxieties of both paranoid-schizoid and manic-depressive natures. Such a position would seem to confirm Glover's (1945) comment that the Kleinian group had committed themselves to a monistic theory of psychopathogenesis. Anna Freud (1943) found "these new theories" to be bewildering. She noted that although the Kleinians maintained that their system of thought constituted local extensions of the thinking of Abraham, Ferenczi, Freud, and Jones, while some existing analytic concepts were stated to be retained, they were concurrently denied.

It is interesting to speculate why this system of thinking which was found to be so controversial and stimulated such bitter antagonism came to have so powerful an influence over a large group of psychoanalysts. Glover suggested that support of Kleinian viewpoints was due to a lack of objective evaluation of the conceptual implications of her extrapolations from fantasy contents which had been ascribed to infants. He thought that psychoanalysts who had been eager to have problems of early development solved for them had uncritically accepted the Kleinians' statements that their ideas were logical extensions of the thinking of the aforementioned analysts. Others have considered the personality of Mrs. Klein to have played an important role in the acceptance of her ideas by a devoted coterie. Whatever the truth may be, we might recall that she introduced her theories during a period which followed Freud's presentation of the structural theory and ego psychology was in its infancy. The lack of understanding of the structural theory and its implications was widespread during the period in which Klein introduced her ideas. Additionally, at that time the work of scientists in other disciplines, notably ethology and neurophysiology, was not so relevant to psychology as is true today and there was less evidence with which one could compare Klein's theories.

Regardless of the degree of logic one ascribes to the Kleinian system of thought, it cannot be denied that the thinking and the technical procedures used by Kleinians in the treatment of children have had great influence on the development of the psychoanalytic treatment of the schizophrenias.

During the 1930's and 1940's, Klein and her followers continued to apply her concepts to studies of children and some articles appeared which delineated studies of psychotic children (Isaacs 1939, 1943; Klein 1946). Fairbairn (1936) treated borderline or psychotic individuals and used Kleinian concepts. His technical approach remained initially closely aligned with that of orthodox psychoanalysts.[16] From the mid-forties on-

16 Fairbairn has extended Klein's conception of internalized objects, "which traces its scientific origin to Freud's theory of the superego" (1944:70), and developed the hypothesis that libido is not primarily pleasure-seeking, but object-seeking. To him, the anal and phallic phases are artefacts. The schizoid and manic-depressive states are not to be regarded as defenses but as states to be defended against. The

ward, an increasing number of the so-called English School have involved themselves in the treatment of schizophrenia; they have reported their therapeutic methods and been optimistic regarding the results of their procedures.[17] The work of Rosenfeld is most widely known; he has been treating psychotic patients of various types, using psychoanalysis which has included the minimum number of parameters and extra-analytic steps he deemed necessary. He, like Garma, has aimed at the systematic analysis of the transference relationships and of the patient's resistances.

In general, Kleinian analysts have not insisted that borderline and psychotic patients lie on the couch, although it seems that patients frequently assume the reclining position soon after a working relationship has been developed. As is consistent with Klein's stress on the analysis of introjective-projective mechanisms, their use is emphasized in treatment in the form of analysis of projective-identification, and all interventions and inter-

---

outstanding feature of infantile dependence is its unconditional character which is focused on a single object. The intrauterine state is the most extreme form of dependence; "on its psychological side it is characterized by an absolute degree of identification" and "Normal development is characterized by a process whereby progressive differentiation of the object is accompanied by a progressive decrease in identification" (Fairbairn 1941:269). He thought the fetus to be aware of its dependence on the mother, a viewpoint which seems once again highly questionable and to be subject to the charge that he has attributed to the fetus psychical capacities which are known to apply to children who are old enough to talk. His ideas on the awareness of dependence of the fetus and new-born baby are hard to bring into consonance with Spitz's (1946) studies concerning eight-months' anxiety, for example. Fairbairn's ideas have been used in an attempt to understand some behavioral and ideational productions of schizophrenic patients (Brandschaft 1964) and they have been discussed critically (Abenheimer 1955; Balint 1957: 281–291; Guntrip 1961; Montano 1965; C. T. Sullivan 1963:56 *et seq.*).

[17] Representative contributions are those by Abadi 1954; Avenburg 1962; Bion 1954, 1955, 1956, 1957; Gioia and Liberman 1953; Grinberg 1959, 1959a, 1965; Liberman 1952, 1957; Nöllmann 1953; Paz 1963; Pichon-Rivière 1946, 1947, 1952; Rolla 1957, 1958, 1959, 1964; Rosenfeld 1947, 1950, 1952, 1952a, 1954, 1956, 1959; Sandford 1952; Segal 1950, 1956.

pretations appear to be made strictly within the context of the transference situation. The majority of analysts stress the need for vigilance on the part of the analyst for evidence that he, too, is using projective-identification in dealing with his patient; there seems to be no consistency among these analysts in regard to whether they communicate their own feelings verbally to the patient. From the standpoint of the non-Kleinian, one of the most interesting technical procedures commonly employed is early interpretation from the side of the id and the analyst's verbalizing his understanding of what he considers to be the patient's unconscious fantasies even during the initial interview. An illustration of the emphasis on projective-identification combined with early interpretation of what the analyst considered to be the patient's unconscious fantasies follows (Avenburg 1962:351–352).

All the analyst knew of his patient was that his parents were living, that he had a sweetheart and a two-year-younger brother. The patient was twenty-five years old, and the day before the first analytic session he had terminated a course of insulin shock therapy. He was interviewed four times weekly, face to face. At the beginning of the fourth interview, the patient waited for a short time before the analyst opened the door of the consultation room, perhaps waiting for the handshake with which the analyst opened and ended each interview. "He waited in silence, observing his surroundings and making his movements very hesitantly. After a short time I interpreted to him:

ANALYST: You are observing what happens inside me.
PATIENT: What happens inside me.

A: What happens to your parts which are located in me.
P: I wish to see why I am mute; today I was dumb with everybody. (He remained in silence, hanging on my movements.) Do you believe that it is possible to converse without speaking?
A: That would be what you are doing with me.
P: I think so, but if I would not be very worried."

Avenburg interpolated: "What has occurred to this moment? He has located determinate parts of his own inside me, although we do not know what characteristics they have, but we are able to see his conduct because of them: he wishes to maintain himself isolated (mute) but not too removed; he must at the same time control those parts with conversation which does not include talking. At this time I interpreted to him:

A: You are in touch with the spirit but you are afraid of physical closeness because you fear my penetration." (Later in the article, Avenburg said he had meant "reintrojection" when he used the word "penetration.")

(Author's translation.)

Another step employed by some Kleinian analysts is illustrated by the following example. A woman patient had been taken from the breast when three months old. During an interview in which it became clear that she was envious of her analyst, he first made her conscious of her feelings, and then said to her, "You feel now just as you did when you were at your mother's breast and there was not enough milk for you."

Both of these interpretations are consistent with the Kleinian framework of thinking as outlined above. No doubt they have some degree of accuracy. However, it seems to me that the analysts arbitrarily interpreted their patients' associations to fit their theory. Regressed patients are most apt to ascribe omniscience to their analysts, especially when the therapists make statements with an attitude which portrays certainty. One must wonder whether the use of such technical procedures constitutes the most important element leading to their improvement, or whether introjection of projections or of distorted aspects of the analyst's personality is more responsible for the reconstruction of the ego of the patient, or at least for his symptomatic improvement.

Contributions of Non-Kleinian Analysts from the 1940's

At the same time that followers of Klein became active in the psychoanalytic treatment of schizophrenia, other analysts continued their studies. It is interesting to note that few of them have tried to use psychoanalysis which does not include gross deviations from the classical technique.

Schwing (1940) provided therapeutic optimism to psychiatrists who seemed to have resigned themselves to treating severely disturbed patients with what amounted to custodial care after ordinary physical and supportive treatments had failed. Her procedure consisted essentially in providing what she called a "loving environment." She was permissive and attended to the patient's bodily needs, an act which may in itself have been therapeutic, since the patients with whom she worked sometimes were incapable of recognizing their own bodily needs. Interpretation played a scant role in treatment. She encouraged the development of dependency and then sought to gratify the patients' demands by direct, nonsymbolic actions. Eissler (1943) believed her therapy was effective because it provided a marked contrast to the care the patient had received from his parents. He suggested that her treatment relieved guilt feelings. While this mechanism may have applied to some of the patients, one wonders why patients who were concurrently depressed were not relieved of guilt by the accusatory and rejecting attitudes to which they had been subjected. It seems possible that some of the improvement can be attributed to relief of anxiety through environmental support of paranoid ideation of mistreatment. Stone (1955) considered her treatment to have proceeded only to the level of establishing contact. Schwing's case reports suggest that the nature of that contact did not progress much beyond that of supportive-dependency.

Sechehaye (1947) treated a seriously regressed schizophrenic girl.[18] During the first three and one-half months, treatment was of a tentative nature. When Sechehaye made her intention to continue clear, Renée, her patient, said she now had a mother. During the first two years, treatment consisted essentially of explaining, reassuring, and bodily contact. Sechehaye wrote (p. 42): "I resolutely take the side of the ego against unconscious self-punishment." Verbal interpretations were given rarely and seemed to have no effect. Eventually it became necessary to rehospitalize Renée. Then Sechehaye began to give her in symbolic form things she considered to have been factually withheld from the patient during her early life, such as an apple for a breast. "Taking an apple, and cutting it in two, I offer Renée a piece, saying, 'It is time to drink the good milk from

[18] See also Sechehaye 1955, 1956, 1957, 1957a.

Mummy's apples'" (p. 51). "The first symbol which represented Renée was a little plush monkey which I had given her." "It personified the ego still dominated by the impulses of the 'enlightening'" (p. 55). Sechehaye reasoned (pp. 142-143):

> The "loving mother" had to find something other than the verbal method of psychoanalysis, because the initial conflict had occurred before the development of spoken language and because the patient had regressed to the stage of magical presymbol participation. The only [mode] that could be used was that which is suitable to the baby: expression by the symbolic signs of gestures and movements.

Various therapists have utilized a combination of the treatments recommended by Schwing and Sechehaye. For example, in Canada, Azima and Wittkower (1956) thought that an aspect of pathogenesis can be understood as the real or imagined frustration of basic needs at the oral and anal levels. Accordingly, they designed a method of treatment which was supposed to gratify needs in an "appropriate setting and with appropriate objects." They provided milk, baby bottles, brown clay, and mud to provide a miniature infantile situation in which "appropriate" feelings can be expressed. They stated that subsequent to the establishment of this type of relationship with the therapist, progressive ego interpretation is made possible or at least potentiated. Von Staabs (1954) stated that she dealt with the behavior and verbalizations of the patient less by interpretation than by her own reactions.

During the past twenty-five years, European analysts have become less pessimistic regarding the treatment of schizophrenia. Many of them have used therapeutic procedures which have included interpretation as an essential element,[19] and the role of transference has been studied more frequently than before.[20] As was the case previously, many articles have continued to present general remarks and to reflect concern about establishing diagnoses and the relative roles of heredity and environment in the pathogenesis of the group of schizophrenias.[21] Isolated articles have studied the state of the ego of schizophrenics (Freeman, McGhie, and Cameron 1957). Hallucinations have been viewed from various aspects (Benedetti 1955, Häfner 1954), and the roles of disordered perception, thought, and consciousness have been considered (Benedetti 1955; Davie and Freeman 1961a). Some authors have sought to combine aspects of existentialism and psychoanalysis.[22] Winnicott, who accepts Klein's depressive position as logically defensible as a theoretical and clinical construct (1958:21–23), has indicated in various articles that he has used psychoanalysis in the treatment of frank psychoses (1958a). He believes that character disorders range between conditions in which the presenting syndrome masks neurotic illness to those in which the hidden illness is psychotic in nature (1963:206–207). The existence of character disorders, according to

[19] Representative articles are: Amendola and Garzillo 1955; Bash 1957; Benedetti 1955a, 1955b; H. Binswanger 1954–1955; Boroffka 1958–1959; Ernst 1957; Fornari 1956; Hill 1955; Khan 1960; Margat 1956; Matussek 1959; Müller, 1955, 1955a, 1958; Müller and Benedetti 1965; Racamier 1956; Rycroft 1960; Schindler 1955, 1957; Stengel 1957; Tolentino 1956, 1956a, 1957, 1957a; Tolentino and Callieri 1957; Vanggaard 1955, 1955a; Waals 1954; Winkler 1957.

[20] Davie and Freeman 1961; Schindler 1955; Winkler and Häfner 1954.

[21] H. Binswanger 1957–1958; L. Binswanger 1945, 1957; Cargnello 1947; Faergemann 1946; Fruhle 1932; Kielholz 1951; Schultz-Hencke 1952; Stengel 1957a; Vowinckel 1930; Weigert-Vowinckel 1936; Winkler 1954; Winkler and Wieser 1959; Zapparoli 1957.

[22] L. Binswanger 1947, 1949, 1952, 1958; Boss 1958; Ey 1958; Storch 1947, 1948, 1951, 1957.

Winnicott, indicates the capacity of ego structure to bind energies "that belong to the stunting of maturational processes and also the abnormalities in the interaction of the individual child and the family" and warns of the likelihood that a character disorder might break down "into paranoia, manic depression, psychosis or schizophrenia" (1963:210), during psychoanalytic therapy. Nevertheless, he considers psychoanalysis to be the treatment of choice for such conditions. Winnicott has striven to bridge the theoretical gap between Melanie Klein and Anna Freud, concerning the psychosexual and psychosocial development of the preoedipal child. His concepts of transitional objects and phenomena (1953) have proved valuable in the understanding and treatment of the schizophrenic disorders.

I will now present abstracts from the writings of some of the authors who have used interpretations as their principal therapeutic tool.

Perrier (1955) noted that in schizophrenia, verbal representations prevail over object relations in the sense that when object relations are abandoned, the investment in the verbal representations of the objects is maintained. The schizophrenic who does not recognize himself in a mirror has rejected and lost his capacity for self-representation; he cannot differentiate himself from the outer world. When the therapist imposes himself on the patient in such a stage of undifferentiated narcissism, his verbal products are made partly communicative by the actions of the therapist. Perrier stated that he made himself into a mirror and reflected to the patient what was meaningful in his productions, an action which made the patient gradually look at himself as he was. He found the patient's aggression to express itself, first in retention and then in explosions. He found the last fundamental resistance was the symbiosis which the patient demanded; that if the symbiosis were accepted, the patient becomes "eager to cure himself through us." However, in contrast to Schwing and Sechehaye, Perrier thought the patient must be given the initiative and feel that his reconstituted image was accepted. During the period when the symbiotic behavior was "rejected," that is, dealt with through interpretations, the patient's aggressions were found to become more intense. Perrier noted that during this phase of treatment the therapist's countertransference causes the most serious problems.

Glover (1955:244–251) found schizophrenics with depressive features to be suitable for psychoanalysis but paranoid cases to be refractory. As a procedure for treatment he recommended first an estimation of the factors which prevent development of a stable transference and then an attempt to deal with such traumatic reactions "as appear to have obstructed those particular channels of libido." He believed that manifestations of love, as Ferenczi advocated in his rapport therapy, were unnecessary. Faced by psychotic crises, alterations of the analytic situation should be limited to those which do not prejudice resumption of the ordinary psychoanalytic technique: Eissler's (1953) parameters. As a general procedure, he suggested: (1) reduction of traumatic reactions to past and present situations of excessive stimulation, which he felt could be best done by giving preference to the depressive aspects of the case, (2) then turning attention to projective manifestations, which will have been rendered more accessible by the preliminary work on pathogenic introjections. He thought that if the pathogenic introjective and projective systems are reduced, the regressive products will diminish without direct analysis.

Glover's final statement is tantalizing and seems tautological, since he did not specify just what he did to accomplish such reduction and the essence of successful therapy could be defined to be the reduction of pathogenic systems.

Nacht and Lebovici (1955)[23] recommended classical analysis for some cases, excluding paranoia and hypochondriasis. Analysis was said to be indicated in various cases, regardless of the diagnostic label, when the anxiety is related to the fear of the superego and in which the ego is strong, but not when anxiety is of instinctual origin and the ego is weak. Lebovici reported cures of three cases of manic-depressive psychosis using a classical technique.

Nacht and Lebovici seem to agree in general with Glover. However, their article is somewhat confusing since they do not make clear either what constitutes anxiety of instinctual origin or a strong or weak ego.

THE CONTRIBUTIONS OF PSYCHOANALYSTS OF THE UNITED STATES

The Period Which Preceded Sullivan and Fromm-Reichmann

The development of psychoanalytic thought concerning the genesis, nature, and treatment of the schizo-

[23] See also Lebovici, Diatkine, and Danon-Boileau 1956–1957; Lebovici, Paumelle, Laloum, and Kalmanson 1954; Lebovici, Roumajon, Morin, and Bourreau 1954.

phrenias in the United States paralleled in several respects that which took place in Europe. There was a period during which Freud's ideas were spread and therapists who attempted to use them seemed to be guardedly optimistic. Subsequently, a system of psychology was developed which was based to some extent on psychoanalytic principles and its appearance encouraged many therapists to turn their serious attention to the psychological treatment of these disorders. Then psychoanalysts who followed the mainstream of Freudian thinking became more interested in determining whether the scope of psychoanalytic therapy should be broadened to include the treatment of the borderline states and the schizophrenias. At the same time, various groups arose which stressed one or another aspect of Freudian thinking to explain or justify their handling of borderline or schizophrenic patients.

If any single psychoanalyst can be singled out as the most influential disseminator of psychoanalytic thought regarding this group of disorders, that man must be Brill. His writings extended over a period of some thirty-three years.[24] He strove to demonstrate the presence of psychological factors in the schizophrenias through the presentation of case histories, indicated similarities and differences between the neuroses and psychoses, and attempted to demonstrate the limitations of psychoanalytic therapy when it is applied to schizophrenic disorders. Brill's orientation seems to have remained consonant with the topographical theory.

Campbell, Jelliffe, Meyer, and White, influenced by Freudian thinking, were among the first to stress the psychological aspects of the genesis and treatment of

[24] Brill, 1908, 1909–1910, 1911, 1919, 1925, 1929, 1934, 1941.

the schizophrenias.[25] Arieti (1955:7) has considered Meyer, along with Bleuler, Freud, Kraepelin, Jung, and Sullivan, to have been responsible for the evolution of our current concepts of schizophrenia. Sullivan at one time credited White with having been his most influential teacher.

Coriat (1913–1914, 1917) shared the optimism of the European psychoanalysts who first used psychoanalytic methods in the treatment of schizophrenia. He wrote (1917:327): "The only hope of combatting the disease must rest on the conception of interpreting it purely as a psychogenetic disease." He thought psychoanalytic treatment could cure mild cases and relieve the symptoms of severe and chronic instances. He recommended that psychoanalysis be tried for all cases and stated that the chance for cure depended upon a "thorough psychoanalysis of the entire content of the psychosis." Clark (1919) was less optimistic and recommended great caution in the use of psychoanalysis for the treatment of the schizophrenias. He continued to emphasize the need for the use of technical modifications.[26]

Others dealt with various aspects of the application of psychoanalytic thinking to the schizophrenias. Gordon (1917) and Silk (1920) studied the meanings and defensive uses of hallucinations, Osnato (1918) concerned himself with pathogenesis, Gordon (1912) and Greenacre (1918) investigated schizoid phenomena in affective disorders, Hassall (1915), Menninger (1920), Shockley (1914), and Wholey (1916) wrote of the roles of sexual complexes in schizophrenia and paranoid ideation, and Isham (1920), Karpas (1915–1916), and Lehr-

[25] Campbell 1909, 1912, 1933, 1935; Jelliffe undated, 1907, 1908, 1910, 1927; Meyer 1911, 1921–1922; White 1910, 1910a, 1921, 1926.

[26] Clark 1926, 1933, 1933a, 1933b.

man (1919) studied the meanings and uses of various schizophrenic mechanisms.[27]

In the 1920's, Barkas (1925) wrote of the treatment of psychotic patients in institutions in the light of psychoanalysis and agreed with Nunberg (1921) that the staff should be oriented psychoanalytically, Lewis (1923) believed he had demonstrated pathology in the vascular and endocrine systems of schizophrenics, and O'Malley (1923) contributed a very superficial study of the transference relations of psychotics. So far as the psychoanalytic treatment of these disorders was concerned, writers continued to recommend its use with gross modifications and were guarded in their estimates of its efficacy.[28]

The Approaches of Sullivan and Fromm-Reichmann

Harry Stack Sullivan entered the psychiatric world in 1920. From the beginning he worked primarily with psychotics and predominantly with schizophrenics.[29] Some of his early innovations paralleled those of Ferenczi, but the two investigators probably had little influence on one another (Thompson 1952). Sullivan credited Freud, Meyer, and White as most significantly guiding his psychiatric thinking, but in his later years he wrote (1940:88): "Aside from Freud's discussion of the Screiber [sic] case and Groddeck's *Das Buch vom Es* . . . my subsequent reading of more purely psycho-

[27] See also Gordon 1924–1925, 1933, 1934, 1951; Isham 1920a; Menninger 1921, 1922, 1924, 1925–1926, 1928, 1930, 1947.

[28] Cassity 1925, 1927; Hinsie 1927, 1930, 1932, 1944; Lewis 1925, 1928, 1929–1930, 1936, 1937, 1944, 1949; Lewis and Blanchard 1931; Lundholm 1932; Malamud 1929.

[29] Sullivan 1925, 1927, 1928, 1929, 1931, 1931a, 1947, 1947a.

analytic contributions has fallen under the law of diminishing return."

He became aware earlier than most psychoanalysts of the characteristics of schizophrenics which must be taken into account in their treatment (Brody 1952:39–88). He knew that Freud's position that schizophrenics are unreachable because they do not develop transference was clinically refutable. He understood that the physician's communications may carry more aggression than the patient's special vulnerability makes him capable of withstanding without panic or unsalutary regression; he also knew that this is a complex issue because the schizophrenic also projects hostility onto the therapist (Menzer, Standish, and Mann 1950). Sullivan stressed the tenuous nature of emotional relationships of schizophrenics and stated that stimulation of the libidinal needs of the patient evokes his destructive impulses (Standish, Mann, and Menzer 1950). He thought it possible that the basic fear of the schizophrenic is that he or his physician may be in danger of magical destruction, usually by oral means, reminiscent of the ideas of Klein and her followers and Lewin's (1950) hypotheses related to eating and being eaten.

Sullivan also stressed that the first step in dealing with the schizophrenic is the establishment of meaningful contact and sought to approach the patient by any possible means (M. J. White 1952). He agreed with and antedated Stone (1954) who stated that any number and degree of parameters can be introduced where they are necessary to meet special conditions and so long as they are directed to producing the ultimate purposes and processes of the analytic end. Anna Freud (1954) has agreed, although she warned that many variations of technique are occasioned by the analyst's outlook and theoretical position, a fact which has been demonstrated previously in this chapter, by the examples of Kleinian techniques. Sullivan did not believe that the positive transference must be maintained. He found the psychotic to attempt to make contact through reenacting in a highly distorted manner the events of his childhood with the therapist and the split representatives of the psychiatrist, the other members of the hospital staff. He thought the difference between neurotic and psychotic transference to be largely quantitative. He viewed almost all of the behavior of the chronic psychotic to constitute transference, an opinion which has found much support (Searles 1963). Sullivan noted that the therapist is conceived by the schizophrenic as an important person of his past. From this he concluded that the actual person and personality of the therapist are highly important, as had Ferenczi and Rank, although their avenues of reaching that judgment differed from his. Other therapists have stressed that kindness, strength, and fairness (Betz 1950), dissimilarity of the physician to actual life figures from the patient's past (Kolb 1956), frankness (Federn 1933), sincerity, insight, and self-control (Kempf 1919), and altruism (Schwing 1940) are desirable qualities. Sullivan would have agreed with all of them, although his emphasis might have varied. He stressed the need for a high degree of tolerance, one which will enable the psychoanalyst to permit the patient to seek individual ways of satisfying his needs, so long as they do not transgress the rights of others. With Menninger (1940) and Schwartz and Stanton (1950), Sullivan thought the psychiatrist's overdependency on cultural standards causes him to disparage rather than to investigate the genetics and dynamics of the patient's productions.

Sullivan never presented a systematic account of his theoretical ideas and the efforts of his critics and apologists have not succeeded in making them clear and consistent.[30] It would appear that the most significant differences between his constructions and those of Freud lie in the relative importance placed by each on the vicissitudes and nature of drives and their importance in the psychic structure. Sullivan was apparently unable to penetrate to basic psychoanalytic concepts and discoveries (Jacobson 1955). He failed to take into account such phenomena as infantile sexuality. To him, there was no Oedipus complex, no infantile masturbation problem, and no castration conflict. His conception of sexuality is reminiscent of the pre-Freudian period, and surely no more advanced than that of Jung (1907). Jacobson noted (1955:151): "Sullivan's complete unawareness of the part that instinctual life plays in child development is the prerequisite for his theory of anxiety and fear."

It has been implied (Mullahy 1940) and overtly stated (M. J. White 1952) that Sullivan's idiosyncratic terminology obscured the fact that he was developing a dynamic theory of ego psychology, but Jacobson (1955: 150) has noted that to Sullivan, structural concepts are unacceptable. He was heavily influenced by anthropologists, notably Margaret Mead and Edward Sapir. According to Sullivan, the child conforms to the standards of his culture essentially from fear of estrangement from individuals in his environment. The role of the superego is obviously depreciated.

[30] Bromberg 1954:225–233; M. Cohen 1953; Green 1962; Jacobson 1955; Mullahy 1940; Salzman 1964; Thompson 1952.

Although Sullivan's theory of personality deviated sharply from Freud's, in regard to therapy, his viewpoints have been widely influential in shaping the procedures of therapists who have been more sympathetic to Freudian views (Mullahy 1948, 1949; Perry and Gawel 1953; Sullivan 1940). Thompson wrote (1952: 107):

> If by psychoanalysis one means recognition of unconscious motivation, the influence of repression and resistance on the personality and the existence of transference, then Sullivan's thinking fulfills all requirements for being considered psychoanalysis.

However, recognition of transference, repression, and resistances constitutes a most incomplete statement of what psychoanalysis as a therapeutic method is: recognition is not systematic analysis and repression is not the only defense. Resistance and unconscious motivation obviously had meanings to Sullivan vastly different from what they have to Freudian psychoanalysts.

Thompson (1952:107) stated Sullivan's unique contribution to the treatment of psychotics to have been his stressing the need to convey the therapist's respect to the patient. He considered demonstrating the fallibility of the psychiatrist to be important and when he requested amplification, he also inquired whether he had missed something. Neither of these attitudes was new with Sullivan, being implicit or explicit in many articles in the German psychoanalytic literature. Sullivan did not know German well, and apparently was unaware of many contributions which appeared in that language.

He considered "why" questions to be incomprehensible and inadvisable, because the patient interprets such interrogations as accusatory. In this regard, his viewpoint was similar to Arlow's (1952). He interpreted expressions of guilt and directed the patient's attention to an understanding of events which transpired, especially during the interview situation. Such an approach and the nature of his interpretations were consistent with his conceptualization of personality. He thought that "To gain satisfactions and security is to have power in interpersonal relations [and that] the self comes into being because it is necessary that one's interests be focused into certain fields that 'work' " (Mullahy 1940: 121). He stated "free" association to be unsuitable for schizophrenic patients, at least insofar as dealing with the patient during the period of establishing meaningful contact is concerned, a position which agrees with recommendations forwarded by most analytic therapists (Bychowski 1953; Eissler 1951; Glover 1955:244–251; Knight 1953, 1953a). At the same time, Sullivan emphasized the importance of "marginal thoughts" and he used directed associations in attempts to catch distortions.

Sullivan was not active in every interview and at times long periods transpired during which there was little intervention. In general, he controlled interview situations by his movements, vocalizations, questions, and minimal interpretations, behavior also found to be beneficial by Boyer (1961) during his "noisy" phase of treatment. In unfolding the patterns of living which had led to the patient's difficulties in getting along with others, Sullivan worked first with the "peripheral field," the relationships with relatively innocuous people. He confronted patients with their distortions of what he and they had said previously and sometimes he made deliberately false statements, designed to be corrected by the patient. At the same time, he recommended complete honesty with the patient and felt it advisable to communicate overtly his feelings, a viewpoint which has been popular with many therapists of schizophrenics. Such a procedure may abet the patient's retention of the unconscious bases for delusions and hamper reconstruction of his personality; indeed, the same procedure was recommended by Federn (1933) as a means of encapsulating the psychosis. It will be recalled that Federn considered the schizophrenic patient to be, in the strict sense, incurable.

Sullivan considered it mandatory to give positive recognition of the patient's forward moves. With catatonics he was reserved, gentle, and kindly; with paranoids he was distant and cold (Mullahy 1940, M. J. White 1952). Bartemeier (1965:31) remembered him to have been "very aggressive towards his schizophrenic patients, and that he combined this attitude with an equal amount of tenderness, affection, and understanding." Despite his advocacy of frankness concerning the therapist's personal feelings, he also stated that he did not reassure except with his attitude of kindly reserve, since he considered the psychotic to interpret overt reassurance as evidence that the therapist considers the patient to be hopeless. It will be noted that this idea is at sharp variance with the usual recommendation that the psychotic requires "ego support," using the term within its popular connotation. After he listened to "primitive pregenital material" for some months during which the working alliance was established, Sullivan began to disparage such communications and to insist that the patient "leave the neologistic hoop-la and discover when he began to feel frightened" (M. J. White 1952:147). However, it will be remembered that Sullivan did not acknowledge the existence of infantile pregenital or genital sexual activity, as the terms are used within ordinary psychoanalytic parlance. According to him, sexual pleasure is genital "lust" and gains importance only at puberty (Jacobson 1955:151). Additionally, just what he meant by the working alliance is not quite clear from his writings.

Nevertheless, Sullivan's work with psychotics was highly intuitive and apparently effective; it stimulated much interest and kindled optimism in psychotherapists, and the present author believes that *this* was his cardinal contribution.

Fromm-Reichmann, too, began to work with psychotics in the 1920's. The principles she worked from were based upon a general dynamic and psychoanalytic orientation, derived from her training in and experience with the application of Freud's concepts of psychoanalytic therapy with neurotics. However, she found Sullivan's operational interpersonal conceptions to be of great value in the treatment of psychotics. She, with Alexander (1954) and many others, postulated a continuum, with no discernible or practical line of demarcation, between psychoanalysis and dynamic psychotherapy (Fromm-Reichmann 1954; Rangell 1954).

Fromm-Reichmann agreed with Sullivan's stand regarding the need to convey respect to the patient. However, she found additionally that the "exaggeratedly sensitive, cautious overpermissive approach to the patient" which had been advocated by Alexander, Federn, Nunberg, and Schwing, as examples, was lacking as a technique to establish an effective treatment background. Such an approach addresses itself to the rejected child in the schizophrenic and encourages perpetuation of regression. She recommended that the therapist address himself to the patient's adult aspects, as had Sullivan with his disparagement of neologistic productions. Fromm-Reichmann (1948) recommended respect and understanding relevant to the patient's chronological age. She also found that when the therapist discourages the expression of hostile feelings toward himself, the patient understands such behavior to indicate that the therapist fears the patient's and his own hostility. Such an ascription supports the schizophrenic's attribution of magical qualities to hostility.

Fromm-Reichmann (1950, 1952) found the interpretation of content to be of secondary importance in the treatment of the schizophrenic and said that interpretation should be directed toward an understanding of the genetics and dynamics which determine content. Her conceptualization and dynamics were much more in consonance with Freudian hypotheses concerning personality development than were Sullivan's. She was very much concerned with the importance of the security and personality of the therapist himself and focused strongly on the importance of countertransference. The therapist must not be bound for his security on the "denizens of the society and the culture of the area," and feel impelled to have the patient conform to them. The recovery of the schizophrenic often depends on the psychoanalyst's freedom from convention and prejudice (1949).

Like the work of Melanie Klein, that of Harry Stack Sullivan and Frieda Fromm-Reichmann has permeated the psychotherapeutic techniques employed by the vast majority of dynamic therapists and psychoanalysts. This does not mean to imply that psychoanalysts who use such techniques agree with the theoretical orientations upon which they were originally based.

More Recent Contributions

As was noted previously, Kleinian ideologies have found little acceptance in the United States, and child analysts have remained sharply cognizant of the "fact that a lifelong, albeit diminishing, emotional dependence on the mother is a universal truth of human existence" (Mahler 1963:307). They have aligned themselves with those who place cardinal importance on the actual life experiences of the growing person. Their observations have been made in longitudinal studies of the child with normal and pathological psychological development,[31] as well as typical analytic situations which provide reconstructive material and hypotheses. Such studies have led to the increasing corroboration of the validity of the structural theory of psychical organization; they have led to the stand taken by Mahler (1963:307):

The biological preparedness of the human infant to maintain its life separately conditions that species-specific prolonged phase which has been designated the "mother-infant symbiosis." I believe it is from the symbiotic phase of the mother-infant dual unity that those experiential precursors of individual beginnings are derived which, together with

[31] Significant references are to be found in the bibliographies of Korner 1964; Mahler 1963; Mahler and Furer 1960, 1963; Mahler, Furer and Settledge 1959; Mahler and LaPerriere 1965.

inborn constitutional factors, determine every human individual's unique somatic and psychological make-up.[32]

Understanding of symbiotic phenomena required following the child into a later stage of the mother-infant relationship, the "separation-individuation" phase (Mahler, Furer, and Settledge 1959; Mahler and LaPerriere 1965). Normal separation-individuation is conceived to be the first crucial prerequisite for the development and maintenance of the sense of identity.

Such longitudinal studies, combined with reconstructive efforts, have indicated that the libidinal availability of the mother, because of the emotional dependence of the child, facilitates the optimal unfolding of innate potentialities and contributes to or subtracts from harmonious synthesis of the autonomous functions in the service of the ego, the neutralization of drives, and sublimation, by activating or hindering the flux of developmental energy (Kris 1955).

But the child does not grow up solely under the influence of his mother. With increasing impact, he comes meaningfully in contact with other members of his immediate and extended family and then other individuals and institutions in his environment. The impact on the personality and the demands and supports which emanate from this widening circle of environmental influences has led to a crescendoing series of longitudinal studies performed by scientists of various social disciplines.

[32] The unique contributions of individual organic endowments in the infant on the nature of the development of the object relationships between the child and his environment have been stressed in such contributions as that of Bergman and Escalona (1949), who stressed the role of unusual sensitivities in young children. Erikson (1966) has concluded that organic endowment is of crucial importance in the development of the autistic child. (See also Boyer 1956; Korner 1964.)

The psychoanalytic treatment of psychotics was formerly conducted largely in the hospital situation. In such an environment, it was learned early that the patients behave as though various hospital personnel and other patients were their actual family members. This finding was probably serendipitous at first. Historically, psychoanalytic therapies of patients had been conducted within the framework of a one-to-one relationship between patient and analyst. The varieties of techniques employed in that predominantly dyadic situation were aimed at enabling the individual to be reconstructed through rectification of earlier pathological relationships, predominantly those of the mother-child dyad, through various means of educative contact, actual and symbolic, and through interpretation.

As has been emphasized frequently, psychoanalytic treatment techniques influence and are influenced by the theoretical positions taken by analysts. With the renewed focusing of attention on the individual's relationships with members of his environment, therapists, extrapolating from dynamic theories of child development, heeding their own intrahospital observations and borrowing from the findings of researchers in other disciplines, have been increasingly interested in devising techniques of treating psychotics within the framework of a family situation. At first, such efforts were directed to including patients only in group situations and later actual family members were brought into the treatment situation and research milieu.[33]

[33] Ackerman 1958; Ackerman and Behrens 1955; Alanen 1958; Alikakos, Starer, and Winnich 1956; Bateson, Jackson, Haley, and Weakland 1956; Bion 1961; Böszörmenyi-Nagy 1962; Brodey 1959; Delay, Deniker, and Green 1957, 1957a; Harris 1963–1964; Jackson 1961; Lidz, Fleck, and Cornelison 1965; Reichard and Tillman 1952; Schaffer, Wynne, Day, Ryckoff, and Halperin 1962; Searles 1964a; Sharp, Glasner, Lederman, and Wolfe 1964; Towne, Messinger, and Sampson 1962; Wassell 1959; Wynne and Singer 1963, 1963a.

All of these contributions have been combined with the observations of psychoanalysts in order to understand various aspects of schizophrenia: such as the relative contributions of heredity and environment to the genesis of these disorders, the role of object relations in influencing psychic structuralization, and the genesis, defensive uses and adaptational functions of such phenomena as language and hallucinations. The nature of the psychotic process, its manifestations, and the use of transference and countertransference phenomena have also been studied.[34] A detailed discussion of these contributions is not possible within the framework of this chapter.

Let us return to the therapy of schizophrenia. As has been true in the past, the practical problem of whether to hospitalize the patient has proved to be troublesome. As Brill (1929) had before him, Boyer (1961, 1965) has advocated avoidance of hospitalization whenever possible. Nevertheless, the need of some families to keep patients ill is a well-known phenomenon.[35] The special problems connected with hospital management have been the object of numerous and penetrating studies.[36]

One of the most spectacular deviations from ordinary psychoanalytical technique to have been introduced in the United States is the "direct analysis" of Rosen

[34] Bak 1939, 1941, 1943, 1954; Bellak 1948, 1949; French and Kasanin 1941; Galant 1933, 1933a; Giovacchini 1963, 1965, 1965a; Hartmann 1953; Hollender and Böszörmenyi-Nagy 1958; Jacobson 1954, 1954a, 1959; Kasanin 1944, 1945; Kasanin and Hanfmann 1942; Katan 1939, 1950, 1954; Kaufman 1934, 1939; Lemieux 1961; Malamud 1950; Modell 1956, 1958, 1963; Namnum 1964; Niederland 1959; Penrose 1931; Pious 1949, 1961; Polatin 1948, 1949; Savage 1958; Searles 1959, 1962, 1963; Sprague 1937, 1940, 1941, 1942; Staveren 1947; Szalita-Pemow 1955, 1958; Wexler 1951, 1953, 1965; Will 1959, 1961.

[35] Bychowski 1963; Jackson 1959; Ryckoff, Day, and Wynne 1958; Szurek and Johnson 1954.

[36] Brody 1952:57–74; Fromm-Reichmann 1947; Morse and Noble 1952; Stanton and Schwartz 1954.

(1962), who has claimed that his procedures are a logical extension of Freudian hypotheses (1964). His techniques have proved sufficiently stimulating to a group of supporters and followers that a special foundation and school continue his research and teachings; recently an international congress of direct psychoanalysis was held (Scarizza 1965).

Rosen's (1947) major description of his technique was presented in 1947. He felt "called upon" to converse with the patient in the language of the unconscious and to untwist, "clear down to the earliest ontogenetic and even philogenetic roots," each symptom, remark, and symbol. He reasoned that when the symbol was clearly unmasked to the patient, it would become purposeless and the patient would be able to relinquish it for more mature ways of handling his drives. Rosen felt the task to be incomplete until the "transference is as completely worked out as we aim to do in ordinary analytic procedures." During the initial period of treatment, he spent several hours each day with his patients and literally fed, bathed, and otherwise cared for their presumed needs. He claimed cures following treatment of three days to eleven months; the average period of treatment lasted two to three months. Needless to say, Rosen's conceptions of what constitutes working through a transference relationship must be considered to be very different from those of most analysts and his ideas concerning the development and uses of symptoms, too, are radically different (Searles 1964; Stone 1955; Wexler 1965a). Horwitz *et al.* (1958) reviewed and followed nineteen of Rosen's original thirty-seven cases, and noted (p. 783): "Whatever the merits of direct analytic therapy for schizophrenia, the claim that it results in a high degree of recovery remains unproven." (See also Sagredo 1955, 1955a; Scheflen 1961.)

It has been remarked frequently that there appear to be as many approaches to the psychological treatment of the schizophrenias as there are individual therapists.[37] Yet, today it appears that all therapists in the United States have been influenced by various aspects of the techniques of Federn, Fromm-Reichmann, Klein, Nunberg, and/or Sullivan, regardless of their individual theoretical position. Psychoanalysts who deal with schizophrenics now seem to be divided into three general groups: (1) Those who agree with variants of Freud's original formulations. These therapists in general offer supportive therapy and environmental manipulation, although some interpretations may be employed. The majority tend to use extra-analytic or parametric procedures to handle anxiety-laden or -producing situations; many also use medicines. They seem to aim at encapsulation of the psychosis. Some of these therapists, as Knight (1953, 1953a), suggest that whenever the physician suspects that the patient's symptomatology masks a borderline condition, he should have psychological tests done; if unusual regressive tendencies are discovered, the patient should have supportive therapy rather than psychoanalysis, although certain patients may, after a suitable period, be given a trial analysis. Eissler (1953, 1953a) has written at length on the effect of the structure of the ego and the emotionality of the patient and their relation to technique. As mentioned before, Bychowski[38] believes that the intro-

[37] For varying approaches see Brody 1952; Burnham 1955; R. Cohen 1947; Ekstein 1955; Feigenbaum 1930, 1930a; Grotjahn 1938; Karpman 1944; Myerson 1939; Tower 1947; Wexler 1951a.

[38] Bychowski 1923, 1932, 1943, 1945, 1947, 1951, 1952, 1952a, 1953, 1954, 1963, 1965.

duction of parametric and extra-analytic procedures is mandatory, but his treatment method more nearly approaches that of the classical analytic than is true of the majority of the therapists of this group. Kolb (1956) has listed the "necessary" modifications of analytic technique for the treatment of the schizophrenias. (2) Those who have greater reluctance to shift analytic technique because of their patients' exhibition of regressive tendencies. The writings of many analysts reveal that they are now knowledgeably treating borderline and psychotic patients with techniques which use interpretation as their principal therapeutic tool and systematically analyze resistances and transference relationships.[39] (3) Those who have turned to family therapy techniques.

SUMMARY

In this chapter I present a survey of the thinking of psychoanalysts other than Freud pertaining to the therapy of borderline and schizophrenic conditions. The chapter is divided into two main sections, dealing with the development of thought of European and Latin American analysts, and those of the United States. However, parallels exist which make it possible to present a unified summary.

Before Freud introduced his formulations concerning schizophrenia and stated that psychoanalysis was inapplicable as a method of treatment, many European clinicians used psychoanalytic techniques and were

[39] Boyer 1961, 1965; Brandschaft 1964; Giovacchini 1963, 1965, 1965a; Hoedemaker 1955, 1958, 1960; Jacobson 1954; Searles 1965; Sperling 1955.

enthusiastic about their results. After Freud's pronouncement, however, there was a period of almost a decade when few articles appeared in which the treatment of schizophrenia was discussed in any detail. After Tausk questioned Freud's diagnosis of one of his "hysterical" patients, there was again an upsurge of therapeutic attempts. In the United States, before 1920, psychoanalytic principles were used in an attempt to understand various facets of paranoia and the schizophrenias, but very few writers indicated they had attempted to use psychoanalysis as a treatment method; their conclusions varied from those of Coriat, who was enthusiastic, to Brill and Clark, who were much less optimistic.

During the 1920's, analysts of both continents became more adventurous and a few turned their attentions strongly toward the use of psychoanalysis in the treatment of these disorders. In Europe, Nunberg treated psychotics, using gross parameters and extra-analytic procedures; Waelder, Landauer, Laforgue, and Brunswick overtly or implicitly suggested that techniques which were close to those of classical analysis could be used, and Bychowski thought that analytic techniques could be used for the treatment of some borderline and schizophrenic disorders, but that various modifications were mandatory. In the early 1930's Garma and Laforgue recognized earlier than most analysts the nature of the schizophrenic superego and the need of the therapist to reduce its archaic and sadistic qualities; they recommended the use of orthodox analysis, once adequate contact had been made between patient and therapist and a working alliance had been established. However, the work of Federn was much more influential; it was similar to that of Nunberg, who, with Alexander, believed that a "positive transference" must be maintained if the analyst were to do effective work. In the United States, Sullivan began his intensive work with psychotics and extrapolated therapeutic methods from psychoanalytic theory as he understood it, combined with his own brilliant clinical observations. The vast majority of psychoanalytic therapists who worked at all with schizophrenics used techniques such as those recommended by Ferenczi for the treatment of neurotics and those of Nunberg and Federn.

Also in the 1920's, child analysis made its appearance as a specialty. Although the work of the Anna Freud school did not stimulate an upsurge of the use of psychoanalysis for the treatment of the schizophrenias, that of Melanie Klein clearly did, both in Europe and later, after Garma's migration, in Latin America. Her system of thought, which seems very difficult to synthesize with the point of view of the structural hypothesis, gave a number of analysts a feeling of assurance that they understood infantile fantasy, which enabled them to interpret the behavior of borderline and psychotic patients. A sizable number of analysts, particularly in Great Britain and Argentina, have undertaken the psychoanalytic treatment of patients who suffer from such disorders, apparently without the use of gross parameters or extra-analytic procedures such as those advocated by the vast majority of analysts whose thinking has followed more closely that of the mainstream of psychoanalysis. Perhaps the best known of the Kleinian analysts who treat psychotics are Rosenfeld and Segal.

In the United States, too, a group of analysts developed a deviant school of thought, that of the neo-Freudians, which has, in the viewpoint of the followers of the structural theory, overemphasized the role of socialization processes and understressed the biological equipment of the infant. Sullivan has been the most influential of this group. The Sullivanian school, as the Kleinian, stimulated far more interest in the treatment of the schizophrenias than did the analysts of more orthodox orientation; both schools have heavily swayed the treatment techniques of other analysts who treat psychotics. Following Sullivan, the work of the much better trained psychoanalyst, Fromm-Reichmann, appears to have been most influential in the development of treatment methods of United States analysts.

During the past quarter of a century, interest in the psychoanalytic psychotherapy of the schizophrenias has increased. In Latin America, Klein's thinking has predominated in determining technical procedures. In Europe and the United States, a number of different approaches have been used or developed. Schools of divergent thought have arisen over the years: In Europe, in addition to that of Klein, there have been psychosynthesis and existential analysis; in the United States, in addition to that of Sullivan, there has been the direct analysis of Rosen. More orthodox analysts have divided themselves into three main groups in both geographical areas: (1) Those whose philosophy has elements of Freud's early formulations or who for other reasons believe that the schizophrenias are essentially incurable. This group use psychoanalytic principles in their work to some extent, but they also believe that uncovering techniques are generally contraindicated; they offer support of existing defenses, environmental manipulation, reassurance, and various symbolic or real gratifications, as did Schwing, Sechehaye, and Azima and

Wittkower. (2) Those who are more optimistic regarding the curability of individuals who suffer from borderline and schizophrenic conditions. Some of these work in hospitals with chronically regressed patients and some see patients in their consultation rooms. Both groups attempt to use as few extra-analytic procedures and parameters as they can in establishing contact and developing a working alliance and seek to analyze systematically the transference neurosis and psychosis and the defenses. In Europe, some of the analysts who belong to this group are Glover, Lebovici, and Perrier; in the United States, Brandschaft, Hoedemaker, Searles, Sperling, and Will. A growing number of analysts are using classical analysis as a method of treating characterological disorders, and, as Giovacchini, borderline conditions. So far as can be determined from the literature, only Boyer has experimented systematically with the use of psychoanalysis with a minimum number of parameters in the treatment of overt schizophrenic conditions. (3) Those who have turned their attention to group and family therapies for the borderline and schizophrenic states.

Chapter Four

Office Treatment of Schizophrenic Patients: The Use of Psychoanalytic Therapy With Few Parameters. Introduction

L. Bryce Boyer, M.D.

During more than seventeen years, I have conducted a study directed toward evaluating the efficacy of psychoanalytic therapy with few parameters in the office treatment of schizophrenic individuals.[1] All prospective patients under the age of fifty years who suffered from borderline or overt schizophrenia or schizoaffective psychoses were included. The seventeen patients who supply the data for this report exclude chronically regressed, "back-ward" individuals and all had average or superior intelligence. Some were seen at reduced rates. No waiting list was kept; patients were accepted when they were referred and therapeutic hours were open.

Bychowski (1957:129) subsumed under the term "psychotic core" three points of special interest for the understanding of future psychotic development:

[1] This chapter is a modification of papers which have been presented before the Department of Psychiatry, University of Illinois at the Medical Center, Chicago, May, 1963; the Extension Division of the San Francisco Psychoanalytic Society, October, 1963, and November, 1964; the Los Angeles Psychoanalytic Society, February, 1964; the West Coast Psychoanalytic Societies, San Diego, October, 1964; the Utah State Department of Mental Health, February, 1965.

1. Persistence and prevalence of archaic forms of functioning such as magic thinking and thinking on the original concrete level;
2. Persistence and prevalence of such primitive mechanisms as introjection, primary identification and projection, though of universal significance for every mental functioning, in individuals under consideration, they assume the leading role and culminate in paranoid formations; and
3. Splitting of the ego, occurring according to the original highly ambivalent attitudes of the child toward essential figures of his environment.

In the present series, the psychotic core has been altered fundamentally within two years, as a rule. All but three of the patients whose external circumstances permitted continuation of their treatment developed transference neuroses which were usually resolved.

It is postulated that psychoanalysis can be used for the successful treatment of borderline and schizophrenic patients of the types included in this study. On the basis of the empirical data, I believe that countertransference problems may constitute the major obstacle to the psychoanalytic treatment of such patients. On the basis of this investigation, it remains questionable whether successful outcome depends upon special qualifications of the therapist. The data suggest that the professional and theoretical orientation of the analyst is a major determining factor.

THEORETICAL ORIENTATION

As outlined in Chapter Two, Freud stated that complete decathexis of mental representations followed by a restitutive phase was the most characteristic single feature of the schizophrenic psychoses. He never changed explicitly his formulations to make them consistent with the structural theory. As has been noted by Arlow and Brenner (1964), interpretations based upon Freud's formulations do not abet thorough understanding of the defensive nature of psychotic regression and withdrawal. Federn (see Chapter Three) believed the psychotic process to be irreversible and used various so-called supportive techniques in the treatment of patients who suffered from this group of disorders. He strove to encapsulate the psychosis.

The roots of all functional psychoses have been traced to the qualities of the symbiotic and separation-individuation phases described by Mahler and her coworkers. The structure of the ego and superego results from the interaction of inborn and socialization factors, which determines the nature of their introjects. Deprivation in infancy alone, whether due predominantly to hereditary and/or constitutional defects within the babies or psychological defects within their mothering figures, does not produce all of the group of schizophrenias. The schizophrenic has traversed to some degree all phases of psychosexual and psychosocial development, has manifold areas of developmental failure and fixations, and uneven levels of ego and superego development, and the various ego functions are affected differently from patient to patient. As observed by Arlow and Brenner (1964) and Glover (1955), defensive regression typically transpires in response to adolescent or postadolescent stresses which reawaken unresolved oedipal conflicts.

No human action can be conceptualized to be free of hereditary factors. The hypothesis that schizophrenia is due especially to environmental influences has led to many investigations of schizophrenic patients and their families (see Chapter Three). Research has shown that schizophrenic behavior serves various functions in particular kinds of family organizations and cultural groups, and that serious impairment of ego functioning may be related to the failure of parents to transmit properly the usual communicational tools of the society. The families of schizophrenic patients have discouraged the learning of methods of communication which are based predominantly on secondary process logic and include generally understood, rather than idiosyncratic, symbolic connotations. Individuals who have been reared in such unfavorable milieux do not learn to exchange information well in extrafamilial or cross-cultural situations. It seems likely that they regress defensively when confrontation with their message-sending and -receiving difficulties is superimposed upon already existent intrapsychic conflicts.

Consistent with this bias regarding the origins of schizophrenia is the notion that the primary therapeutic task is to restore and/or develop a reasonable ego and superego. Theoretically this can be accomplished by modifying or replacing cold, unloving, and archaic ego and superego introjects. The introjects of those psychic structures must be warm, loving, and reasonable in order for the individual to be capable of loving himself and others. Simultaneously, therapy must be directed toward the growth of intrapsychic and interpersonal communication techniques. With these orienting notes in mind, let us turn to the methodology which has been employed in the present controlled observation.

METHODOLOGY

I shall first describe my procedure with prospective patients who appeared at the office. All individuals of the groups mentioned above were accepted for treatment except those for whom there was inadequate time or who could not pay minimal fees. Once the diagnosis was made, the patient was told that the object of therapy was to make him comfortable with himself, that treatment was to be of an experimental nature and that an indefinite period might be spent in our collaborative work. During the vis-à-vis hour or hours, I explained the analytic procedure as one does with neurotics. In addition, clear criteria were set regarding vacation periods, interview attendance, and payment arrangements (Boyer 1961: 390–392).

Couch treatment was begun after the patient had been seen no more than four times; usually after one or two face-to-face interviews. Free association techniques were used from the beginning. Once couch therapy was instituted, few parameters were employed, and they were, with one exception, of ordinary varieties which are used in the analyses of neurotics, as the arbitrary setting of the termination date in one instance, the demand bills be paid on time in two cases, and the instruction to face a phobic object in several analyses (Boyer 1961:392–393). None of the seventeen patients who are included in this series was given medicine at any time while being seen in the office. Telephone contacts were discouraged and occurred rarely, except in two of the three cases with whom failures resulted. Direct communication with relatives was rare and almost nonexistent after office treatment was undertaken. Patients were not called by their first names. They were seen four times weekly, except for one of the two women whose treatment failed; she was seen five or six times weekly during some months of treatment. As Searles (1963) has noted, the techniques employed in the care of the patients included in this study have more nearly approached orthodox psychoanalytic treatment than has been reported previously in any detail in the literature.

Five of the six patients who were first interviewed in hospital were under the care of other psychiatrists at the time. A fragment of the case history of the sixth is included below. With that exception, I did not involve myself in the physical or drug therapy of any of those patients. I restricted my activities to observation and interpretations; all of these cases then came to the office for therapy and, although they were still actively psychotic, were begun in analysis, after having been given the conditions of therapy while still in the hospital. Only two of the patients included in this study were hospitalized during treatment with me. Aside from the one mentioned below, one woman was immured and treated by a psychiatrist while I was absent from my office for a period of two weeks. Her hospitalization was at her request.

Although the treatment of these patients constituted a continuum, for purposes of amplification it can be divided conceptually into two phases. In the first, reasonably stable, loving introjects appear to be established within the patient. Coincidentally, psychotic thinking patterns and behavior are removed or their cathexes are markedly diminished. At the end of this artificially divided first period, a tranference neurosis has developed, replacing the use of transferences and transference psychosis.

The words *transference, transference neurosis, transference psychosis,* and *countertransference* are used with variant meanings in the psychoanalytic literature. The following paragraphs will clarify their use in this contribution.

French (1946:71) noted that the word *transference* has been used to include everything from the transference neurosis proper to the "emotional relationship existing between patient and analyst" to the "treatment situation as a whole." When Freud used the word *transference*, he meant reactions to the analyst as though he were not himself but some person from the patient's past. Such a definition implies that a patient's transference to the analyst is but that part of his reaction which repeats his responses to an individual who has previously played an important role in his emotional life. When a patient is neurotic, his continuing, predominant partial misidentification of the analyst is properly said to constitute a transference neurosis. During the course of analysis with most neurotics, the therapist is reacted to for varying periods, usually for months or years, as though he were one or another person from the patient's past. In addition, the patient responds realistically toward the analyst and also with phenomena which are properly called transferences. Derivatives of the repressed may be attached to various individuals and situations in the environment so that in everyday life, too, there are transference situations. When the word *transference* is used in this sense, it means an irrational repetition of a stereotyped reaction which has been adjusted to the present situation (see Fenichel 1954:29–30; Sharpe 1930).

Countertransference is likewise a term used with variant meanings (Orr 1954; Tower 1956). In its most nonspecific application, countertransference means all of the analyst's reactions to his patient. Freud's (1910: 289) first reference to it said: "We have begun to consider the 'countertransference' . . . arising as a result of the patient's influence on (the physician's) unconscious feelings." In this conceptualization, countertransference corresponds to the word *transference* as used above, although it may mean more. Sometimes analysts unconsciously identify patients with important persons from their own pasts. In this communication, the word *countertransference* will be used to designate those reactions of the analyst which correspond to the transferences of the patient and the phrase *countertransference neurosis* will be used to indicate the state in which the analyst has unconsciously identified the patient with an important person from the life of the therapist, and that identification has remained unconscious for a period of weeks or months. This formulation appears to agree with Greenson's (1965) latest formulations. The counteridentifications described by Fliess (1953) would appear to form one group of the countertransference neuroses.

Psychotics, too, develop transference reactions to the therapist. They have been called *transference psychosis* (Rosenfeld 1954) and *delusional transference* (Little 1958). Searles (1963:251) has written:

The difficulty of discerning the transference aspects of one's relationship with the (chronically schizophrenic) patient can be traced to his having regressed to a state of ego-functioning which is marked by severe impairment in his capacity either to differentiate among, or to integrate his experiences. He is so incompletely differentiated in his ego-functioning that he tends to feel not that the therapist reminds him of or is like his mother or father . . . but rather his functioning toward the therapist is couched in the unscrutinized assumption that the therapist *is* the mother or father.

The matter is further complicated by the fragmented nature of the patient's introjects which are projected onto the therapist, so that the analyst may, during the course of even a few minutes, be reacted to as though he were an actualization of a mental representation of a part of first this person and then that. Additionally, under the influence of the primary process, cathexes are sometimes loose and easily displaceable, so that an intense reaction which is present at one moment may be misjudged by the therapist to indicate a more serious involvement with the introjected and usually distorted aspect of the person represented than later analysis will indicate to be the case. (See also Cameron 1961; Jacobson 1954.)

One further datum should be indicated. The psychotic patients who are included in this study had, at all times, areas in which their regressions were similar to the regressive level of neurotics. Thus, intermixed with the use of transferences and the presence of the transference psychosis which developed during the treatment of each, elements of transference neurosis were present simultaneously. A very complicated transference relationship was the rule. Some patients who had been hospitalized immediately before entering analysis quickly projected fragmented introjects onto me. At the same time, their relationships with other individuals had varying degress of objectivity. Others, who appeared to be less psychotic, first developed a relationship in which a transference neurosis was evident and only later were transference psychosis elements obvious. Since those individuals simultaneously functioned better in their everyday lives by that time, it was considered to be a sign of progress when they began to focus their reexperienced infantile emotions onto me, rather than to maintain them in their previously generalized state.

Psychotherapists have sought usually to avoid states of further regression in the treatment of psychotic patients. I believe the data provided by this study indicates that the patient's ability to regress in a controlled manner in the therapeutic situation is a sign of development of trust and psychic structuralization. It would seem that if no psychotic transference develops to be analyzed, there is little likelihood of cure: the most one can hope for is isolation or encapsulation of the psychotic process.

The course of the treatment, then, constituted a continuum which can be viewed from the side of changing transference relationships. After there had been more or less controlled regression to a stage where psychotic transference elements were obvious and these had been effectively analyzed, a neurotic transference relationship ensued. Sometimes this neurotic transference seemed to have the same content as that which had developed before the regression to the psychotic transference state, but the bases of the initial neurotic transference had been cleared of parts of their meanings and they could be analyzed from the standpoint of a more advanced period of psychosexual development.

To state the case slightly differently, the second phase of the arbitrarily divided continuum constituted the analysis of the neurotic character disorder and its attendant symptomatology. Most therapists of psychotics have not sought to continue treatment to the resolution of these elements. However, the patients included here gave no indication of a desire to discontinue therapy after they had lost their psychotic symptomatology and thinking patterns. I wished to continue the investigative procedure because of the possibility that neurotic elements might be masking further psychotic mechanisms or process, inasmuch as a goal of this controlled observation was to test the hypothesis that psychoses can be cured by the use of psychoanalysis. My remarks in this chapter are directed to the first of the artificially divided phases, since there appeared to be little to distinguish the second phase from the usual analyses of neurotics. Nevertheless, during the second phase, in times of stress, the patients sometimes defensively recathected psychotic thinking and behavioral patterns for short periods, but the intensity of such recathexis was less than that observed during the first phase and, when the reasons for such regressions were determined, quickly abated.

As the result of more than two decades of work with schizophrenics, I believe that few, if any, patients are truly inaccessible. In the present series, no chronically and severely regressed schizophrenics are included, because none applied for treatment when time was open. At the present time, such a patient is being analyzed and the course of events supports the stand just mentioned, but it is too early to report details of his treatment. Nevertheless, the seven patients who had been hospitalized just before they began the study believed in the reality of their hallucinations and/or delusions; thus they belonged to Eissler's (1951) "acute" group. Four had received courses of electroplexy and one had undergone insulin shock therapy. Seven cases were borderline schizophrenics whose psychotic thinking became obvious only after they lay on the couch. Examples of the emergence of psychotic thinking in such patients has been published previously. I quote from the case fragment of a woman whom I thought to be a classical hysteric before the following material emerged (Boyer 1956a:459):

> During the second week of a trial period of psychoanalysis, as she lay on the couch, she heard noises outside the window. A gardener was filing his shovel. What she thought she heard was a man's hand rubbing a "hard object." A dog barked outside. Her interpretation of this sound was that I was rubbing my hand on some "hard object," probably a thick, long stick of wood. Her dream that night depicted a man masturbating. She insisted that she could recall seeing her father masturbate when she was about 4 years old, while her mother was pregnant. She was convinced that I was masturbating openly behind her; nevertheless, she had no inclination to leave my care. As she lay speaking of such things, she thoughtfully rubbed her pubic area.

Psychological tests were done and interpreted to be diagnostic or schizophrenia, the accuracy of which judgment was ascertained during her subsequent successful but lengthy treatment.[2]

[2] This case is the only one whose analysis was not conducted solely by me. The psychotic core seemed to have been resolved after about two and a half years of analysis; a transference neurosis developed in which I was reacted to as though I were her mother and she were a pregenital child. A year and a half later her care was transferred to another analyst, Dr. Charles B. David, because I was leaving the area for a year and a half to be involved in a research project of a different

Therapy during the first phase is directed toward the replacement or modification of undesirable introjects, that is, to restoration and/or development of a reasonable ego and superego. Clearly, the first step in preparing the patient to accomplish such goals is to establish meaningful and lasting contact with him. Aside from the common denominators which are inherent in systems of referral and the patient's first interviews, each psychiatrist has techniques which are more or less individual. I strive to make contact in an atmosphere of abstinence and through the use of interpretation. I believe that such a technique is most apt to offer true ego support, through the integrative and structuralizing effects of interpretation (see Chapter Six), and through the immediate establishment for the patient of an atmosphere in which symptoms are treated calmly and as subjects for investigation. I shall present a vignette of the effects of interpretation with a floridly psychotic patient. I do not mean to imply that her dramatic response is typical, but only that it can occur under some circumstances.

A thirty-six-year-old woman had suffered intermittently from a psychosis manifested by hebephrenic, depressed, and manic behavior for fourteen years, requiring almost constant care by psychiatrists and repeated hospitalizations. She had undergone insulin shock therapy. I saw her first while she was slightly confused from electroplexy. I asked her to tell me the history of her illness. When she could not remember dates, she

sort. During her analysis with me, the mother-transference had been analyzed almost completely and she was beginning to view me as a father figure. Dr. David was reacted to from the first as a father substitute. Her analysis with him reached successful conclusion after another four years; there has been no regression of any kind during the ensuing three years.

became flirtatious and joked. I said she tried to hide her embarrassment because of memory deficiency by seeking to divert my attention through humor. She gratefully responded that she had always sought to make people laugh when she thought they might be angry with her. She was able to eschew such behavior for the rest of the interview. At its end, I offered her participation in the study and she accepted. However, her husband forbade me to see her again. During the next week, she regressed seriously. She spent most of her time in seclusion, hallucinating, soiling herself, and terrified.

Her husband was a physician who had undergone a period of psychoanalysis for assistance with a psychosomatic complaint. He subsequently "forgot" his reason for undertaking therapy, read a great deal, and convinced himself he had studied analysis for intellectual reasons and become a "nonpracticing analyst." Accordingly, he knew that psychoanalysis is not recommended commonly for the treatment of psychotic conditions. However, it was generally known that he interfered grossly with psychiatrists' care of his wife and he was unable to obtain the services of anyone else for her care.

The patient was aware of her husband's actions and the nature of his relations with me before I saw her again.

The second interview took place in the seclusion room. We sat on the floor. She faced away from me and talked through clenched teeth about the dangers of gamma rays. I asked whether she feared she might harm me, were she to face me and open her mouth. She turned to me, agreed, and asked if I were going to "buckle" her. I ignored the sexual connotation of her question, choosing to hear instead, "Are you going to put me in a strait jacket?" I said if she were afraid she would harm people on the ward, she could ask directly to be put into isolation and that it was unnecessary for her to be noisy, silly, and provocative as a means of getting there. After she smiled, I said if she controlled her behavior for a while, we would start interviews in my office, although she could return to the hospital if she chose.

Following that interview, she refused further sedatives and voluntarily requested seclusion when she became fearful. I saw her for five further interviews but made no additional interpretations. Then she came to the office with a nurse. She lay on the couch after the third hour and left the hospital soon thereafter.

During this initial period of interchange between the patient and me, I made two interpretations: (1) I suggested a reason for her flirting and joking and (2) I implied that I both understood her attribution of magical qualities to her hostility and was unafraid. However, it is obvious that the interpretations were made in a framework which had other significant elements. I believe that her startling improvement and the establishment of contact which, as it proved, quickly developed into a working relationship, cannot be ascribed solely to the effects of the interpretations. Of some importance must be the fact that her skilled and beloved psychiatrist had given up and her husband had been unable to find anyone else to care for her. Later developments indicated that these factors were understood by her to mean that others attributed magical powers to me and considered me to be some sort of shaman, as she did.

My objective, observing, optimistic, and relatively calm attitude was important and promptly introjected in part; she also responded to my appeal to her own ego strength, her self-control. I believe these elements to be the most relevant in the framework within which the interpretations were made and that it is not possible to distinguish their relative positions of importance. The example serves to illustrate that from the beginning of my contacts with psychotic patients, I strive to make contact especially through the use of interpretations. Nevertheless, we cannot forget that all interpretations made by psychoanalysts while acting in their positions as therapists are made in special contexts (see Chapter Six and Boyer 1961:394).[3]

Throughout this project, I have considered the pri-

[3] This woman's psychotic core was greatly alleviated after about two years. The psychotic transference was less florid than might have been expected and after a few months, she reacted to me largely as though I were her pregenital mother. During this period, much of her self-punishing behavior and thinking had disappeared and her previous sense of worthlessness and emptiness had been greatly modified. She then made of me a father figure and worked through some of her heterosexual incestuous conflicts. As a result, she began to be consciously aware of sexual urges toward her husband, who had denied her physical contact throughout her analysis. His need to keep her ill had been patent from the beginning, and his overt support of her self-evaluation as being dirty and without value had been disruptive. When she indicated she might be a better sexual partner than erstwhile, he informed her he had had mistresses for many years and was planning to divorce her to marry one with whom he had been intimate for the duration of her analysis. She responded by recathecting psychotic thinking for a brief period and her ideas of worthlessness for a longer time. While she again considered herself to be valueless, he proceeded with the divorce action. She refused to get a lawyer of her own and accepted as joint attorney a close personal friend of her husband's, a man whom she knew to be a misogynist. In consequence, her husband was awarded their children on the basis of her past mental illness and she accepted a meager alimony settlement which provided for but six months of further medical or psychiatric care. During the last six months of a three-year-long analysis, she made substantial strides in regaining self-esteem. During the ensuing two and a half years, she has remarried and been happier than ever before; there have been no obvious periods of regression. Although she has not come to my office, we have had chance meetings and brief conversations. During them, her embarrassment indicated to me that the erotized transference which was being analyzed at termination was incompletely resolved.

mary initial goal of therapy is to enable the patient to develop altered introjects. At the same time, I have attempted to use interpretations as the ultimate therapeutic tool. I have attempted from the beginning to present consistent examples of the scientific attitude, a quality the patient gradually acquires. In doing so, he develops an attitudinal shift from a predominant primary process orientation to one in which he achieves the capacity of self-observation. The patient learns to view his conflicts as subjects for study and develops a working alliance (see Chapters Six and Seven).

Thus, treatment begins with steady but gentle confrontations with distortions, contradictions, and other abandonments of reality, coincident with interpretations which are, as a rule, of the defensive functions of the products of his psychotic thinking. However, a review of the research data indicates that I have gradually shifted my technique over the years, in the following ways. Initially, I responded rather indiscriminately to the patient's productions, interpreting defensive products of the derivatives of both sexual and aggressive drives. Now, I tend to ignore material stemming from sexual drives per se, unless an erotized transference threatens to develop which may prove to be unwieldy, and to restrict my interpretations to the aggressive aspects of whatever material is presented. Of course, at the same time, such interpretations are made through the technique of stressing the object relationship aspects of the utilization of such aggressive drive derivatives.

Another shift in my technique over the years has been in the direction of choosing to deal with depressive material when possible in preference to persistently pursuing the products of paranoid ideation, an approach which has been recommended by Glover (1955) and others (see Chapter Three). Both changes in technique reflect my growing conviction that ego introjects cannot be altered efficiently unless simultaneous changes take place in the superego introjects, in the direction of reducing the archaic, sadistic nature of that psychical structure. However, in contrast to Wexler (1951) and others, I do not give direct superego support. The delineation of specific rules of conduct during treatment constitutes an indirect support. As another example, I stress the patient's anxiety when he factually has transgressed morality and label asocial and antisocial actions by their common names. When his "sins" have been moral infringements in thought only, I ask him to consider whether his thoughts have harmed anyone. Within the framework of the therapeutic situation, such support is not limited to the prohibitive functions of the superego.

I have called the initial period of treatment the "noisy phase." It is unusual that such patients can tolerate my silence for long periods. When they seem to be developing too great anxiety, I make noncomittal noises or request amplification. Almost any sound seems to reassure the patient that he has not been deserted or magically committed murder. I believe, with Arlow (1952) and Fromm-Reichmann (1950, 1952), that interpretations of content which emphasize forbidden or frightening wishes are not of primary importance during the period while the patient is still psychotic, although to make them is technically expeditious at times. In general, an interpretation regarding such content arouses feelings of guilt, whereas one concerning defense gives the patient the sense that the therapist, whom he perceives to a large degree as a superego figure, appreciates how much he struggles against his impulses. However, content interpretation can at times serve as a means for regaining contact with the patient when it becomes necessary to demonstrate to him that the therapist does understand some small part of what he tries to communicate. In addition to the use of content interpretation as a gambit, there are times when one has no choice. Occasionally neurotic symptoms will demand attention. The following case fragment serves as an example.

A woman underwent a paranoid and depressed psychotic regression during the last months of pregnancy and became excited and confused following childbirth. A psychiatrist hospitalized her twice and administered electroconvulsive therapy. Soon after her second hospital discharge, she fled from his care and was included in this study.

During one of her early interviews, she recalled having seen her mother and a maternal uncle having sexual relations when she was a small child and confessed that she had wanted to take the place of each of them in the act. Her feelings had caused her to wet her pants. She was startled that I was not disturbed by her accurate screen memory and did not reprimand her because she wanted to urinate on the couch as she recalled the scene. She was also incredulous that her recitation did not excite me and thus make me want to urinate. She then related that, while hospitalized, she thought her psychiatrist was really her father and that he had sexual relations with her in the presence of a nurse while she was unconscious from the shocks. Although she ascribed the actions to his lechery, at the same time she was aware that she had awaited each electrical treatment in a state of sexual excitement and was a willing victim. She withdrew from his care in part because she was afraid they would have sexual relations in his office while she was awake and responsible for her acts. Then God would kill her as punishment for the overt incestuous crime.

Soon thereafter, she decided that she had distorted the event in which her mother and uncle had cohabited and she began to picture her mother as asexual, forgiving, kind, calm, and supremely intellectual and to have had an attitude of "scientific detachment." Although her mother may have had such qualities to some degree at times, she was factually a chronic manic-depressive psychotic whose dominant characteristics were quite otherwise. The patient had ascribed her evaluation of me to her mother. She then began to describe herself to me in the same terms, a distortion as great as had been her picture of her mother (see Boyer 1960). This series of events illustrates an early modification of archaic, sadistic superego introjects, no doubt preoedipal and maternal in origin, combined with or followed by projective identification (Klein 1955).[4]

She then had a dream in which she obviously combined the figures of her mother and me and when she entered the office the following day she was startled to see that I was factually a man. She promptly developed a street phobia, a symptom which was new for her. One of its purposes was clearly to prevent her coming unaccompanied to the office; she wanted to be brought by a woman. My interpretation of that defensive aim of the

[4] Although I have used here Klein's term as happily applicable, there is no implication that in my understanding of this process I call upon her theoretical orientation.

neurotic symptom relieved no anxiety. I then suggested that her perception of me as a woman had been motivated in part by her fear that she would be unable to distinguish me from her father, whom she visualized as sadistic, lewd, stupid, and totally dedicated to satisfying his own lusts. I said she was now afraid that what she had feared would happen with the psychiatrist whom she had fled would now transpire with me in my office. She was vastly relieved and the street phobia disappeared, never to return. During the next interviews she recalled having seen while a teen-ager her father making love to a neighbor woman. The patient had tried soon thereafter to get her father to make sexual advances to her and was bitterly disappointed that he rejected her thinly veiled offer. The preoccupation with her parents' sexual lives then disappeared from the content of the interviews for some time and her attention turned to a closer examination of her relations with her husband. The therapy moved along smoothly for some weeks.

As has been stressed, the intended purpose of the first phase of the treatment of these patients is conceived to be the replacement or modification of introjects. Both case fragments illustrate descriptively some results of this process, with larval evidence of concomitant taming of drives. It may be that in the first of the examples, there was simultaneously a redirection of the aggressive drive toward self-control or mastery.

Numerous writers have called attention to the fact that in the presence of inadequate differentiation of id and ego, tensions are frequently fixed to physical phenomena. In the treatment of psychotics, the analysis of the meanings of phenomena that result from automatic actions of bodily systems which are innervated by the voluntary and involuntary nervous systems is sometimes mandatory before further differentiation of id and ego can transpire. Reference is made to skeletal muscular tensions, postures, and gestures (Deutsch and Murphy 1955; W. Reich 1933), emotional attitudes (Greenson 1949, 1951), and the so-called psychosomatic disorders (Alexander and French 1948; Scott 1948; Sperling 1955). My practice has not included patients who have suffered from severe and chronic psychosomatic disturbances. In the analysis of muscular tensions, postures, and gestures, I have found the extra-analytic and parametric procedures recommended by Braatøy (1954) to be unnecessary. Such analysis is usually indicated during the period while the patient is psychotic; like Searles (1963) I have found it to be an essential step during the resolution of the transference psychosis. Subsequently, as in the case of recathexis of psychotic thinking and behavior during the second phase (see above), defensive regression to the utilization of such phenomena must be repeatedly analyzed.

It is a noteworthy and mysterious fact that no patient to whom participation in this controlled observation was offered has refused. This datum gives evidence that in these cases a potentially favorable transference relationship existed from the beginning. Whether this can be attributed to the nature of the individual cases or of the referrals, or to the patients' initial contacts with me, I cannot say. It was quickly evident that many patients projected megalomanic expectations onto me; they ascribed omniscience and omnipotence to the analyst and expected some form of magical performance. The data I have which are relevant suggest that such ascription resulted in part from my apparently successful attempt to treat the patients' productions with calm and neutrality. Those subjects who have spoken to this point have stated that they interpreted my not having been upset by their recitations of material which seemed extremely dangerous to them to signify that I was too strong and wise to be made anxious. I have had some experience in dealing therapeutically with people whose healers are shamans (Boyer 1964, 1964a) and have been struck by the similarity of expectations of those Indians and my schizophrenic patients.

Various authors have discussed the importance of accurate interpretations in dealing with the schizophrenic. Fromm-Reichmann (1950, 1952) in particular has emphasized the dangers of incorrect interpretations. However, what constitutes an accurate or a wrong interpretation presents a most complex problem. At times I have made statements which were subsequently determined to have been dynamically, economically, and reconstructively wrong. Patients have responded to them in widely varying manners, ranging from no evident reaction to acute, although brief, psychotic regression. Not infrequently, I have found faulty interpretations to have been accidentally beneficial. Sullivan (1940) consciously used misstatements for the purpose of having the patient correct them, and I, too, have used this technical procedure for the purpose of having the patient reconsider data and remove distortions, thereby strengthening his powers of discrimination. However, here I write of unintentionally faulty statements. One patient, commenting to this point, said:

When your understanding of what I've said is just wrong, I'm not bothered at all. If it has been partly right, I am angry and frightened because I expect you to be completely right when you're right. What disturbs me most, though, is when you have overestimated how much *I* can understand and have been *too* right when I wasn't quite ready.

In general, in my experience, *accurate* interpretations are more detrimental to the course of treatment than are totally inaccurate or partially wrong statements and explanations, when the correct statements are faulty as to *timing*, that is, when they pertain to phenomena which are not near enough to the conscious, economic, or dynamic agenda, to paraphrase Loewenstein.

Fromm-Reichmann has also written of the dangers of pretense of understanding. When I think I have failed to understand, I let the patient know of my lack of comprehension and invite him to amplify and clarify. Additionally, I never consciously play a role.

It is obvious that I disagree with Alexander (1931), Federn (1933), and Nunberg (1921), who advocated nonanalytical and parametric methods of fostering a "positive transference" as a means of establishing contact. The schizophrenic is terrified of the potential destructiveness of his impulses and when the emergence of hatred of former love objects is discouraged, he interprets the therapist to fear the patient's or his own hostility. I refer here to hostility which is expressed in words or symbolically and not that which shows itself in assault. No patient has ever attacked me in the office, and when I have been attacked or threatened obviously with attack by a hospitalized patient, and have been unable to mollify the patient's panic or rage by interpretive means, I have commanded cessation or directed attendants to calm the patient physically. When hostility is expressed in words or symbols, they are interpreted from the standpoint of their defensive or testing functions. The appearance of hostility is not discouraged, but the rate and intensity of its emergence are slaked by the timing of interpretations.

Patients who no longer ascribed magical destructiveness to their aggressive impulses commented that during the courses of their treatments they considered their repetitive and timid attempts to express hostility to have been beneficial and necessary. It is known that children's repetitive activities are highly cathected and that interruption of practice or prevention of completion of acts sometimes upsets a tenuous balance of psychic energy. Hartmann, Kris, and Loewenstein (1946) suggest that experiments on act completion in normal adults and obsessional patients indicate that the same may be true of man's life (Gerö 1933; Hartmann 1933; Zeigarnik 1927). The child's tendency to respond aggressively when he experiences restraint can be modified, usually without great difficulty, by the behavior of the restraining adult, or, in the therapy of the psychotic, by that of the parent-substitute. When the child is distracted by nonhostile, loving attention, cathexis which was directed previously toward action is transformed into loving cathexis. When the psychiatrist recognizes the patient's release of aggression, here viewed as a practice phenomenon, is accompanied by too-great anxiety, he can shift the patient's attention considerably to possible meanings of his behavior. This, then, would constitute a learning situation, lead to psychic structuralization, encourage the development of object cathexis, and make possible further mastery of reality by reducing the patient's fear of his own hostility.

Above all, I wish to emphasize the importance of consistency in attitude and technique; my attitude and technique can best be described by the terms calmness, indirectly communicated optimism, and scientific detachment. All of these phenomena are superimposed, obviously, on a capacity to understand productions which are influenced heavily by primary process thinking and some knowledge of why they are used at the times they are employed. I periodically remind patients that interpretations are made tentatively and solicit their active cooperation in validation and modifications of answers to enigmas. This procedure enhances the development of at least the observing and synthesizing functions and reduces the severity of the patient's primitive superego introjects by permitting him to view his new parent-model as fallible.

Let us now turn to the results of this study to the present.

RESULTS

The treatment of this series of seventeen patients was terminated at least two years ago, except for one patient who took his own life. Fourteen appear thus far to have outcomes which can be classified as satisfactory, or, in some cases, most encouraging. Because of numerous reports of spontaneously remitting schizophrenias, perhaps some of them might have encapsulated their psychoses (to use Federn's term) without such therapy. In addition, the number of cases involved and the shortness of time which has elapsed since their termination of treatment makes this an interim report.

It has been noted regularly that psychotic states which include overt anxiety and mood changes, particularly depressive manifestations, have a better likelihood of therapeutic success. All of the patients in this series manifested overt anxiety and the majority could well have been labeled as suffering from schizoaffective psychoses, with depressive aspects prevailing over manic, although several patients experienced periodic hypomanic episodes.

Glover (1955) found schizophrenics who manifested depressive elements to be the most suitable for psychoanalytic therapy. Nacht and Lebovici (1955) recommended classical analysis for cases of schizophrenia, excluding paranoia and severe hypochondriasis. They, as had Glover, felt that anxiety which was due especially to fear of the superego, was a favorable sign. In all of the cases in the present series, evidence of an extremely punitive superego was present. However, in my experience, this state has been observed uniformly. Authors have discouraged regularly (since about 1908) the use of analytic therapy for paranoid schizophrenics. In this series, two patients, both male, had systematized persecutory delusions. In one, there had been hallucinations during a period of late adolescence and early adulthood, symptoms of which reappeared during one phase of his selective analytic regression, but the other man never experienced hallucinations and in previous years might well have been labeled as paranoiac. Both recovered from their paranoid states although they both remained hampered by obsessive-compulsive character disorders. Each man had been psychotic for many years before analysis; neither has regressed since termination of analysis. The treatment of one man lasted six years and ended ten years ago; that of the other lasted five years and was terminated eight years ago. Each reentered analysis at a later time for relief of depressive symptomatology and received further assistance in overcoming obsessive-compulsive rigidity.

Three cases of this series ended in outright failure. The lack of success with two of them appeared to have been related more to my problems than theirs; I believe the third failed because of faulty judgment on my part.

I shall present two clinical abstracts which illustrate apparent success. I have chosen these cases above others, because they show that analysis can take place with the same therapist after a change in treatment method, whereas in the other instances of apparent success only analytic therapy was used. Each of these patients had been treated by me before I decided to conduct this controlled observation.

A twenty-nine-year-old woman sought treatment because she thought she was going insane; she had numerous obsessive fears. She was afraid she would bite her tongue off if she were openly angry and that she would jump from windows; she barricaded those of her apartment. She also suffered from claustrophobia and had an intense fear of pregnancy. She was sexually anesthetic.

Her parents had immigrated from a southern European country and were ardent Catholics of peasant stock. They had never been happy together and lived apart during most of her life. The mother resided in a city with the children and the father attended a vineyard in the country. He came home on weekends when she was small and at much rarer intervals as she grew older. From puberty, she sided with her mother and avoided her father.

She was the youngest of many children, being seven years younger than the next sibling. She was treated always as though she were an incompetent baby; her decisions were made for her, and she was protected from all extrafamilial dangers. She was a devout Catholic and sincerely believed in the healing effects of confession. Her principal libidinal outlets were in the home and the church. There were no sanctioned aggressive outlets except contempt for the father and outsiders. At the same time her extended family, succumbing at last to the ideals of their new cultural environment (Giovacchini 1961), pressured her into becoming its only college graduate, a role which was perceived to be masculine. She did well in school, was popular and apparently happy.

Following her graduation from college, she was rewarded with a trip to an Eastern city. She had dated when in the university but experienced no sexual encounters beyond nonpassionate kisses and had never drunk liquor more intoxicating than watered wine. The female relative with whom she lived led a relatively Bohemian life. In that environment, the patient drank too much one evening and had the first genital experience she remembered during all of her psychotherapy and subsequent analysis. She believed she was in a trancelike state while she was being kissed and fondled. She knew the man's penis touched her legs, but did not know that she had intercourse. However, she was impregnated.

She remained in the East, had her baby without letting the man or her family know of her pregnancy. She confided her state to a schizoid man whom she had known while she was in school, with whom her relations had been platonic. He asked her to marry him, the marriage being contingent upon her getting rid of the baby. She had her baby adopted out. The man joined her in the East and she returned to her home environment as a housewife.

Following her homecoming, she became withdrawn, obsessive, phobic, and depressed, and retired from church and family activities. The marital partners had little personal contact and almost no sexual life. He worked during the night by choice, and she during the day. He had affairs and otherwise his social life was spent with his widowed mother, who dominated him through her hypochondria. The patient was terrified of pregnancy but both partners insisted on the rhythm system of contraception. Although her husband never threatened overtly to betray her to her parents, she always felt she must obey him implicitly and did so, achieving some semblance of expression of hostility and independence only through passive aggression and the use of her fears.

In her work, she was grossly inefficient but the general pattern in her office was lax. She had no friends. She felt her miserable life was just retribution for her sin. Her social life consisted largely of rare visits to her mother and an older sister, who were solicitous and nondemanding.

After eight years of marriage, her husband became more than usually interested in some woman and the patient feared he would leave her. She then began to fear she would go mad and sought psychotherapy.

During two years (150 hours) of vis-à-vis psychotherapy, she was an exceedingly tense, largely silent patient. Treatment was directed toward making her aware of her suppressed and repressed hostility and her manipulative uses of passive aggression and fears.

When treatment began, she stopped taking sedatives. She made me into an omniscient and omnipotent figure and used my words, perceived at times as concrete phenomena, as protective amulets. Her behavior outside the interviews did not seem to change, but her anxiety abated. Eventually she began to have vague sexual fantasies concerning me and began to demand sedatives. It was clear that the demand for pills reflected an equation of genital and oral gratifications. Various data indicated she had blamed herself for her parents' separation and believed her father left home to avoid succumbing to her sexual desires. Oedipal interpretations were ineffective and she discontinued treatment.

In conjunction with a separate research project, all of my patients were required to undergo psychological tests which were administered by a colleague at six-month intervals. The test protocols of this patient were interpreted to mean that she suffered from undifferentiated schizophrenia throughout this period of treatment. There were also strong indications of hysteria and depression.

She was seen at six months, one year, two years, and five years following treatment, at my request. She seemed much improved. Although all of the old complaints persisted with the exception of the fear she would go insane, there was little anxiety. She apparently lived with me, quite totally, in fantasy. We held long conversations, no matter what else she was doing, and I cared for her and guided her as though she were a small child. Psychological tests done at the same intervals indicated no change.

Seven years after she left treatment, she became intoxicated with her husband one night and got pregnant, again without knowing for certain whether she'd had intercourse. When she ascertained that she was pregnant, she tried to reach me, but I was out of town. She presented herself at a hospital where she had learned I sometimes treat patients and was admitted as my patient. She was terrified that she was going insane and would rip her tongue out. She had the delusion that I was God and had impregnated her. During the two days before I saw her, she regressed into a catatonic state and there were vaguely systematized persecutory ideas. When she first saw me, her terror left and she was discharged from the hospital the next day.

She was then included in the project. Her delusion promptly disappeared. Thereafter, attention was directed primarily toward alleviating superego pressures. She soon resumed church activities, including confession. No clear-cut oedipal memories ever emerged. Under the influence of reconstructive remarks, she seemed to attain some intellectual understanding, although I was never sure that she was not simply responding to what she interpreted to be suggestions or commands. Concurrently, her obsessions and fears were alleviated to a large extent.

Her pregnancy proceeded without difficulty and she delivered a son. Her period in analysis lasted for one year (140 hours). She had become grossly involved in the care of her son and seemed otherwise symptom-free. Analysis was terminated, however, because of absence of funds and because her husband's hostility toward her involvement in her treatment, superimposed upon that toward the baby and the church, led him to threaten to leave her and to tell her family about her first pregnancy if she didn't stop.

Soon after termination, she became pregnant through choice and was unafraid. She became reconciled with her father.

She was seen again at the follow-up intervals described above. Psychological tests done on termination and at those intervals revealed no evidence of psychosis. It is ten years since termination. During the first five years, she was a doting mother and seemed very happy. She was able to enjoy some of her sexual experiences. Aside from a letter she wrote seven years after termination, there have been no further contacts with me. In that missive, she said she had resumed working, was no longer so preoccupied with her children, and getting along better with her husband, who had become a devoted father.

A second married woman was thirty-two years old when first interviewed. Material concerning her history and care has been published previously, under the names Mrs. Y. (Boyer 1955), and Mrs. L. (Boyer 1961). She was intensely dependent and grossly inhibited in both the sexual and aggressive spheres, traits her husband strongly encouraged. The couple had reached a relationship in which the symptoms of each supported the illness of the other. At a time when his dependency on female relatives was interpreted by the patient to mean he would leave her, she underwent an acute, excited catatonic episode which I treated by electroplexy. She was seen in supportive therapy for some months but then suffered a relapse to the same severely regressed state, and I again gave her electroconvulsive therapy. She was then included in the study, as one of the first patients to be involved. During a period of four years, she was seen 750 hours. No clinical evidence of psychosis remained after the first year, during which the psychotic transference was resolved. Psychological protocols, however, continued to be interpreted to be diagnostic of schizophrenia. The analysis of her transference neurosis, in which for a long period I represented her oedipal father and then her oedipal mother, resulted in her becoming much less fearful of her hostility. She began to be better able to accept her sexuality, but her increased independence frightened her husband. Analysis was terminated prematurely because his anger at her was being taken out destructively on their sons.

She remained at the same level of integration for four subsequent years, during which the psychological tests continued to indicate the presence of psychotic trends. Then she underwent a schizomanic regression. She was hospitalized for two weeks and sedated with tranquillizers. Then she resumed analytic therapy.

Soon after her return, while she was still actively hypomanic, her husband had a sudden, serious illness. She reacted with great guilt and severe depression. However, interpretations pertaining to her ascription of magical powers to her hostility and sexual fantasies enabled her to continue office treatment without rehospitalization. Material related to her early life emerged and her childhood ideas that her oedipal wishes had resulted in various catastrophes, including her father's imprisonment and her mother's becoming a lifelong, severely withdrawn hypochondriac, were analyzed. The second period in analytic treatment lasted 13 months (225 hours). At its end, her sexual inhibitions were greatly relieved and her fears of her aggression had lost their magical qualities. When the analysis was terminated, psychological tests revealed no evidence of psychotic thinking.

She enrolled in a graduate school to prepare for a profession within the next year. Almost immediately, her husband became acutely and seriously ill once again. She has remained clinically well for seven subsequent years and has successfully practiced her profession for two years.

DISCUSSION

Psychoanalysis was designed for the treatment of neurotics and in its classical milieu, their projections are analyzed. The neurotic who assumes the couch position is invited to regress selectively. When a psychotic takes the couch, certain facets of his ego and superego are already in a deeper state of regression than we usually expect the neurotic to reach in his therapy. He reenacts the early mother-child relationship, although the areas of ego and superego regression which permit such a reliving differ from patient to patient. We recall that the unfolding of conflict-free ego spheres is dependent upon the mother-infant relationship. In the treatment situation, identification with the actual frustrator is enhanced and there exists a danger of the patient's becoming too like the therapist and being unable to develop subsequently in a manner optimal to his personal potential. The therapist appears for a time to become a variant of Winnicott's (1953) transitional object or Balint's (1959) ocnophilic object. Hopefully, the second phase of treatment eradicates much of this danger. Empirically, none of the individuals in this study has become professionally like me, but one. The ego and superego structures of a number appear now to approximate my own. The psychotic, I believe, makes the treatment situation, as he probably does of many others, one in which he acts in terms of innate strivings toward ego maturation. He also reaches for new objects to replace the old ones to which he ambivalently clings.

When a person lies down on the couch, his contacts with the therapist are diminished abruptly and he maintains contact primarily through hearing. Thus, the attitudes of the analyst, as reflected in his words, voice tones, and other sounds, assume great importance, and cannot be disguised. As with the pregenital child, and particularly the child who has not yet learned to communicate in words, the introjections of the analysand are dependent upon the actual attitudes and qualities of the analyst. The psychotic patient wishes consciously to validate his auditory perceptions through other perceptual experience, notably visual and tactile, and sometimes presses to be allowed to sit. When he is met with questions concerning his desire to sit, he develops anxiety which stimulates the emergence of data, serving the analytic purpose. Patients have verbalized subsequently their gratitude that they had not been encouraged to face or touch me. As an example, during the third year of the analysis of a borderline schizophrenic who had used every technique I have ever witnessed in her attempts to seduce me to abandon following rigorously the analytic technique, she suddenly blocked in her associations and had an intense desire to sit and look at me. I asked her to tell me what her wish to see me brought to her mind. She became furious and hurled the following words at me. The transition in her vocal expression mirrored the change in the content of the sentence. First she shouted a few words, then her voice tone became scathingly sarcastic, then softer and ultimately loving. She said:

You God-damned rat fink, you buddy, you pal, you dear sweet kind man. Do you know that if you had not been incorruptible throughout my analysis, I'd have been dead long ago? I used to be afraid, too, that you'd grate off like a potato. I'm so glad you're ungratable and haven't been destroyed.

Patients have commonly said that their remaining on the couch had made them aware of the magical nature of their fears of being destroyed by me or of destruction of me which at times they sought to achieve through fusion via tactile or visual contact.

A therapist cannot remain completely objective about a patient. My patients' introjection of my attitude that they were worth helping served the valuable purpose of increasing their feelings of self-worth. I did not tell them overtly that I liked them. During the early period of treatment, the most important step, in my judgment, has been their introjection of my relatively calm, hopeful, expectant attitude with its consistent implication that gratifications can be postponed, or even renounced, with benefit.

The question has been raised frequently, "How can introjection take place in a milieu designed for the analysis of projections?" This query implies that introjection takes place principally through visual perceptions of the psychiatrist's overt communication of factual data concerning himself. Discussants have offered such a viewpoint as a reason to have the patient face the therapist. The results of this study surely affirm that successful introjection can take place as a result of auditory perceptions. Such information has long been available to us, since congenitally blind people, too, develop ego structures.

It is my impression that the notion that visual and/or tactile contact is of primary importance in the treatment of psychotics has been overstressed. In infants, such contact promotes the differentiation of id and ego. In certain acute episodes of psychotic regression, such contact is also mandatory for the reestablishment of some degree of autonomy, as is evident by the terror expressed by patients at some times when they are deprived of the sight or touch of the therapist. However, it is my opinion that the helplessness of the psychotic is exaggerated in the minds of many therapists and that their attitudes encourage patients to remain deeply regressed at times by rewarding them for such infantile behavior, that is, by their supplying the secondary gains sought by the patients. When we work with psychotics, in order to develop a working alliance, it behooves us to appeal to the more mature aspects of the patient's ego whenever possible. Clearly, in the presence of too great anxiety, no analysis can take place. I am suggesting that in the analysis of psychotics, especially during periods of acute regression, too little importance has been placed on the value of words and therapists have underestimated the resiliency of their patients. They appear to have forgotten sometimes that the psychotic patient is not *all* psychotic and that he has both normal and neurotic aspects which can be called into service by directing attention to them.

Freud's original formulation was that the aim of psychoanalytic therapy was to lift amnesias. Since psychoanalysis has come to consider the result of defenses other than repression, the need has arisen to understand the role of the synthetic and organizing function in the therapeutic process. Now we aim not merely at bringing into consciousness but at gaining analytic insight. We seek to produce changes in the ego which make warded-off functions available to the conflictless sphere of the ego, a process which entails both the bringing into consciousness and the reestablishment of connections (Bibring 1937; Fenichel 1937; Kris 1950; Loewenstein 1951; Nunberg 1937). The role of language is of cardinal importance in the accomplishment of this goal.

The psychoanalytic dialogue differs from all others and is made unique by the fundamental rule and the role of the analyst. The patient is asked to relinquish the aim-directed nature of conscious thinking. A controlled regression of the ego (Kris 1950) results, and elements of the Preconscious are made available to the Conscious. The analyst protects the patient and draws certain affects of the patient onto himself but his main role is of lending his own ego functions to the weakened, although to some degree autonomous, ego of the patient. All of these functions are, of course, even more graphically portrayed when the patient is psychotic. The analyst forms what might be characterized as a variant of the maternal protective barrier (Boyer 1956). He supplies the knowledge of mental phenomena, the understanding, and the objectivity which help the patient to understand them (see Chapter Eight).

Loewenstein (1956) has differentiated among three

functions of speech: the cognitive function, the expressive function, and the function of appeal. In the neurotic, the first two functions predominate at first and that of appeal emerges soon thereafter. In the psychotic, the latter two functions predominate initially. The analyst refrains insofar as he can from responding to the appeal function. He attempts, through using interpretations, to transform the appeal function to the expressive function. He demonstrates to the patient that he expresses something about himself when he speaks of other persons or things. The analyst attempts to exclude both the functions of expression and appeal from his own speech.

Nunberg (1932) wrote of the magical function of speech and also of speech as a substitute for action. With the psychotic, the analyst seeks to reduce belief in the magical effects of speech. While his nonverbal behavior assists the patient to accomplish this goal, I believe the analyst's interpretive words to be of more lasting benefit.

Superego, id, and ego contribute unequally to the actions of speech. So far as the superego is concerned, the confession of acts or intentions may lead to an actual change in the person, when such admissions do not create anxiety and retributive acts on the part of the confessor. Communication through speech is often in the service of the id. Speech may be a poor substitute for sexual gratification but so far as the expression of aggression is concerned, words may indeed constitute actions. As discussed earlier, the patient's being encouraged to express his hostility verbally serves various purposes; here attention is called to its discharge function in an atmosphere of safety. The role of speech from the standpoint of the ego is perhaps of more interest at this point.

Our patients teach us that a barrier exists between the *Ucs.* and the *Pcs.*, but also between the *Pcs.* and the *Cs.*, since they frequently delay relating known information. No doubt this barrier results from fears of loss of love and esteem or other punishments. The analyst is both a superego and witness to the patient; these roles are of inestimable importance in the treatment of the psychotic. As witness, he serves as an accessory, reminding memory, an autonomous ego. When the patient has verbalized data, those data become more real and more easily remembered, which may result, in part, from auditory perception. The analyst stores previously imparted data and recalls them to the patient at appropriate times. Communicated private data become objective and social data, especially if they are not allowed to become repressed.

It has long been known that catharsis in analysis is not enough. The experiencing of emotions must be followed by their verbal expression and, for ultimate structuralization, they must be connected with specific contents. Then the affects can be reintegrated as parts of defenses as well as of drives. In the formation of analytic insight, verbalization is an essential step and the interpretive role of the analyst is his most important function.

Language plays a decisive role in the formation and development of thought processes. In analysis, the thought processes of especial interest are those dealing with self-knowledge. When words bring to conscious awareness a thought and an affect which have been previously unconscious, language performs the function of a scaffolding which permits thought to be built inside. Interpretations given by the analyst also provide such a scaffolding, although interpretations may also be misused in the service of resistance. Possibly when such is the result, the interpretations have been made when some aspect of them is untimely. The receptivity of hitherto pathogenic memories into consciousness makes them become harmless because insight and verbalization subject them to reality testing and unravel the effects of pathogenic entwinement between past and present (Loewenstein 1956).

Particularly with psychotic patients and those with characterological disorders it is necessary consistently to analyze idiosyncratic efforts at making himself understood in order that the patient may learn to communicate in a generally acceptable manner. The analyst's understanding of the meaning of the patient's communications enables him to break through resistance and to learn about interpersonal and intrapsychic realities. In addition, the patient's becoming consciously aware of his use of attitudinal and bodily language helps him remove body-ego deficiencies and to separate self from nonself.

Many analysts have stressed the role of the superego in schizophrenia (Hoedemaker 1955; Pious 1949; Wexler 1951). I have spoken of my means of giving superego support. In general, I communicate indirectly my philosophy that guilt is appropriate when one's behavior, without rational cause, jeopardizes the rights and comforts of others.

A major thesis which the empirical data supplied from the present controlled observation have strongly suggested is the following: revision of faulty ego and superego structures in certain psychotic patients can be accomplished by the analytic process. The success of that process is dependent upon two main phenomena: (1) In a controlled situation, qualities of the new parent-model, the therapist, can be introjected and such introjection can alter unhealthy nuclei (Glover 1930) of the patient's ego and superego. (2) Interpretation has a structuralizing effect (see Chapter Six). Clinical observations have revealed that schizophrenic patients partly fear potent results of their rage; that they worry that their aggressive tendencies will destroy the object or, projected onto the object, result in their own destruction. Psychic structuralization is dependent upon neutralization of the aggressive drive and its internalization into the ego and superego for which it supplies motor power (Hartmann, Kris, and Loewenstein, 1959:71). It is probable that interpretation is the principal tool which leads to neutralization of the aggressive drive and to its being made available for such internalization. These data suggest that, in contrast to the prevailing attitude of psychoanalysts regarding the therapeutic procedure of choice for such patients, the analytic method, modified as little as possible, may be not only preferable but mandatory, if the psychotic processes of the patients are not to be merely masked or isolated.

Clearly the internal security of the therapist is of signal importance. If he is too anxious, it is unlikely that a lasting therapeutic alliance can be attained. Since his attitudes and relative lack of anxiety will affect his understanding and judgment, he must understand himself well, be proud of his skills and accomplishments and be optimistic. Surely, if he understands primary process thinking and has the capacity to regress selectively in the service of the therapeutic process, he will be better able to understand his patient's productions and to elicit additional usable data from that patient. I would assume that most properly trained psychoanalysts could become relatively free of anxiety while dealing with psychotic patients and proficient at treating them.

A number of therapists have stressed that the role of countertransference is of great importance for the successful outcome of treatment of schizophrenics (Fromm-Reichmann 1950; Rosenfeld 1952). My analysis of one patient was supervised. When treatment had reached a frustrating plateau, it became obvious that the problem lay within myself. I returned to analysis, where I learned more than intellectually that I had entered the practice of psychiatry and later psychoanalysis for the unconscious purpose of healing an important person of my past who had periodically regressed into psychotic states. I learned that when dealing with patients whose conflicts struck literally too close to home, I developed a countertransference neurosis. My return to analysis made possible the resurrection of the treatment of my patient. The therapy of two individuals who are included in this study had failed previously. Review of their case histories and the course of their treatment made amply clear that I had acted out with them, too.

The third failure may be attributable to bad judgment on my part. The young male patient had had a particularly tense oedipal period. His father had been absent from the home much of the time and the patient had believed his father had abandoned him to the sexual desires of his mother. In treatment, he was in the midst of a transference psychosis in which he believed I was his father. At the same time, he was having great difficulty in restraining himself from sexual activities with a relative whom he periodically believed to be his mother, a woman who he thought had strong sexual desires for him. This was the state of affairs when I announced to him that I was to be away from the office for a few days, some weeks thence. The patient seemed to take the news well, and I misinterpreted his turning to other subject matter. Nevertheless, I arranged for him to be able to call a psychiatrist whom he knew and trusted and for him to enter a hospital if he were frightened during my absence; he was aware of these provisions. One day after I left, he went to stay with family friends. He became fearful he would harm himself and was taken to a hospital where a psychiatric resident decided he did not require hospitalization. The next morning he killed himself.

SUMMARY

For seventeen years I have treated borderline and overtly schizophrenic patients by the analytic method that has ordinarily been reserved for the treatment of neurotics. In seminar groups, colleagues have remarked at times that I was more strictly and consistently analytical while treating psychotics than they were with neurotics. In this chapter I discuss the theoretical orientation upon which this study has been based, the methodology, and the results.

The patients included were all of average to superior intelligence; the symptom picture of almost all of them included strong depressive tendencies. No chronically regressed, withdrawn patients were studied.

Although the cases number only seventeen and the time elapsed since termination is not long, fourteen of the cases have achieved satisfactory or striking improvements, and there has been no psychotic or serious neurotic regression among them during periods which range from two to ten years. The data suggest that, with patients such as those included, therapists have used more parametric and extra-analytic procedures than have been either necessary or, perhaps, advisable.

It is suggested that the psychotic process is reversible in some patients and that we, as analysts, might aim not at encapsulation of at least some psychoses, but at their cure. Stone (1963) voiced the opinion that the analyst shirks his responsibility at times if he does not give decisive help beyond interpretation. To me, as it does to Giovacchini (1964), such a statement implies that we have something better to offer than psychoanalysis. Hartmann and Kris (1945:12) wrote: "Those who do not appreciate the importance of genetic interpretations change their technique." It is emphasized here that the role of genetic interpretations is at least as important in the treatment of psychotics as it is with neurotics and that the likelihood of successful therapy will be enhanced by the therapist's taking only such actions as do not jeopardize subsequent use of interpretations.

Chapter Five

The Psychotic Identifications in Schizophrenia: The Technical Problem

Edward D. Hoedemaker, M.D.

It is my purpose to draw attention to one of the ways in which the schizophrenic asks for help and at the same time communicates or reveals to his therapist the plight in which the ego finds itself. The area of treatment to which I wish to call attention has to do with some of the manifestations of hostility and aggression. This must include the defensive role of such phenomena, the implications for the handling of countertransference, including the technical demands upon the therapist, and the resulting therapeutic benefits. Finally, and most important, the insights which both therapist and patient gain through such experiences in regard to the psychodynamics of the illness deserve consideration.

First, let me sketch briefly my experience in the treatment of schizophrenia. I find that I have treated fifteen schizophrenic people since 1947, four of whom are now in treatment. All of them have been seen four or five times a week and, except those who have started recently, treatment has lasted for from four to seven years. All have spent most of this time on the couch, but several have sat, either in a chair or on the floor, during the early phases. Twelve were hospitalized some time prior to the beginning of treatment or were in a hospital when treatment began. Of these fifteen, there were three failures, two of whom committed suicide. Five have made good recoveries with adequate social, emotional, and economic adjustments. Of the four now in treatment, all appear headed for recovery with insight. Of the remaining three, none has decompensated or has been hospitalized, and two earn marginal livings, but all three have a below-average psychosexual adjustment. Both suicides, one during treatment and one after transfer to another therapist, were precipitated at least partially by errors in technique.

My first insights into the psychopathology of schizophrenia occurred in the recognition of the needs of such patients for firm, consistent, and realistic limit-setting as reflections of an important part of ego failure. It was by utilizing this first area of insight and experience as a base that I found myself working toward a broader understanding of the remaining pathologic mechanisms in this illness. Only when I thought I could perceive the entire illness as a meaningful system of defenses did I encounter well-rounded success in any given patient. It is difficult to imagine that a therapist could approach the manifestations of schizophrenia without running full tilt into the appalling aggression and destructiveness of the patient's introjects and also without being forced to set some limits. And it is equally difficult to think of lasting therapeutic success without the destructiveness being successfully encountered in the treatment. Finally, it is the introjection of the perceiving, understanding, and consistent therapist which is the *sine qua non* of recovery. Whether this introjection occurs through interpretation, confrontations, or limit-settings is a moot question, and all probably play important roles. The above statement applies to a considerable degree to the psychoanalysis of neuroses and of character neuroses as well, the great difference with the treatment of the psychotic being the much greater degree of regressive empathy demanded of the therapist while he at the same time figuratively struggles to maintain one foot on solid ground. As I have stated elsewhere (Hoedemaker 1960), I find myself becoming more convinced that the apparent differences in work with schizophrenics as compared with analytic work with neurotic character disorders are differences in degree rather than in kind. In this Boyer and I are in agreement (Boyer 1964).

The technical problem posed by the pathological introjects leads directly to the question, namely, can functioning introjects be effectively provided for the schizophrenic early in treatment which will stay with him and provide a psychologic graft to his embattled ego and allow him to work in an analytic partnership with his therapist? I am satisfied that they can be provided and must be provided or treatment will fail. For illustrative material here I have turned to my sickest patient, who, only after six years of work, is able to perceive (and I too!) the distorted, regressed, fragmented, cliché-packed, primitive identifications from the past with which she has literally been stuffed. This deluded, hallucinating woman whose schizophrenic father committed suicide when she was fifteen, and whose cold impersonal mother had from the start been unable to tolerate her crying as an infant, has, as an outpatient, never missed an appointment, has lain on the couch most of her hours and talked throughout almost every hour, has computed her bill each month, paid it promptly, and has not acted out since the third month of treatment when a specific and definite limit-setting crisis was successfully passed. Without going into details, this limit-setting crisis dealt with her ego's inability to prevent destructive and intrusive behavior on the part of others. In addition to the above ego-syntonic behavior, she has progressively become able to distinguish clearly the all-important difference between, on the one hand, being aware of such delusions and not expressing them after recognizing their pathologic origin. That is to say, secondary process ego functioning is present in a very important way and she makes use of it. The early introjection of one of my traits appears to have served as an ego graft upon which a progressive and accretive process has continued. At the time when this limit-setting was carried out I only knew that her failures in control were critically self-destructive. Now, six years later, we both can see that her impulsiveness was the expression of the introject derived from her suicide father, and it is now evident that my relatively blind and intuitively carried out limit-setting was a successful confrontation of her behavior as though she were this pathological introject.

This ego functioning has persisted and improved throughout the six years during which she has deluged me with a cacophony from the past. Such outpourings have driven me close to despair and appeared at times to threaten my psychic organization, with the impulse to drive her from my office in a rage. What prevented my doing so was my awareness of her ego-syntonic behavior described earlier. This leads me to ask this question: Is it not possible that our failures or the length of treatment with any particular schizophrenic patient are due often to the vulnerability of the therapist to the trauma of the psychotic transference upon him? I will refer to this matter later with a specific clinical illustration, but I think success or failure depends in any case on whether the specific necessary introject can be fashioned by the patient from the specific therapist.

Turning more specifically to the hostile and aggressive manifestations of the schizophrenic patient and to the technical implications for both treatment and psychotherapy, it is generally accepted that problems arising in connection with the countertransference are of major importance. To begin with, the patient fears his own destructive capabilities. This rage, directed as it is against former objects, must eventually be encountered in the transference and, therefore, directed against the analyst. Because of the intensity of this feeling and because the patient himself has been unable to express this rage directly in the past for fear of its effects on others and himself, he naturally fears that it will destroy his therapist. I agree with Boyer that if this hatred of former objects is discouraged by the analyst, the patient senses that the analyst fears his own hostility. It follows that the analyst is perceived as both unable to cope with his own hostile urges and with those of the patient as well. The patient's developing identification with the analyst, in such an eventuality, increases the patient's fears of his hostile impulses. I, early in my experience with these patients, precipitated a psychotic decompensation when I retreated (by denial) from a patient's accusation (in the transference) that I was just like his father. It follows that when such expressions are turned aside or otherwise discouraged, the patient immediately senses the analyst's fear of his own aggression and his wish to avoid looking at that part of himself. This countertransference problem of the therapist unwittingly reinforces certain portions of the pathologic introjects from the parental figures of the past who, in addition to their other shortcomings, have been notoriously unable to recognize and deal with their own aggressiveness and, therefore, that of their children.

There is a companion idea which appears to be equally important to the ability of the analyst to allow the expression of the patient's hostile wishes. It is this: While the therapist must not discourage the expression of such hostility, he must not, by the same token, deny his own realistic fear and concern of these manifestations. The analyst needs to behave with his patient as he would behave when crossing a busy street corner: to be terrifed at the traffic, never to realistically encounter it, is certainly contraindicated; but, if he denies such fear and if he dashes blithely across the street, he will be hurt. If an analyst is hurt by a patient, it is damaging to the patient as well as to the therapist because introjection of this behavior of the therapist will be the introjection of a counterphobic approach to realistic dangers. There is a middle ground which contains realistic appreciation of the potential dangers which derive from the tremendously hostile urges of the schizophrenic patient. It is necessary to confront the patient with the fact that therapeutic success will depend on the patient's ability to control these urges in regard to the therapist, and an effective way to do this is for the therapist to admit realistic concern. Recently, a young schizophrenic man in treatment six months told me that he thought I was afraid of him. I promptly told him that I was, but that I didn't think I was too afraid to let it affect my work with him. He has since been noticeably more comfortable. Introjection of this position of mine allowed him to maintain both healthy fear and respect for his impulses.

One familiar source of countertransference trouble stems from the demands which some analysts tend to make of themselves when working with psychotic patients. This appears when, in the face of accusations by the patient that they are unloving and do not really like the patient, they find themselves denying this and insisting that they really like the patient! Respect for the patient as another person can be confused with the terms "love" or "like" with all the subtleties of meaning involved. Such respect for the patient is better left unverbalized. I think, when confronted by accusations of being unloving, the analyst provides better introjective material for the patient if he lets him know at an appropriate time and in appropriate ways the simple truth that in many ways he does not like him. When the schizophrenic with his highly tuned sensitivity to the unconscious of the therapist says that he does not think that the therapist likes him, I think it is most helpful to both participants for the therapist to admit the simple truth that in many ways he does not like his patient any more than any doctor likes some manifestations of disease that he is called upon to face. I usually let the patient know about this negative feeling toward him by asking him (or its equivalent and when it is fitting), "Am I supposed to like everything about you?" This is a countertransference problem having to do with the analyst's guilt feelings about his own aggressiveness. I think it was Fromm-Reichmann who said that the therapist of the schizophrenic cannot afford the luxury of guilt feelings.

The question of the analyst acting in his own best interest oftentimes is overlooked in our analytic work. It seems to me that Western civilization is still suffering from a sense of guilt about each individual acting first in his own best interest. Most of us do this, but many find themselves talking about doing things in the best interest of other people first. There is no contradiction for a doctor to act truly in his best interest and, in this way, to act in his patient's best interest. The schizophrenic's ego has been prevented from acting in its own best interest in many ways, and, because of this, I am suggesting that, as analysts, we learn to think without guilt of what our own best interests as professional people are. If we do this carefully and realistically, we will have to act in the best interests of the patient's ego as well. Obviously, with any given patient, if we do not strive for our own success, we cannot strive for the success of the patient under our treatment. This is not moralizing, but merely a part of my attempt to test the reality of the therapeutic situation with these difficult patients. This problem having to do with the therapist's best interests is more clearly seen with the patient who repeatedly behaves destructively against others and himself outside of the therapeutic hour. In such instances I take the time to explain to the patient that I want to work as efficiently as possible and that that in turn will give him the best chance to recover. I go on to say that, if I can't see the possibility of working efficiently because of his continued misbehavior, it is true that I will sooner or later have to withdraw from work with him. This leaves the choice clearly where it belongs, it shows him the power he possesses over his fate, and at the same time shows him that he cannot trap the therapist and destroy him. Furthermore, I have come to realize that such early confrontations, necessarily intuitively done as they are, will later in the analytic work appear as important confrontations of manifestations of hostile introjects which threatened the treatment relationship in its early days. As an introjective "package," this confrontation which delimits the therapist's position is of high value. There are two things which this position is not. First, it is not a threat of abandonment because of one false step on the patient's part. Second, it is not moralizing, but rather it is a confrontation of the possibility of the necessity of an abandonment under certain circumstances. I think to do less than to take this position is a form of abandonment in itself. In my experience the healthy partnership with the patient is *always* strengthened by this position. Regardless of how carefully this is described, it is always misunderstood by some; a young author in a draft of a paper referred to this position and its implementation as "Hoedemaker's violent acts of rejection"! This theme is more clearly seen in the analogous surgical situation wherein a surgeon may work at his top efficiency and his patient may later die in spite of his skill, but the surgeon has succeeded and he, too, cannot have a need for the recovery of all his patients, only the wish. Pertinent to this is Searles' recent comment about "therapeutic dedication" in work with chronic schizophrenic patients: "It seems to me that, if a therapist sets out to save the schizophrenic person from his illness, then the therapist gets put into a 'meat-grinder'; . . . he cannot take that great responsibility for the patient's care; he can only help the patient to become well, insofar as the patient becomes aware of his own wish to become well" (Searles 1964). It is my position that such necessary early limit-setting, without committing the analyst to some dedicated crusade to cure the patient, demonstrates to the patient that he is not too afraid to attack the pathological introjects, and this in turn, through introjection, strengthens the patient's ego, brings him hope, and immediately brings him to some degree of cooperation and conscious desire to recover.

In turning now to some of the manifestations of the psychotic identifications, the following clinical examples will be helpful. These clinical encounters emphasize a way in which the schizophrenic communicates and at the same time invites help. My attention has for some time been drawn to the psychotic identifications and their clinical disclosure. Jacobson (1954), in reviewing Klein's (1952) term "projective identification," discussed in considerable detail the differences between the identifications of manic-depressives and those of schizophrenics and their influence on behavior. She pointed out how the schizophrenic behaves *as though he were the object.* To quote Jacobson, "The ego and the superego systems deteriorate to a much more dangerous extent (than in manic-depressives) and the conflict between the self and the superego becomes retransformed into struggles between the self and magic, threatening love object figures, and the pathologic identifications are the expression of alternating introjective and projective processes leading to more or less total fusions between the self and the object images within the deteriorating ego-Id" (Jacobson

1954). It is these alternating introjective and projective processes to which I wish to call attention. In the psychotic transference after new and healthy introjects have been successfully introduced and are playing their important role in the ego and superego, the terrifying figures of the magic-ladened past are seen alternately as characteristics of the environment including the analyst, then of the patient, back and forth, sometimes with bewildering rapidity. We are all familiar with the kaleidoscopic manner in which some schizophrenics shift from one to the other of the archaic forms of the hodge-podge of partial identifications. Here I wish to draw your attention to the alternating introjection and projection of the same image of the past and the bearing this process has on the ways in which the patient communicates with the analyst, the technical problems posed by the hostility involved, and the attempt of the patient to recover.

A deluded schizophrenic woman working on the couch for over four years had with considerable regularity projected upon me in the psychotic transference the nonattentive, fundamentally hostile, image of her mother. She believed that I cared nothing about her, was not interested in her welfare, and only wanted her money, and that actually I was probably wondering how soon she would go away and leave me alone. Attempts to interpret this projective phenomenon by the usual methods met with total failure because, as we know, such interpretive work requires the help of a relatively healthy and perceptive ego, as found in the neurotic. She saw others as having the same traits and I was like them all. Now at work also was the schizophrenic's need to see everyone, including the therapist, as rejecting figures as a defense against underlying painful feelings becoming conscious if, in his hostile world, he discovers the therapist as being truly loving. Thus, the realization of this contrast threatens the patient with consciousness of overwhelming poignancy and rage regarding his past. However, while the schizophrenic defends against this painful awareness, he also works toward recovery and has, in my illustration, worked in an analytic setting toward it by projecting the pathologic introject of the cold mother onto the analyst, thereby giving the analyst an opportunity to deal with it. Now, in this setting, and by this I mean the projection upon me, in the psychotic transference, of the inattentive cold mother, my patient one day reported a telephone call from her mother concerning the patient's youngest son, and said that obviously her mother was attacking her in this way. She then said that she had called her mother back and reported some news about another son. She then said, "I don't know why I called her and told her this." She hurried on, obsessing about this and unrelated topics. I interrupted her to ask, "Doesn't it strike you as odd that, on the one hand, you know why your mother called you but you do not know why you called her?" Paying not the slightest attention to me, she continued to verbally wring her hands about the purpose of her mother's call. Again I stopped her and said, "Apparently you don't understand me. I am trying to draw your attention to the paradox that you know your mother's motives but not your own." She again brushed this aside and continued on as before. I repeatedly interrupted her and each time confronted her in different words with the apparent paradox. After each confrontation, she would brush aside what I had said and rush on. Finally, with considerable irritation, I pounded my hand on the arm of my chair and said, "I insist that you pay attention to me; I have an idea that you haven't looked at. *Apparently I have to fight for my own existence here.*" She then saw what I had been trying to point out, namely, the apparent contradiction as I have described it. After commenting, showing that she had understood me, she said, "*That's what has been troubling me. I think I know how you feel now. Now you know how I feel about my mother. That's exactly what happened to me a long time ago. I guess I have been trying to tell you something about this.*" The importance of the content of these telephone calls and their meaning in terms of the patient's life experience is not denied. However, in my inquiry concerning the apparent paradox, I was literally forced to confront her with her rejecting behavior before dealing with the content. Searles has clearly described this phase of work with the patient who behaves as the parental introject toward the therapist, especially in the need for the therapist to experience anger and to express it without guilt (Searles 1961:177–178).

The overwhelming oral aggressivity which holds the schizophrenic's ego captive must first be seen and successfully encountered by the therapist before a meaningful interpretative relationship between patient and therapist can exist. In the quieter atmosphere with the neurotic character this would be simply working with behavior before content, but, with the schizophrenic, it is more like working in a howling gale. Characteristically, this patient paid no attention to my attempts to draw her attention to the content of what she said. We have all had the experience of having a patient sound as if he were answering a question, but in fact paying no attention to the content of our question and the appropriate answer. The patient had in some way placed me in the position of her own ego structure and then had turned loose upon me the cold disdain and rejection of the pathologic introject of a figure from the past. I thought that if I could survive this attack, she, by introjecting this part of me, could survive the internal attack of this pathologic introject and come to see the process more clearly within herself. To a large degree, my reaction in this instance was spontaneous with some recognition that she needed to have me successfully defend my intactness in the face of her sadistic attempts to eliminate me. Having had such experiences with other schizophrenic patients, I had been through this before, but this type of experience is always accompanied by an awareness by the therapist of the crucial and of the desperate need for one's own defense. I am convinced that my patient literally had to place me in a position where I either survived or did not. The alternative would have been to tacitly agree to listen, not interrupt, to relegate my anger to the limbo of ineptness and analytic incompetence with its attendant sense of loss of professional identity. However, the position I took and successfully defended gave the patient, as I understand it, very important introjective material to stand side by side with her embattled ego against the terrifying threats of these pathologic introjects. If I could survive her attack, by introjecting this aspect of me, she could survive and come to see the pathologic process within herself more clearly, just as I could. This type of confrontation in some form was necessary for many months and was accompanied by steady improvement with insight. It was, in fact, the turning point in her treatment and led to a steady improvement in the analytic partnership to the point where she could fully project this hostile identification with her mother onto me in the transference. With this new ability she at first would leave the analytic hour in its midst in cold fury, "knowing" that I had never loved her, only to return for the next hour with decided improvement and insight. She then developed the ability to remain throughout the hour of this transference phenomenon. In this transference phenomenon she was at last able not only to project her hostile identification with her mother, but she could express her rage directly at me. She could now do this in the transference and survive, knowing that at a deeper level both of us could live through the attack. My confrontation led in this instance to good, healthy analytic work in the transference, tempestuous though it was. I think this could be termed part of the transference psychosis. This patient is headed for a good recovery with insight. A quote from a few months ago shows the insight she has developed. "I've had to fight the Medea in me—this has been my battle to make sure that this part of me cannot actually hurt. Medea first loved Jason and, when he became free, she turned on him. You couldn't believe how much hate I have in me." I was tempted to say, "Oh, yes I could!" The work of the therapist in empathizing with the threatened child, in which he must feel the poignant isolation and the resulting rage and then vigorously assert himself, brings a rich reward to the patient. The patient, by introjecting this ability of the therapist, can better express his needs and aggression both internally, and, when appropriate, toward the outer world.

In my clinical example I have reached the point where the patient was able to bring into the open the full fury of her hatred of her mother, projected upon me, and vent upon me the cold retaliatory rage so long repressed. The content of this rage contained such expressions as, "You don't love me and you never have and you know it and I have always known it." The accompanying feeling cannot be expressed in writing. This to my mind was no different from similar phenomena in the analyses of neurotics, except for its almost overwhelming intensity and its attendant difficult countertransference problem. There is no place for guilt feelings on the therapist's part. In what way does the analyst love the patient? Disgusted and enraged at the patient at times, there must be an abiding object relationship with these patients which will not become unseated and which will hold steady during these transference crises. The usual failure on the part of the unseasoned therapist takes the form of protests that the patient is mistaken and perceives him incorrectly. This robs the patient of the promised opportunity (in the analytic contract) to express whatever thoughts and feelings he needs to express. Thus, the patient's chance to discover the nature of the pathologic introject which so closely invests his weakened ego is taken from him because of the therapist's technical failure. Certainly one element of the therapist's love for the patient, then, is his ability to hate and attack the patient's objectlike behavior and then to tolerate the patient's hatred in the transference storm without becoming too frightened (Hoedemaker 1955, 1960; Searles 1959, 1961).

At the risk of repetition, the two aspects or phases of this work done by the patient-therapist team which deals with the emergence of the pathologic introject into consciousness must be carefully differentiated. The patient's behavior as though he were the pathologic introject is understandably determined by several factors which include: the parents' personalities and the interchanges between the parents and the patient in the course of their lives including the regressive alterations and misperceptions of the parent figures. As beginning insight came the other day to a moderately sick schizophrenic young man, he was able to say, "It's not how father really is or was, but how I saw him that I have to fear." In my experience one important element in the patient's behavior toward the therapist is his massive psychic blindness to the therapist's needs as a presumed working partner. This explains my patient's indifference and insensibility to my needs in the encounter dealing with the apparent paradox in her account of the telephone conversation. Unless this indifference and other behavior (as though the object) is *perceived* by the therapist, it cannot be dealt with by confrontation, and, of course, to perceive this indifference the analyst must allow himself the needs of the symbiotic ambivalent child and then assert them with feeling, a formidable stint of regressive empathy. It then follows that if the patient's indifference is not dealt with, the work with the transference phase is ineffective. Once this insensitivity of the patient is perceived, it demands activity by the analyst-therapist even though his training has taught him receptiveness and passivity. In order to become active in these confrontations he must be sensitive to his needs and rights as a partner in the relationship and he must recognize that his failure is the patient's failure and his success the patient's success. While the behavior of the patient as though he were the object may be multifaceted, it is behavior and without conscious thought content concerning the therapist. The therapist's role here, and in the transference phenomenon as well, is highly charged with feeling and always severely tests him, especially his temptations to feel guilt.

The therapeutic benefits of the successful handling of these manifestations include the resultant increases in the ego's strength. When the patient acts as though he were the object and the analyst confronts this behavior and obtains deserved recognition, the patient's ego through introjection of this ability of the analyst is better able to perceive and confront the pathologic introject from the past. When the pathologic introject is successfully tolerated by the analyst in the transference, the patient's ego through introjection of this ability of the analyst becomes better able to tolerate and survive the internal attacks of the pathologic introject.

A schizophrenic woman withheld information concerning her sexual play with a male acquaintance, behavior that I had forbade because it interfered with treatment. Just as the father had concealed from the patient's mother his thoughtless seduction of the patient, she concealed her forbidden sexual behavior from me. This concealment on her part was one of the important ways in which she behaved as though she were the object, the object-representation of her father. For her to behave in this way (the concealment) it was necessary for her to completely lose sight of my needs as her therapist, including my need to be kept informed as to the occurrence of the sexual behavior described. It was necessary to repeatedly make myself known as someone who could not function if she remained oblivious of my needs, that I was in fact dependent upon her. Following a series of such confrontations she began to project upon me characteristics of the introjected secretly seductive father, and only then could she express her hatred and fear of me in the transference.

Hopefully, the above clinical examples and this brief account of the technical problems show how insight into the dynamics of the massive identifications is increased for both analyst and patient with consequent growth of ego strength. Clearer perception of the meaningful past as noted in the first patient's recall increased her ability to hate and to mobilize healthy aggression in the service of the ego; introjection of the intelligent perceptibility of the analyst, of his healthy fears, and of his courage are only some of the important products of such patient-analyst interactions. While not a part of this brief study, the gains to the analyst are very great as well.

As to the defensive operations of the ego in these instances, there appears to have been massive introjections and resultant hostile identifications with attempts to cope with this pathology by alternating projection and reintrojection. In spite of the defensive regression, splitting, and dedifferentiation of the ego, if the analyst can allow himself to empathize with both the rejected child and then the hostile introjects and still do analytic work, the patient's ego somehow is able to provide the material which the analyst needs for his work.

Chapter six

Psychoanalytic Treatment of Character Disorders: Introduction

Peter L. Giovacchini, M.D.

The psychoanalyst seldom sees cases that are similar to the ones reported in the early literature. Reichard (1956) questioned whether Breuer and Freud's (1895) cases were hysterics. Instead of classical hysteria one is faced with a variety of conditions that are sometimes called character disorders. These patients usually complain of an inability to adjust to their milieu. They feel as if they are misfits, that there is no purpose to their existence, and that in general they "do not belong." When they are studied in analysis, one does not see the usual neurotic preoccupation with manifestations of intrapsychic conflict and defense. Such patients may not complain of discrete symptoms, but one notes confusion about their identity and special problems in dealing with reality.

A seminar, under the auspices of the Chicago Institute for Psychoanalysis, has been studying these clinical entities for the past five years. Although we have learned considerable about their ego structure and the problems encountered in the analytic setting, very little progress has been made in distinguishing these cases from psychoses. Most of us agree that there must be nosologic distinctions, but when we attempt to enumerate differences in terms of narcissistic fixations, object relations, and a variety of ego functions, we find we are unable to construct sharp and definite boundaries.

However, here it is not particularly relevant to be too concerned about exact diagnostic categories since the focus in this chapter will be to consider the applicability of the psychoanalytic method to cases suffering from severe characterological problems regardless of whether they might be phenomenologically psychotic.

In 1896, Freud (1896) believed psychoses could be treated psychoanalytically and he stressed the defensive techniques of a case of paranoia. He had not as yet distinguished between the narcissistic and the transference neuroses or made precise nosologic distinctions. Today, as noted above, one is faced with a similar diagnostic vagueness. However, when Freud was evaluating patients from a psychodynamic viewpoint exclusively, he felt that the psychoanalytic method was applicable to most cases. He stated (1898) that psychoanalysis was a method of treatment designed only for psychoneurotics, but later in the year (1898) he included paranoia as well as the hysterias and the obsessionals among the psychoneuroses.

Later, in "Freud's Psychoanalytic Procedure" (1904), contraindications to analysis are discussed, and, although psychoses are not specifically mentioned, it is apparent that cases suffering from severe psychopathology are not considered as being suitable. The following year (1905) he states that psychoanalysis is indicated for cases with a "normal mental disposition" and contraindicated for psychoses as well as other groups of patients. While constructing a model for paranoia (1911), he concludes that the paranoid patient is difficult to analyze. This is due, Freud explains in a discussion of narcissism (1914), to the psychotic patient's withdrawal of libido from the external world and his inability to form a transference. This formulation emphasized that libido becomes detached from an external object and defensively turns toward the self, a megalomanic-hypochondriacal phase. But Freud elaborated his theoretical model into the structural hypothesis, one that considered the ego as a precipitate of past object relations. At least once in *The Ego and The Id* Freud writes of withdrawn libido and the introjected object as occurring together.

One finds considerable discussion of withdrawn libido in "On Narcissism" (1914), "Instincts and Their Vicissitudes" (1915), and "Mourning and Melancholia" (1917), but it is with his final formulation of the structural hypothesis (1923) that the role of the object, internal and external, is stressed. Although Freud does not explore the subject of transference in this context, it is theoretically compatible that even in cases of withdrawn libido (the beginning phase of Freud's model for psychosis) transference can develop. Since libido that is returned to the ego is still connected with object representations, or insofar as it is projected back onto the outer world in the restitutional phase, it can once again attach itself to objects even though this may occur only in the context of a delusion. Arlow and Brenner (1964) have pointed out that the structural hypothesis enables one to construct a model different from the hydrodynamic model that will account for the formation of transference, although Freud also stressed that not all the libido is withdrawn from objects in the paranoid psychosis as it might be in dementia praecox.

Nonetheless, even though transference has been reported as occurring in patients with severe psychopathology, the question of whether the classical psychoanalytic technique is feasible is an unsettled one, since there are other factors besides transference that are necessary in order to conduct an analysis. One also has to distinguish between a transference neurosis and a transference psychosis.

Consequently, one is faced with the need to reevaluate the applicability of the psychoanalytic method. Insofar as these patients have been so deprived and traumatized during their development, some therapists feel that they have to modify their technique in order to give the patient an experience that makes up for or corrects the effects of early disruptive object relations. Other analysts, Boyer (1961) in particular, believe that the so-called classical technique is effective in the treatment of schizophrenia, whereas Eissler (1953) believes that one can concentrate on an interpretive approach after having introduced some modifications that lead to psychic integration, modifications that are required before the patient can benefit from introspection. Jacobson (1954), Little (1958), Searles (1963), and Modell (1963), among others, believe that one can work with the psychotic transference, but specify how their therapeutic activity differs from the treatment of the neurotic patient. Hoedemaker (1960) illustrates how such patients attempt to intrude into the therapist's "ego activity" and demonstrates how he handles such a complication, mainly by not allowing the patient to do anything disruptive to analysis, emphasizing by his behavior that he values the psychoanalytic method and will not permit the patient to devaluate it.

Aside from such pragmatic considerations, the reevaluation of psychoanalytic technique is a natural extension of the theoretical elaborations of ego psychology. As any science progresses and its ramifications became widespread, both pragmatically and heuristically, there comes a time when it becomes natural to pause and to reexamine basic fundamentals and premises. Psychoanalysis started a general reevaluation of its theoretical scaffold with the development of ego psychology and the examination of the ego operations of the therapeutic process.

Freud (1911–1915) was the first scientist to design a method of psychotherapy founded on a consistent theoretical rationale. It is, therefore, a logical sequence to attempt to integrate the theoretical extensions of ego psychology with the conceptual framework that underlies psychoanalytic treatment. Concentrating on the ego and using it as a framework causes us to sharpen our metapsychological focus of the therapeutic process. Many of the questions regarding the applicability of the psychoanalytic method to the treatment of characterological defects and psychosis can be restated as we understand the underlying treatment problems in terms of ego psychological theory.

SUPPORTIVE ASPECTS OF PSYCHOANALYTIC THERAPY

Frequently one hears about two types of therapy, one concentrated upon supporting the ego, and the other focused on uncovering, which is the essence of classical psychoanalytic technique. The definition of classical technique, however, is an ever-evolving one. Freud outlined certain practical tenets, but naturally could not, in the early days of psychoanalysis, discuss treatment in a comprehensive theoretical fashion that would include modern ego concepts. Freud was aware of the integrative features of interpretation, but some recent writers point out there is a dichotomy between helping the patient and analyzing him.

For example, Stone (1964), in his recent monograph "The Psychoanalytic Situation," believes the analyst is shirking his responsibility if he doesn't give "decisive help beyond interpretation." He is talking about patients in general and not restricting himself to characterological and psychotic disorders. Although interpretation is not dismissed as valueless, one gets a definite impression that it is insufficient. If interpretation is the essence of psychoanalytic technique, it implies that, as analysts, we have something better to offer than analysis. Nacht (1962), in a recent panel, felt the analyst has to feel some kind of love for the patient. Because the patient has been traumatized by life experiences, the analyst in some way is supposed to make up for resulting developmental deficiencies.

In the treatment of patients with characterological defects, it has often been stated that the patient cannot turn to external objects in order to receive gratification. In early developmental stages his parents or guardian have failed him in one way or another, and the patient has later manipulated himself into similar positions. Still, very often, such patients have made appeals to persons who have not helped. That may be one of the reasons he comes to analysis. Do we have any special qualifications to gratify the patient when everyone else has failed?

Deviations from analysis in patients suffering from severe psychopathology are often referred to as a more human approach than classical psychoanalytic technique. This implies that analysis for these patients is inhuman, or relatively so, and that the analyst has to step outside his role of "mirrorlike" anonymity and relate as a "real" object. I feel these are unfortunate distinctions, for every analyst is familiar with the patient's needs, based on transference projections, to distort his perception of the analyst. The distortion itself becomes the central theme of the analysis and the "real" presence of the analyst may confuse the picture. On the other hand, there are cases where, even though the analyst has maintained strict anonymity, the patient will not be able to involve himself in a workable transference. It may be natural to want to help the patient, but this does not mean that we should not utilize our professional approach in order to give such help. Commitment to analysis by being receptive to the patient's projections is more important than gratifying his curiosity or being primarily interested in "helping" him. The maintenance of a professional attitude is potentially helpful even though at the beginning of treatment it may seem that what the analyst offers is different from what one would ordinarily consider helpful.

Such questions cause us to examine our concepts of what constitutes analytic help. I feel, as do Gitelson (1962) and other writers, that help is intrinsic to the analytic process and need not involve any extra-analytic factors. Winnicott stresses the same point when speaking of reassurance, a feeling of security the patient experiences because he is in "a reliable setting with a mature person in charge, capable of making penetrating and accurate interpretation, and to find one's personal process respected . . ." (1955).

Being helped, as with any psychic transaction, can be considered in terms of a spectrum that is arranged in the form of a hierarchical continuum. The continuum can be correlated with different stages of psychosexual development. For example, during the early neonatal period the mother's care is global, the infant's survival depending (anaclitically) almost exclusively upon her. One can view this type of help in terms consonant with this early developmental period; that is, a megalomanic kind of help where boundaries between self and outer world are not yet established and the mother's role is cosmic. With psychic differentiation, this initial state of cosmic fusion is changed into a more circumscribed one and the child becomes able to make some discrimination about the source of help which up to now has been synonymous with the nurturing substance. The child begins to differentiate the sources of homeostasis, the milk, the warmth, or the soothing kinesthetic or equilibratory sensations. Later the person (the parent) who supplies is specifically identified, and the presence or absence of this person becomes the mediator of satisfaction or of disruption and frustration. Summing up momentarily, with psychic development there is greater structure and differentiation of perceptual ego systems which are associated with more highly structured needs and increasingly more sophisticated means for their gratification.

Both the needs and the techniques of satisfaction

acquire greater coherence, flexibility and mastery, attributes which are characteristic of the secondary process. Delay and postponement of gratification, qualities which are the essence of reality testing, promote autonomy and make the psyche less dependent upon external objects.

Piaget (1952) draws a hierarchical continuum when discussing the development of thought processes, the beginning point consisting of a sensory-motor modality and characterized by egocentricity and the most advanced stage being what he refers to as formal thought, a form of thinking characterized by self-observation. In other words, such thinking is reflective and involved with an awareness of what is occurring within the self, a process that occurs with introspection. To understand what is going on within the psyche becomes, according to Piaget, the most advanced form of thinking.

To draw an analogy, understanding the nature of one's needs represents the advanced continuum of our need-satisfaction series. Thus, I am postulating a gamut from biological satisfaction to self-knowledge and awareness of our psychic requirements. The latter is self-understanding and is associated with a well-integrated, autonomous ego.

It is precisely this kind of understanding that the analyst offers. Analytic help is associated with the highest order of development where self-observation is dominant. To know about one's needs is of greater adaptive significance than the narrower gratification of the need. The former puts matters, in the context of structure, on an objective level and enables ego systems to be aware of all the implications of internal requirements and outside gratifying facilities.

The study of cases with characterological defects and of psychoses highlights the lack of awareness of inner needs, of understanding what they need and want as well as the lack of experience of ever having felt understood. In order to develop basic ego capacities there has to be some satisfying and gratifying relationships in early life. The psychotic patient has never felt understood. His early relationships were characterized by a lack of empathy for his needs. His mother or his guardian never really understood his needs; instead she reacted only to her own needs and he experienced either rejection or assault. As a consequence, his ego development is both narrow and defective and the hierarchical development of needs is also a constricted one. Many so-called borderline cases complain of never knowing what they want and experience a hopeless dejection, not simply because they feel the outer world to be frustrating, but because they do not feel anything. This lack of feeling applies to such elemental sensations as hunger, heat or cold, excretory functions, etc. A patient who had been diagnosed as a character disorder was aware in a gross way of such feelings but he was not aware of any finer sensory discriminations. Not being able to feel was often experienced as nonexistence and a complete alienation from objects, a state of panicky dissolution. The patient felt dead (but still panicky) and believed that no one could see anything within him, that is, understand him, because there was nothing there to see or understand.

To be understood, therefore, has many implications and offers the patient the type of help he has never had before. Kind and helpful friends may try to give him wise counsel, but their needs are somehow also involved. The analyst tries to make the patient aware of his needs and conflicts but he does not take sides in his ambivalence. The patient begins to learn that the analyst's understanding indicates that there is something within him worth understanding. As the analyst recognizes the patient's inner processes and reveals them to him by integrative interpretations, he is pulling together (synthesizing) disparate fragmented elements and thereby helping the patient to structuralize what was previously felt as vague, diffuse, and perhaps painful. *The analyst has not only helped the patient become aware of something within himself, but by synthesizing fragmented elements has, in a sense, helped create a need.* The previous sense of emptiness is, to some extent, alleviated as the patient begins to develop an ability for self-observation. Patients with ego defects do not use repression as much or as effectively as the psychoneurotic, one reason, among others, being that the ego is insufficiently structuralized to support the function of repression. For both types of patients, however, interpretation has an integrative effect that expands the self-observing function and, in cases with character disorders, also leads to a structuralization of needs.

Granted, many such patients have only a limited ability to form a therapeutic alliance and, instead, demand some form of nurturing. However, their frustration is eventually intensified if the analyst tries to minister to their needfulness. The patient will inevitably experience a disruptive agitation since he demands an omnipotent, megalomanic type of help. He will find it impossible to maintain the delusion that the analyst is supplying magic. A conflictual and primitive need is then experienced in the transference. To be aware of its existence rather than attempting to gratify it, shifts the patient's cathexis from the product that he thinks would bring gratification to the phenomena of the existence of such a need and its constricting effects. This can be compared to a creative achievement because psychic equilibrium is achieved by adding a segment (insight) to the ego, resulting in an ego expansion. This is the essence of the unique quality of analytic help.

TECHNICAL FACTORS IN THE TREATMENT OF CHARACTER DISORDERS

Boyer (1961), Will (1964), and Eissler (1953) conceptualize the treatment of schizophrenia as consisting of two phases: (1) a more or less supportive phase where the therapist attempts to get the patient sufficiently oriented so it is possible to work with him analytically, and (2) a phase that can be considered analytic where the emphasis is on interpretation and insight formation. This same type of division into two phases has been considered also applicable to nonpsychotics who suffer from ego defects. This separation strikes me as being an artificial one, although perhaps of value in organizing one's thinking; but clinically the two phases are so merged that they are indistinguishable. Still, many therapists would disagree and remind one of the patient who is so excited or withdrawn that it is impossible to make analytic contact.

Although such cases rarely come to the analyst's consulting room, they still exist, usually in institutional settings, and, consequently, cannot be dismissed in any discussion of clinical interaction and therapeutic process. One has to admit that there are cases so completely inaccessible that it would be utter folly and even ludicrous to attempt a standard analytic approach. Still, one might wonder whether many cases that have been thought of as being far out of reach, might have been amenable to analysis if it were tried. For example, cases have been recorded where the initial phases of therapy have been extremely stormy. The patient has been distrustful and suspicious, and his behavior has been antagonistic and rejecting. The therapeutic approach has been viewed as an assault and an intrusion. Under these circumstances, the therapist has often tried to make himself felt as a person, indicating his interest and concern for the patient's welfare. Until a "real" relationship is established, it is felt that interpretive work is impossible; the patient's libido is so narcissistically fixated and withdrawn that transference projections will not occur. However, as has often been the case, when the patient regards the therapist as an intruder and sees him in a negative light, this is already of tremendous value and an important and significant step in the establishment of a transference relationship. The severe paranoid distinguishes between good and evil. By projection he constructs a bad and persecutory external reality, one he hopes to escape from. Although this defense is primitive, it also means that the patient is able to make some evaluation of internal distress and has methods at his disposal that might achieve some equilibrium.

What is being described appears, on the surface, to be withdrawal. But this does not indicate that the patient's libido is completely introverted. On the contrary, very often such patients have turned away from us in anger and this means that the therapist has been connected with his destructiveness. By so doing, the patient indicates an investment in the therapist, one that he hopes will give him relief from internal tension. This also implies that a concept of the future exists and that the patient is able or has the capacity to be able to imagine or fantasy a situation which is less painful or more pleasurable than the current one.

A hostile rejection of the analyst has an element of structure to it and can eventuate into a workable transference situation if the therapist can keep these feelings focused on himself and prevent them from becoming generalized. *The analyst, by making himself available for the projection of negative feelings, which are often embodied in destructive introjects, is removing an obstacle to psychic development.* The analytic process is, therefore, set in motion from the very first contact with the patient.

A clinical vignette to illustrate the above point is that of a young man in his middle twenties who, although he came to therapy voluntarily, was extremely suspicious as to what the analyst would do to him and felt vulnerable, fearing that he might be taken advantage of and exploited. During the middle of the first hour he became very angry about doctors in general. He believed they made much more money than he did, and he decided not to go on with the interview because he did not want to contribute to what he considered to be my already sizable financial estate. He had revealed considerable paranoid ideation about several people, especially his immediate superior on his current job. I showed an interest in his rejecting and hostile attitude and conjectured as to whether there might not be some advantage in feeling exploited by me, that this might represent some security rather than having to feel at the mercy of and vulnerable to his boss. After all, he could leave me but this would be a somewhat more difficult thing to do with the job upon which his livelihood depended. He visibly relaxed at this point and nothing more was said about discontinuing therapy for a long time.

I will not go into the details of this patient's interesting analysis, but will mention one particular crisis that emphasized the analytic gains that can occur when the patient is hostile and rejecting and seemingly analytically inaccessible. This patient had an acute delusional episode following an important business success where he thought he had destroyed his immediate superior and, in a sense, he had, insofar as he demonstrated that his employer's judgment was faulty. He became angry and disappointed with me because I was unable to protect him from being overwhelmed by destructive feelings, and at this point he had an acute paranoid episode. He heard tormenting voices accusing him of being a homosexual and sneering and laughing at him. He heard babies crying through the ventilator system in his apartment building, and he suffered from uncontrollable waves of panic. He became so agitated that his relatives finally called the police and had him dragged bodily to a hospital. He quickly calmed down, but continued to be plagued by his own thoughts and the voices. All of this happened over a weekend, and, surprisingly, despite all the turmoil, he asked for permission to keep his appointment with me. The attending psychiatrist granted it and the patient came alone to my office. At first he would not lie down on the couch and insisted on maintaining a distance of at least fifteen feet between us. I pointed out that he need not fear for my safety, that he wouldn't destroy me, whereupon he shouted he wasn't concerned about my safety, but was worried about his own, and what I might do to him. Nevertheless, he lay down and revealed that he felt I was his persecutor, exploiting him, picking his mind and becoming rich, since I was being paid $100,000.00 a year by a business rival to drain all his mental abilities from him. This other person and I would learn a good deal from him, but he would be intellectually destroyed. I had, up to this point, asked some questions as to the details of his paranoid delusion, but when I was satisfied that I understood its content, I asked him why he had to bring another person into the picture, why did I have to be paid such a large sum of money to persecute him? He was astonished at my question and interpreted it as meaning that I wanted exclusive rights to persecute him, but he also saw the humor in this interaction and was able to recognize the transference projection. After he left the hour, he signed himself out of the hospital and continued his analysis as previously.

His delusions disappeared with partial transference resolution. A patient who reacts in this fashion may not be considered as a typical example of a seriously disturbed schizophrenic; still, if all the details of this patient's delusional system were given, not only during this particular episode, but including those present at the onset of therapy, he would be indistinguishable from any bizarre, paranoid schizophrenic, at least on a phenomenological level. This raises an interesting question because patients who have been to some extent analytically influenced are considered as being nosologically different from another group where it is postulated, in fact it is a criterion of diagnosis, that analysis is contraindicated.

There is a very important difference between this

patient and many other patients who reject their therapists. I feel it is highly significant that he sought therapy on his own and was able to come to my office. This particular capacity may be of crucial significance, and it cannot be denied that no matter how correct our interpretations may be, there are some patients who will not respond to our efforts to conduct analysis. These patients are so withdrawn, as in some catatonic stupors, that external objects are either not recognized or completely denied. One can raise the question, however, as to whether any form of psychotherapy will be effective. To repeat, is there anything better than analysis which can be offered within the frame of reference of psychotherapy if analysis is ineffective? Other therapeutic approaches may be relevant, but we are limiting ourselves in this discussion to the consideration of outpatient relationship type of therapy, and, at this point, not considering the environment outside of the analysis.

In the beginning of treatment, interpretations may not involve much in the way of specific content. However, from the very first interview, the patient is making projections, some quite obvious, and others subtle. By constantly interpreting the projection, one causes an internalization of conflict. The analyst's purpose is to focus on the intrapsychic, and when the patient succeeds in doing likewise, he has gained considerable security. The following vignette is an example of the reassurance a patient can receive by converting external chaos to a topic for intrapsychic consideration.

This middle-aged housewife had been rejected as analytically unsuitable by two different analysts in another city. Although neither one of them believed she was psychotic, they felt that the degree of narcissistic fixation was sufficiently intense that she could be considered a borderline character. The patient had been in a state of utter confusion and despair for many years and had reached a point where she was incapable of carrying out routine activities. She was unable to care for the house, the children, do the shopping, etc. She lay in bed crying all day, and complained of numerous physical symptoms including migraine headaches.

She arrived fifteen minutes late for her first appointment and presented herself in a state of utter dissolution and chaos. She was dirty, dishevelled, and her face had a pained, agonized expression. She gripped her stomach, moaned, and, in a helpless feeble voice, asked where the nearest toilet was because she didn't know if she could get through the session without having to rush out. She then pleaded for something to alleviate her distress and intense pain. Throughout all of this I kept looking at her and, despite this display of helplessness, I could not feel any sense of urgency. I was puzzled and felt immensely curious as to why she was behaving in this fashion and what it could mean. I motioned her into the consulting room and made what I felt to be an interpretation. I told her that she wanted something from me but she didn't know precisely what it was because she was unable to put it into words. She had a need to create confusion and make others feel anxious. On the basis of all this we would have to try to find out why she had to go to so much trouble making herself sick for my benefit. She looked me straight in the eye, accepting this challenge of putting matters on an intrapsychic level, composed herself and indignantly said she felt fine. This immediate change was striking, one that I considered a resistance. However, she lay down on the couch and, without any instruction, started free-associating. It became apparent that the patient was attempting to manipulate and destroy the analyst with her helplessness as she had done with everyone else. By relating her behavior to a transference situation, one was able to make certain observations that were designed to internalize a conflict. What the patient presented was seen as a phenomenon that both the patient and therapist could study together. In this instance, the interpretive activity consisted of indicating that her seeming chaos had: (1) an intrapsychic origin, and (2) adaptive significance. This activity was integrative and, if one wants, one can say it was also supportive, *but it was supportive because it was analytic.*

Pointing out to the first patient that he was afraid of killing me was an interpretation of a defense. He was basically afraid of being killed, but both the fluidity of his ego boundaries, which made the distinction between the two of us a blurred one, and his projective defenses caused him to feel panicky, fearing he would destroy me. Still, his basic fear was that he would destroy part of himself, the hated part that he had projected onto me. His agitated response to my comment highlighted the more basic fear of being destroyed. The fact that one could talk about all of this and relate it to the transference enhanced his self-observing tendencies.

THEORETICAL ASPECTS OF INTERPRETATION

Is self-knowledge and awareness of inner processes a structuralizing experience in its own right? Perhaps it can be, but this can occur only in an ego that has considerable resources and is capable of functioning at high levels of autonomy. In schizophrenia and characterological defects, structuralization does not occur *sui generis,* and autonomous boundaries cannot be established without a positive object relationship.

However, this does not mean that one has to give support in addition to interpretation. Interpretation is more than just a verbal exchange between analyst and patient and, as the clinical examples demonstrate, the giving of an interpretation conveys an attitude, an integrative one, that is based on understanding. Furthermore, effective interpretation, that is, therapeutically useful interpretation, can occur only in the setting of the transference. Therefore, intrinsic in interpretation is an object relationship that is composed of various elements. Interpretive content cannot be pulled out of context and viewed as a disembodied stream of words. Rather, it is a communicative aspect of an object relationship and its integrative value is, to some extent, due to its object relationship qualities.

The object relationship qualities of the transference consist of many different levels. The patient's perception of the analyst is determined by a projection of infantile archaic imagos as well as reactions to current impressions. Projected archaic imagos, however, are not exact reproductions of early introjects, since any introject undergoes numerous revisions throughout the course of psychic development. The essence of the transference neurosis, at any particular moment, depends upon what aspect and level of a particular introject is projected onto the analyst. During the course of analysis, there is a broad spectrum of transference projections ranging from primary process infantile elements to relatively nondistorted secondary process percepts.

The ego gains structure by the formation of functional introjects. Through the incorporation of satisfactory and gratifying object relationships, the ego's adaptive capacities are increased. The introject at the highest level represents an operational technique that leads to mastery rather than simply being a nurturing object. The transference neurosis is an introjective-projective process, and the patient's perception of the analyst, one that contains many levels, is finally incorporated into his ego. One result of the introjective aspect of the transference is the formation of what I have referred to as the *analytic introject,* and I believe that Zetzel's (1960) concept of the therapeutic alliance includes the formation of such an introject. The analytic attitude, one that scrutinizes intrapsychic processes and archaic fixations, leads to integrations. The patient, by incorporating this observational quality which is identified with the analyst's interpretive activity, can look at his problems to some extent objectively and place them in their proper perspective.

Integration takes place, and what had previously been fragmented, disparate, and inchoate, is now brought together into a synthesis which can be definitively experienced and structured as a coherent goal-directed drive. Loewald (1960) believes this type of synthesis is a cardinal feature of the analytic relationship.

Is a patient with severe characterological defects and intense narcissistic fixations capable of forming and sustaining an analytic introject? The above clinical examples indicate that even a severely disturbed patient may rather quickly identify with the analyst's viewpoint, which also includes the ability to respond to interpretation. Still, one has to consider what general factors are important in determining the limits of analyzability. Three variables, the patient, the environment, and the analytic setting, are conditions which have to be explored relative to each other before one can conclude whether analysis is possible. This chapter emphasizes the integrative effects of analytic activity, but the patient and the environment cannot be dismissed, although they are not focused upon here. Insofar as the environment intrudes into the analysis or the patient's ego is totally involved, defensively or otherwise, with an infantile relationship with the external world, the patient is decreasingly analyzable. *Specific psychopathology is not the chief determinant as to whether analysis is possible, but the reciprocal interplay of the patient's psychic organization, the supportive or disruptive factors in his environment, and the constant nonanxious reliability of the analytic setting all have to be included in our final assessment.*

However, in terms of the analytic setting, the analyst is not overwhelmed with anxiety, because what the patient consciously or unconsciously perceives as dangerous is considered as an intrapsychic phenomenon that has become the focus of intense interest. The analyst, by wanting to understand the intrapsychic, is not responding to it as a reality which the patient fears, but as a subject deserving of his analytic skill. Even when the ego is precariously balanced, the patient gains considerable reassurance and esteem by being treated as a person worthy of study rather than a pitiful human tragedy. This occurs in a steady, reliable setting (Winnicott 1955) which, in itself, promotes integration. The analytic atmosphere is characterized by calmness which fosters introspection. The analyst does not share and, consequently, does not contribute to the patient's inner sense of urgency. He is particularly effective in achieving the latter, which is also reassuring to the patient, since he relates in an entirely different frame of reference than one determined by the content of the patient's intrapsychic conflicts.

Freud (1910) emphasizes the futility of giving a patient direct advice aimed at gratifying instinctual impulses. Winnicott (1954, 1960) repeatedly points out that the unstructured ego reacts to many external stimuli as if they were traumatic impingements. Very often the helpful analyst unwittingly interferes with the patient's autonomous potential. The patient may not be aware that he feels "assaulted" by good advice and direction, although the character disorders, in particular, with their poorly formed identity sense, tend to react sensitively to external manipulation.

The analyst listens to free associations derived from all levels of the psychic apparatus, representing varying proportions of primary and secondary process. A particular association will be predominantly characteristic of a specific developmental phase, but it will also include to a lesser degree other phases and systems of the psychic apparatus. Patients with severe psychopathology produce associations which often lean heaviest on the side of the primary process, but the analyst is perceiving and responding from all levels of his psychic organization. Intuition may be due to the primary process element of the analyst's response to similar elements in the patient. On the other hand, the analyst is simultaneously reacting with his secondary process too. As in creative activity, he is refining and synthesizing primary process-oriented stimuli into terms which have the integrative and coherent features characteristic of secondary process activity. Elevating the analyst's perception to a verbal level and communicating it to the patient involves the progressive abstraction of psychic elements which are responses to primitive aspects of the patient's intrapsychic organization. The interpretation, therefore, is an upward extension, so to speak, of an aspect of the patient's psyche and in the character disorders a psyche whose range of development is narrow. The interpretation by superimposing the analyst's secondary process upon the patient's primary process, adds a significant element to the patient's adaptive capacities. The patient's ego gains organization and structure as the analyst supplies an auxiliary secondary process through his interpretations. The integration which replaces the previous inner chaos leads to a solidification of the analytic introject. There has to be some degree of ego synthesis before introjection can occur, be maintained, and be functionally significant. The introject, in turn, because of its emphasis on introspection and understanding, creates order from the previous primary process disorder and thereby leads to further structuralization. *This process constitutes a positive feed-back for, insofar as the ego gains structure from an interpretation, its capacity to form an analytic introject is increased; the introject leads to further integration which enables the ego to introject more effectively and expansively and respond to further interpretations.*

With reference again to patients with a poor identity sense, one often notes eagerness to identify with the analyst in order to obtain some coherence for their self-representations. What one frequently sees at the beginning is not a true identification, since the analyst is not smoothly incorporated and integrated into the patient's ego. Rather, one sees a somewhat clumsy imitation of the analyst, but as the analysis continues to focus on observing and understanding the patient's inner chaos, what was an unsynthesized and unintegrated incorporation becomes gradually integrated and contributes to a more secure identity sense. This does not mean that the analyst is imposing his standards or values on the patient. *The analyst's main interest is to foster the patient's autonomy, and it is this aspect of the analyst that the patient ideally incorporates.* The analyst represents autonomy or the patient's hope for autonomy, a feature that is the essence of a secure, well-delineated self-representation.

Interpretation, therefore, leads to structuralization. It has an intrinsic supportive value. From another viewpoint, it is also educational in the sense that the patient learns new adaptive techniques, but he does so by correcting inner distortions. This adds to the patient's capacity for reality testing. From this viewpoint, one can take the position that the analytic method is indicated for patients who have defects in reality testing, that is, schizophrenics and character disorders, and who particularly need the integration that is intrinsic to analysis. The superimposition of the analyst's secondary process upon the patient's primary process is especially valuable for a patient who has only a minimum of his own secondary process. Much that is considered as being extra-analytic can be achieved by adherence to analytic principles, principles which become sharper as we clarify our theoretical framework, rather than by altering our role.

SUMMARY

Early dictums concerning the applicability of classical psychoanalytic technique to the treatment of cases with severe psychopathology assert that these patients are not suitable for such an approach. With the theoretical expansions which have occurred with increasing focus on ego psychology, one must reexamine the metapsychology of the therapeutic process relative to the psychopathology of ego defects.

As the treatment process is examined from such a viewpoint, the integrative and supportive aspects of interpretation become apparent. For a fuller understanding of the effects of interpretation, one has to define more precisely, in operational terms, what constitutes analytic help. Help can be considered along a broad spectrum ranging from the gratification of needs associated with primitive levels of psychosexual development to analytic help conveyed through interpretation. Analytic help leads to introspection resulting in a broadened perception of inner needs and their integration with the perceptions of the outer world rather than in the narrower constricting gratification of the need.

Interpretation is then understood as a special aspect of an object relationship with the analyst. As the analytic imago is introjected and as interpretive activity becomes internalized, the patient's range of secondary process functioning is expanded. The analyst superimposes his secondary process upon the patient's primary process, leading to greater ego structure. In a positive feed-back sequence, this enables the patient to introject more helpful aspects of the analytic relationship, which, in turn, leads to further structuralization and then to greater ability for internalization, etc. This increase in secondary process activity gradually extends to the patient's everyday life and no longer requires analytic reinforcement.

Patients with faulty ego structure are in particular need of auxiliary secondary process activity. The analytic method is an integrative one and need not be altered to supply greater structure. These patients have had only a minimum of understanding during their childhood; the analyst's willingness to focus exclusively upon his intrapsychic processes constitutes an acceptance which he has never had before. To scrutinize content of conflictful needs leads to resistance, but wanting to understand how the patient's mind works fosters the therapeutic alliance. Giving the patient an awareness of what goes on within himself, to help him see himself as a psychic phenomenon rather than as a human tragedy, not to participate or take sides in archaic self-destructive conflicts and defenses, in other words, to analyze him and make him understand there is a core within him worth analyzing, is treating him with the greatest dignity and highest respect possible, and represents, in my mind, the ultimate in human responses.

Chapter Seven

Some Elements of the Therapeutic Action in the Treatment of Character Disorders

Peter L. Giovacchini, M.D.

The extension of the classical psychoanalytic method for the treatment of cases with characterological disorders is intellectually exciting and its successful application is of tremendous clinical significance. However, as with any innovation, one does not expect universal acceptance. There will be and should be a certain amount of disagreement on both major and minor issues.

It must also be recognized that, in presenting a particular viewpoint, we are working within a frame of reference that is not necessarily the most comfortable one for another investigator. This symposium was addressed exclusively to psychoanalysts but psychoanalysis does not impose homogeneity upon its practitioners, especially in regard to technical issues. As Boyer has demonstrated in his review, there are many "schools" stemming from the mainstream, each encompassing a discrete theoretical orientation and each claiming some therapeutic validity. Others may prefer to work within a theoretical subsystem founded on principles which differ from classical analysis but are still related in some way to the psychoanalytic realm. Undoubtedly, there is much to be learned from such differences and similarities, but, at the moment, it seems premature to attempt a rapprochement. Our task is not one of evaluating but of focusing on our approach and exploring its rationale.

In dealing with patients with character disorders we have found it unnecessary to alter the basic psychoanalytic model Freud provided. However, there are areas of metapsychology referring to the therapeutic process which are vague and require both extension and clarification. In our pursuit of theoretical and therapeutic clarification, one must expect differences of opinion even among the three authors of papers in this volume. Although basically we are very much in agreement, it is precisely at the junctures where our ideas differ that we hope to open up vistas which will not only lead to new insights, but will cause us to look at our therapeutic interactions in a new perspective. This can lead us to make explicit many attitudes and strategies of which we may have been previously unaware or have not considered as being particularly important in the treatment setting.

GRATIFICATION OF INSTINCTUAL NEEDS

Boyer (see Chapter Four) believes that, at times, it is necessary to behave in a manner which is aimed at direct gratification of the patient's instinctual needs. He does not, however, consider this activity therapeutic in and of itself. He believes that in some cases it is necessary to gratify the patient, such gratification leading to a situation in which analysis becomes possible. Boyer considers this a parameter, but a minimal one. As with all parameters, the sooner it can be eliminated, the less hampered will be the course of analysis.

The gratification of instinctual needs in an emotionally deprived patient has frequently been considered desirable for its own sake, since it is postulated it may bring about an equilibrium favorable for psychic development. As mentioned above, this does not impugn the value of an interpretive, introspective approach, but merely emphasizes that there may be necessary conditions before interpretation can be effective, and these conditions, in addition to the transference neurosis, may be an important aspect of the treatment of patients suffering from characterological defects. Winnicott (1955) believes that the analyst offers the patient a reliable setting that leads to an organized regression. The latter is valuable and becomes the subject of transference interpretations, but it would not have occurred without a secure setting.

Various nonanalytic psychotherapeutic approaches attempt to gratify basic needs as well as to reinforce defenses without the utilization of insight or the aim of altering character structure. The purpose of such therapy is symptomatic improvement and to facilitate adjustment to reality. Such treatment is occasionally considered a preparation for analysis. This is not what Boyer describes.

Nevertheless, since this issue is encountered so frequently in clinical discussions and in the psychoanalytic literature, it behooves us to examine it as a phenomenon rather than casually to accept such "supportive" interaction as a therapeutic necessity.

Instinctual frustration contributes to ego defects and fixations. Can psychoanalysis undo these deleterious effects? To put the question more cogently, is it possible for the analyst to give a patient gratification which would have been appropriate during his infancy or childhood and would have led to psychic growth? Does such gratification lead to emotional development when one attempts to give it in the analytic setting? Many therapists have made the casual assumption that they have the capacity to undo childhood trauma by a direct response to the patient's needs. If we are to assess the effectiveness of the attempt to gratify such needs, they must be considered in terms of the psychosexual stage to which they are appropriate. Through the transference projection the patient relives infantile conflicts. He relates to the analyst as if he were a significant person from the past, one who can withhold and frustrate or minister to his needs and provide what is required for emotional sustenance. The types of needs the transference regression evokes are related to earlier stages of psychosexual development and are characterized by a preponderance of primary process elements. In order to gratify these needs, the analyst would have to be able to respond to primitive elements within the patient's personality while at the same time being able to maintain his own professional orientation.

The transference regression is not an exact replica of a childhood state that is revived and projected into the analytic setting. The patient is biologically an adult and has been exposed to a variety of experiences throughout the course of his life which have had their effect upon his psychic structure. He has acquired many skills and adjustive techniques that were not present during his infancy. During the therapeutic regression there is a selective loss of these later accretions, but not a total one. Although the patient may feel a need to make up for his infantile deprivations, he is considerably more complex despite his regression and his current requirements have many elements which could not have been incorporated and integrated by his infantile ego.

He needs more than he once did. Mother's milk is no longer an adequate nutriment even though the patient may not know it while in the regressed state. His dietary requirements include a variety of substances which would not have been digestible when he was an infant. Similarly, at the psychic level, an attempt to give the patient something that would have been appropriate for an earlier developmental period is not adequate or even relevant to his current needs. Trying to gratify the patient does not fill a gap in his psyche, nor does it correct the traumatic and disruptive effects of early frustration, for even if the analyst were able to gratify infantile needs, what would enable the patient to benefit from it? Undoubtedly the patient has had many subsequent experiences that had adjustive and developmental potential, but because of intrapsychic conflicts, disruptive, constricting introjects, and ego defects, he was not able to profit from them and to use them for the expansion of various ego systems. Without the resolution of these archaic conflicts, activities designed to satisfy relatively primitive drives neither gratify them nor promote psychic structure, as noted by Freud (1910) in his paper " 'Wild' Psychoanalysis."

The patient frequently demands gratification of what he considers to be urgent needs. This may be expressed as a cry for help or by clinging to the analyst for succor.

He often is asking whether the analyst will be able to rescue him from his destructive self. He feels helpless and vulnerable as well as hateful and unlovable. The analyst is cast in the role of an omnipotent savior sufficiently powerful to counteract the patient's "badness." The patient's needs are megalomanic in quality and dominated by primary process elements. To be consonant with such needs a response would have to be preponderantly primary process in quality. One is then faced with the situation where a primary process-oriented need is responded to with a primary process-oriented reaction. Can such a transaction lead in the direction of secondary process structure? It is difficult to conceptualize how experiences founded on primitive infantile expectations can lead to the acquisition of adaptive techniques, techniques that are the consequence of ego structure and enable the patient to master the complex and subtle problems involved in relating to external reality.

Any attempt to give the patient something that may have been required during childhood is a way of relating to him as if he *really* were a child. This interaction emphasizes his helplessness and vulnerability and enchances his potential for the projection of omnipotence. Similar to disruptive and constricting introjects, this kind of activity may result in corresponding fixations. To attempt to relate directly to such needs is perceived by the patient to be an acceptance of their reality. Not infrequently, patients subsequently complain of having felt depreciated and threatened because they believed the analyst shared their fear of their disruptive impulses. Even though they may ascribe omnipotent powers to the analyst, they often resent it if he assumes such powers and one finds that the analysis of the transference becomes inordinately complex.

The patient regresses during analysis. But as Winnicott (1955) emphasizes, there are different types of regression, some analytically useful, and others disruptive to analysis. In a previous communication (1965), I discuss how the regressed state can create a setting in which the ego is not hampered by destructive, constricting introjects and can incorporate experiences that enhance self-observation. *In contrast, relating to the patient on the basis of infantile needs leads to a hypercathexis of archaic introjects. The corresponding regressed ego state is then unable to incorporate and synthesize ego-expanding experiences because of the fixation on these primitive introjects.*

A frequent objection regarding the utilization of the analytic method in the treatment of patients suffering from severe psychopathology is that the patient will not be able to tolerate it. It is felt that the use of the analytic method may lead to serious repercussions, such as further decompensation or a complete psychotic breakdown. The author has found that even incorrect and poorly timed interpretations, by and of themselves, do not lead to psychotic disintegration. It is not easy to penetrate prematurely the patient's resistance so that primitive underlying impulses will flood the ego and cause a state of psychic dissolution. *However, stepping outside the analytic role and making promises that cannot be kept or further hampering the patient's autonomy by trying to run his life in the interest of helping him, according to the experience of many analysts, is more likely to lead to disruptive panic states and psychotic decompensation.* The patient's ego becomes inflexible and nonadaptive when he places himself in an infantile setting and lets the analyst take over basic caretaking functions. Insofar as his dependency on the analyst is such a total one, his vulnerability is intensified if the analyst disappoints him. He sacrifices his autonomy for the promise of omnipotent nurture. His adjustment, therefore, hangs on the thread of the analyst's power to supply, and, at best, is in a state of precarious balance.

SPECIFIC ASPECTS OF THE ANALYST'S PERSONALITY

Boyer has stated that the psychotherapist who is able to remain within the psychoanalytic frame of reference while treating psychotic patients may need special personality qualities. It is important to consider whether this is a question of degree or whether there are differences in kind. Should the analyst have a specific characterological or psychodynamic constellation that contributes either to his skill or capacity to deal with what are generally considered to be difficult patients? This question is, of course, of interest regarding psychoanalysis in general, but is there something additionally specific to what is required of one who treats patients who have been so traumatized during childhood?

While I agree that the analyst has to be very much in tune with the patient's needs and to some extent even have some fondness for him, I do not believe this is above and beyond what one must feel for every patient. There are patients who ostensibly seek help but are insincere or have ulterior motives (usually some manipulative needs) and who are so unlikable that the analyst finds himself unable or unwilling to work with them. I doubt whether such patients are more common among those nosologically categorized as suffering from character disorders. In fact, the needy person is less apt to have sufficient structure to resort to subtle manipulative maneuvers. His hatred and self-hatred, however, may reach disturbing proportions and evoke rejecting responses in those about him.

One has to consider the question of what enables us to tolerate patients at all. Is it solely some specific internal need of our own? The desire to help the patient sometimes represents a desire to help ourselves at an emotional level which may be at approximately the same level of fixation as the patient's. One would hope, however, that our needs are not too deep or intense, and that our desire to treat patients is based largely on mature motives; otherwise, we would run the risk of indulging in a neurotic interaction which does not lead to analysis and psychic development.

If the analysis of patients with severe psychopathology demands specific personality features of the analyst, then the "standard" analytic method is inadequate. It is implied that analysts without such qualities and yet able to use the psychoanalytic method will not, in spite of their technical skills, be able to deal with these patients. What is required is both special emotional features and technical psychoanalytic skills. The analyst's personality will, of necessity, affect his psychoanalytic style. If it is assumed that he has to have specific emotional features, then his psychoanalytic style will reflect them. This would constitute a modification for, although the personality of the analyst is, to some extent, always reflected in his technique, here we are considering the effects of special personal qualifications. When one speaks of qualifications one is not necessarily speaking of skills which are the outcome of optimal development and training. Oftentimes we are referring to a residual or core of severe psychopathology which has been to a large measure resolved, and which can now be used to empathize with the patient.

Searles (1965), Staveren (1947), and Szalita (1955), among others, emphasize the importance of the analyst's reactions and the extent of personal involvement with the patient based on the analyst's intrapsychic requirements. However, what is being described is often idiosyncratic. It is a moot question whether one's "deeper" motivations hinder or help one's analytic capacity, although to separate motivations completely on the basis of the level of the personality from which they stem is an artificial dichotomy. In creative activity optimal conditions consist of a balance between primary and secondary process operations. Our motivation springs from all levels of our psyche but the clinical situation determines which attitudes are appropriate in terms of psychic level and the proportionate amount of primary and secondary process.

If our assumption that the psychoanalytic method need not be altered, or only minimally altered for the treatment of borderline and some psychotic patients, is correct, then the analyst's personal orientation should not be a distinguishing factor. There may be some homogeneous factors found in all analysts, but one is also impressed by the diverse qualities which are compatible with sincere motivation and analytic competence. Consequently, if we are to be consistent in our assertion that these patients can be treated analytically, it must be postulated that no particular type of intrapsychic orientation or psychopathology is a necessary condition for conducting analysis with either psychoneurotics or patients suffering from characterological defects. Conversely, if special emotional constellations are required of the therapist, then the treatment of the latter group cannot be effective without some radical revisions of our psychotherapeutic approach.

The above does not mean, however, that there are not psychic constellations and forms of psychopathology that hinder one's capacity to analyze. There may also be regressions and acting out by the patient which may evoke feelings within the analyst which are incompatible with analysis. Such feelings have to be examined by the analyst and brought sufficiently into focus so that he will not allow the analytic situation to be disrupted.

THE PATIENT'S MOTIVATION

Hoedemaker makes some interesting points about the disruptive aspects of his patient's behavior. He emphasized, in a previous communication (1960) that certain types of acting out may preclude analysis and the patient has to be able to curb his behavior if he is to continue. This idea brings several issues to the fore, a particularly important one being that of motivation.

Analysts often gauge analyzability by an assessment of the patient's motivations for treatment. Such an assessment is often impressionistic and intuitive. If there isn't a "proper" amount of motivation at the onset, it is sometimes believed that analysis is not feasible and this supposedly occurs more often with "sicker" patients. Commitment to analysis is a progressive step, one which is realistically oriented insofar as it involves a judgment and appraisal of one's emotional state and the recognition that something can be done about its painful and self-defeating aspects. Patients with characterological defects are not very skillful at making such appraisals, and this deficiency, which is in part due to faulty reality testing, will be reflected in their seeming motivation for analysis. The character defect itself handicaps the patient's desire to be analyzed.

Lack of motivation is similar to any attitude or behavior that is a consequence of intrapsychic conflict or an ego defect. The patient brings many varied attitudes to the consulting room which are determined by specific emotional constellations and conflicts. Usually these are symptomatic and the analyst uses attitudes, behavior, and symptoms to assess what is going on within the patient. This is material, and it would be unrealistic to expect the patient not to have symptomatic manifestations or to expect him to give up some of his symptoms if he is to be analytically acceptable.

The patient's motivation for treatment, to repeat, is a manifestation of attitudes which are the outcome of his psychic organization. From one viewpoint, it is a symptomatic manifestation and, as with all symptoms, one can question the wisdom of expecting modification as a condition of acceptance for treatment. Granted there may be certain qualities to the patient's behavior that may preclude analysis (to be discussed later), but can one make relevant a priori judgments about motivation, per se, before the formation of an operable transference neurosis and analysis?

It is valuable to consider motivation in terms of its object relationship qualities as well as its intrapsychic determinants. The patient must be willing to involve himself in a relationship with the analyst; whatever anxieties and defenses were directed to significant objects from the infantile past will be repeated in the transference neurosis. The patient has some awareness of what is going to happen and is understandably reluctant. Even in the first interview (sometimes even before the patient has met the analyst), there is already some projection of archaic imagos, that is, an object relationship is partially established which, to some extent, is imbued with the same conflicts that were present during a vulnerable childhood. Motivation, therefore, has to be considered in the context of a setting that is object directed. The patient undergoes some regression, even at the beginning, and his judgments are already impaired. His sense of discrimination and reality-testing will function at the level of his ego state of the moment, one which has infantile elements. These important ego functions will be influenced more by primary process operations than usual and cannot be taken at face value. As with earlier object relationships, the patient's motivations will be unstable insofar as he is either manifestly wary and distrustful or extremely positive because of projection of omnipotence and idealization of the analyst. In either case, these attitudes represent psychopathologically distorted perceptions and are only of limited value in judging the patient's suitability for analysis.

The analyst's reponse to the patient is of crucial significance. Considering motivation as an aspect of an object relationship brings the analyst's reactions into focus. Motivation is no longer considered as something that happens exclusively to the patient. The analyst is involved too, and his reactions, conscious and unconscious, are communicated to the patient at some psychic level. Hesitancy or reluctance to analyze are reacted to by the patient, who may then withdraw. The analyst's indecision and scepticism stimulates a similar indecision and scepticism in the patient which is manifested as insufficient motivation. What has to be emphasized is that this lack of motivation is not a singular phenomenon but one which exists in both the analyst and the patient. Rather than viewing this situation in an absolute sense, it may be valuable to consider it as a subject worthy of investigation. As with all analytic material, countertransference attitudes also must be assessed.

The manifest expression of motivation and the actual circumstances which bring the patient to analysis are often deceptive. It has often been stated that one of the worst possible circumstances for beginning treatment is when the patient is forced to do so. The patient ostensibly does not seek treatment; due to circumstances, someone has imposed it upon him. In some instances, in spite of an apparently impossible obstacle, treatment may proceed in a relatively unobstructed fashion.

For example, a young man in his early twenties was apprehended by a policeman who let himself be homosexually approached in a public washroom. The patient, being well educated, held a position of responsibility. The judge was sympathetic and wanted to spare him a jail sentence and the jeopardy of public disgrace. Still, he was firm in his insistence that the patient get psychiatric treatment and made treatment a condition for a suspended sentence. The patient was to report to a probation officer every three months so the latter could ascertain that he was still in treatment. If not, he would be put in jail immediately. A court edict not only demanded that the patient start treatment, but also imposed the further condition that he couldn't discontinue treatment if he so desired. Many therapists believe that the patient has to have the freedom to leave therapy in order to foster his autonomy.

In spite of these severe circumstances, this patient's treatment did not present any unusual problems. The problems encountered were related to intrapsychic conflicts and defenses and the external situation did not seem to enter into the therapeutic interaction. This, in itself, was pertinent and only later in the analysis did it become apparent why he showed such little resentment at having analysis imposed upon him. He remembered having been rebuffed during childhood and, at times, physically attacked if he dared to ask for anything. This developed into a component of his masochistic submission and homosexuality in which he was usually the passive partner. On occasion, he would use reaction formation, as in the washroom, and, at least momentarily, adopt the aggressive role. It is tangential to the thesis to go into any further details of this patient's analysis except to mention briefly that the patient really wanted treatment but had to manipulate himself into a situation where he was "ordered" to do what he was afraid to ask for directly.

One might conclude that this case is an exception, but when it was presented at a seminar, other members of the group reported similar experiences. Such cases should cause us to pause and wonder when we are presented with material which seems to indicate a lack of motivation and to try to understand the patient's reactions in terms of the intrapsychic rather than being discouraged. The fact that the patient comes to the analyst's office often indicates sufficient "motivation." A court order "forcing him" to seek help or a painful symptom may each be sufficient reason for analysis. The analyst is interested in the patient's reasons for wanting treatment, and a court order and a symptom may be equivalent.

RESISTANCE

There are many other kinds of reactions which have been considered by analysts as incompatible with analysis. Hoedemaker (see Chapter Five) presented examples of actions he considered to be attempts by the patient to sabotage the analytic relationship. What his patient did might be considered a resistance, one that threatened to be totally disruptive. He described the case of a middle-aged woman who ignored his interpretations. Whenever he attempted to point out what she was doing, she paused to let him speak and then went on without overtly acknowledging that he had spoken. Finally, Hoedemaker became irritated and expressed his anger. He banged his hand on his chair and insisted that the patient listen to what he had to say, not just for the sake of making himself heard, but to convey what he felt was going on within her.

Hoedemaker knew why the patient ignored him, and was able to understand that she was reenacting in the transference neurosis an infantile relationship with her mother. The patient always felt ignored by her and couldn't get through to her; in the analysis she reversed roles, identifying with her mother and rejecting the analyst as she perceived she had been rejected. The analyst broke through this pattern by "insisting" he be "heard."

I will direct myself to the wider implications of behavior similar to that of Hoedemaker's patient, behavior that has been viewed as resistance and which is frequently considered to be detrimental to analysis.

Freud presented several viewpoints about the nature of resistance. In "Remembering, Repeating and Working Through" (1914), he states that overcoming of resistance is a major therapeutic task. The resolution of "resistance due to repression" leads to a filling in of memory gaps. Acting out which is accentuated by resistance is a further obstacle to remembering, and impedes analytic progress. He concludes that the aim of removing resistance distinguishes psychoanalytic therapy from other forms of treatment.

The transference neurosis became the center of Freud's interest in his two papers, "The Dynamics of Transference" (1912) and "Observations on Transference Love" (1915). In the former, he remarked that as one approaches the unconscious sources of the patient's associations resistance occurs. However, transference enters the picture at this point. We need not pursue the process of transference development here, except to point out that Freud believed the transference itself to be a potent form of resistance. Specifically, in the case of the erotic transference, the patient tends to suppress or to repress it. In the latter paper, Freud notes that a frequent manifestation of the transference is that the patient falls in love with the analyst. He asks the pertinent question as to whether the analyst should prohibit or exhort the patient to overcome these feelings, since they present a resistance to analysis in that the patient wishes to destroy the analyst as analyst and convert him into a lover. He answers his questions by concluding that such an attitude would be merely asking the patient to repress, while the aim of analysis is to undo repression. Such an exhortation would be contrary to analytic principles.

Consequently, one is impelled to reexamine the concept of resistance in terms of whether one should seek to eliminate it. We have a situation in which, on the one hand, it is acknowledged that resistance is a hindrance to analytic progress, and, on the other hand, to attempt to get "rid" of resistance introduces parameters that may in themselves obscure material that is necessary for the understanding of the patient's intrapsychic processes. Freud resolved this dilemma by not resorting to parameters. He expressed this by advising against any deliberate role-taking, and suggested that resistances must be viewed as material to be analyzed.

If one follows Freud's line of reasoning, one may view resistance as something of analytic value. The patient has to reveal himself and there is nothing more revealing than his characteristic defensive modes. Resistance, according to Freud, is the way the patient manifests his defenses in the therapeutic setting. He defends himself against his unconscious, and the defense manifests itself in behavior which is reflected in object relationships. The analytic relationship is also an object relationship which fosters a variety of infantile elements depending upon the dominant transference theme. Resistance becomes part of the transference, insofar as projected archaic imagos contain the reactions and defenses the infantile ego constructed against the more disruptive aspects of the threatening persons of the past. These reactions and defenses constitute resistances when projected onto the analyst and reveal characteristic adjustive ego modalities. In cases with characterological defects, the distortions and defects of the ego's adjustive modalities reveal the personality style and highlight the psychopathological core. Consequently, in this group of patients the development and quality of resistance is especially important to the significant transference trends. Resistance is an important aspect of an ego state which reveals as much about the patient as does any other type of material.

THE ANALYST'S REACTIONS AND COUNTERTRANSFERENCE

The specific questions stimulated by Hoedemaker's clinical material are intriguing. In his clinical example, he emphasizes the value of the hostile transference, and discusses personal reactions which include some countertransference elements. He also discusses behavior which he feels was in his own best interest, but, as a consequence, was in the patient's best interest, too.

The type of transference described, that is, the patient identifying with her mother and treating the analyst in the same way her mother treated her, involved projection of the memory of an infantile self-representation and is characteristic of character disorders. It is also found, however, in the psychoneurotic patient. Frequently, neurotic patients bring in dream material where the role of analyst and patient is reversed. Usually, this represents a reaction formation against passive dependent or passive homosexual impulses. Anna Freud (1936) described a similar role reversal when she described the important defense of identification with the aggressor.

Hoedemaker recognized he felt irritated by his patient and then he responded accordingly; he did not suppress his anger, but, instead, conveyed it to the patient in the context of not letting her devalue the analytic situation. He felt that the analytic interaction was important and that he must not allow her to ignore him. Being ignored meant being depreciated and represented the destruction of his analytic role. He felt his interpretations were integrative and did not allow the patient to reject them, the essence of his response being, "I have an idea you haven't looked at."

Other analysts have written of their reactions to patients and discussion of the countertransference in recent years has proved to be fruitful. The analyst's response should be examined, especially when the patient is able to provoke anger. Of course, any affective reaction, positive or negative, is meaningful and sexual responses, in particular, have to be considered.

Analysts are, after all, human, and patients are usually, for defensive purposes, quite skillful in discovering their sensitive spots. They learn rather quickly how to evoke a response from the therapist. Once the analyst is able to place the patient's behavior in an analytic frame of reference, the particular affective reaction often disappears immediately. If he can understand that the patient, at some level, wants to evoke such a response and if he is able to see this as an aspect of a transference projection, the analyst is adopting a viewpoint which goes beyond any constrictive personal reactions. For example, as Freud described, a hysterical patient may wish to manipulate and destroy the analyst by evoking erotic feelings within him. The analyst may actually feel sexually stimulated by a patient who is able to be seductively attractive. But once he understands that being chosen a sexual partner or the victim of her seduction is representative of a fantasied relationship with some figure of her infantile past, and that the patient has to behave in this fashion because it has adaptive and defensive significance to her, then his outlook becomes clinical and no longer a personal sexual one. This shift in attitude eliminates responses which could be disturbing and interfere with the course of analysis, but does not create an affectless state. The analyst is then looking at the patient from an entirely different viewpoint. She is still the subject of intense interest but now it is an analytic interest, one aimed at understanding the patient's behavior and needs rather than reacting to them.

There is no unanimous consensus as to whether it is always necessary to respond first with affect, and then to use such a response as a stimulus to place the patient in a clinical perspective. Winnicott believes that with the psychotic patient the analyst has to feel "objective" hate, and this response can eventuate in a constructive experience for both the analyst and the patient. He views the analyst's feelings as an intrinsic aspect of the therapeutic interaction. Once the psychotic patient can feel hated, then it is possible that, at some future time, he can feel loved. Winnicott (1949) reminds us that in order to experience affect there has to be considerable ego structure, so an interaction founded on a degree of structure greater than the initial fixed state represents an advance. The experience of being hated is potentially constructive, according to Winnicott, if it is conscious and if the reasons for it can be recognized by both the analyst and patient.

That the analyst's response can act as a "signal" to place the patient in a clinical perspective has been discussed; but is it absolutely necessary to have such a signal (a potentially disruptive affect such as hate) to set the analytic process in motion? With greater experience and familiarity with patients' defensive and adaptive modalities, it is possible that the therapist can adopt a clinical viewpoint from the very beginning. The analyst may perceive the patient's material in a total perspective in addition to the primary process qualities he detects. He may be familiar with a total pattern, a gestalt, that enables him to make an immediate evaluation. His secondary process is brought into play and his ego continues to function with high degrees of integration and synthesis. His psychic balance is maintained without any disruptive affects.

In considering Winnicott's proposition about the psychotic patient needing to feel hated before he can experience love, the analysis of the transference projection might achieve the same result without the analyst necessarily having to hate the patient. When hatred occurs, it has to be analyzed and its countertransference components have to be recognized and resolved. This viewpoint stresses, contrary to Winnicott's, that hatred, by and of itself, is an impediment to analysis. The analyst has to overcome this feeling which hampers his ability to analyze. Once he recognizes what factors within the patient stimulated certain personal inner conflicts, he has gained considerable understanding which can be analytically useful. The same kind of understanding, even with the psychotic patient, could conceivably be achieved without the analyst having to feel threatened. If he is able to continue viewing the patient's material in the context of transference projections, then he can maintain objectivity and his analytic role. He still has considerable feeling for the patient, but it is feeling founded on his desire to analyze rather than on the basis of other personal intrapsychic needs.

Hoedemaker emphasizes that he sometimes has to react forcefully in order to preserve the therapeutic relationship. In his clinical example, he felt it necessary to intervene and stop his patient from ignoring his interpretations. This case presents us with a fascinating paradox. If the patient defends herself by not hearing the analyst's interpretations, then she will be unable to learn from them and to achieve analytic integration. Besides feeling frustrated, Hoedemaker felt it necessary to intervene in order not to allow the patient such a total withdrawal and insulation. On the other hand, the patient was reliving (with a reversal of roles) an early relationship with her mother. In other words, this was a transference projection which included a defensive reaction to a maternal imago. The analytic relationship is set in motion by just such a transference projection. Is it advisable then to interrupt a pattern which is part of the spontaneous unfolding of the transference?

Phrasing the question in such a manner carries an implicit answer. Since the unfolding of the transference neurosis is our most valuable therapeutic tool, one should use it and analyze it rather than attempt to eliminate it. In Hoedemaker's case, the nature and content of the transference neurosis would seem to preclude analysis. One wonders, however, if he had persisted in interpreting the transference implications of her ignoring him whether it might have been possible for the patient to integrate it. She might not immediately have changed her behavior, but making explicit the adaptive value of what she was doing might have made her behavior less constricting and eventually capable of integrating the analyst's interpretations.

DISRUPTIVE BEHAVIOR

One may still ask whether there are certain types of behavior and acting out which, in spite of being important elements of the transference neurosis, are so designed that it is not possible to subject them to analytic scrutiny? Hoedemaker's patients may have furnished us with an example of such behavior. Other patients may act out with such violence that the analytic decorum is disrupted and analysis cannot proceed. In other instances, the analyst may not be able to tolerate the analysand's behavior and thereby loses his analytic objectivity.

The latter, of course, involves countertransference. In spite of countertransference elements, there are conditions which every analyst imposes upon the patient, conditions he feels are necessary in order to conduct analysis. One expects the patient to be able to get to the office most of the time and to pay his bills. He should be reasonably presentable and not do anything that would unduly disturb the analyst. These are general conditions most analysts require. In addition, there are other conditions, more subtle and idiosyncratic and determined by the analyst's specific personality patterns. In the optimal analytic relationship these conditions are kept at a minimum. But it still is important to recognize that we make some demands which impose limits on what we permit the patient to present to us, and on what we choose to analyze. No therapeutic relationship is completely spontaneous and uninhibited, and the unfolding of the transference neurosis is, to some extent, guided by some extraneous factors.

If then, the patient's behavior reaches unmanageable proportions, that is, unmanageable for a particular analyst, what avenues are open to the therapist? He may forbid the patient to continue with such behavior. As Hoedemaker states, such curtailment is in the analyst's best interest, but, as a consequence, it may then be in the patient's best interest, too. If, for example, a patient makes a gesture threatening the analyst's life, no matter how free from conflict the analyst might be or how immersed he might be in viewing the patient's behavior as an intrapsychic phenomenon, he will still feel anxious. An adolescent boy picked up the letter opener from my desk and using it as a dagger made threatening gestures with it. At first I could view what he was doing with relative analytic calm, but when he came dangerously close to my chest my previous objectivity left me and I became frightened. Because of my anxiety, I could no longer function as an analyst and in spite of the rich transference significance of what the patient was doing, it was no longer available to either of us. This patient by frightening me succeeded in disrupting the analytic relationship. In order to preserve it (and perhaps my life), I had to stop this behavior. As one might suspect, he wanted limitations imposed upon him, so I forbade him to continue what he was doing. However, I made it quite plain that I could not tolerate such behavior because by exposing personal vulnerabilities he would destroy my role as analyst and this I could not permit. He could either stop voluntarily or I would call the police and have him taken away. I admitted this was unanalytic behavior on my part, but I had to deviate from the usual interpretive procedure in order to be able to return to it later, if he decided this was what he wanted. To persist in such behavior would stimulate such levels of anxiety within me that I might never again be able to look at him with analytic detachment. He stopped acting so flamboyantly, and we were then able to look at some of the provocative and self-defeating elements that were inherent in his behavior. This was possible because I was again able to look at his behavior as a transference phenomenon, as he became relatively less threatening and as my anxiety gradually diminished. As we were able to shift back to the analytic frame of reference, he stopped altogether and went back to the couch, where he continued free-associating. This is an extreme case but, even though extreme, it was possible to make a prohibition, one made in the context of preserving analysis. Many other less traumatic but thoroughly disruptive situations occur, especially in the analysis of cases suffering from severe psychopathology. In these cases, setting limits might be helpful, but this is necessary only if the patient's behavior cannot be handled in an analytic context, and if the analyst feels that he cannot otherwise continue functioning in a professional capacity (see Chapter Five).

In some instances the patient cannot stop himself and the analyst is unable to influence him. Under these circumstances, it may be necessary to temporarily discontinue therapy. The patient may unconsciously want to sabotage treatment and seeks rejection. Nevertheless, it is often possible to demonstrate to him that discontinuing treatment is not the same as termination and that this course of action is taken specifically because the analyst does not want the treatment to degenerate into a confused, unworkable relationship. The patient makes the decision when to return, the analyst keeps himself available, and the interruption may be only for a very short period of time, and sometimes only the interval until the next scheduled session. An instance of this kind occurred when another adolescent patient drove to my home office on a hot summer day. He was wearing a beach robe and, after having entered my consulting room, he took it off. He was completely naked and mockingly taunted me; insofar as he was supposed to reveal himself, he was now displaying himself and hiding nothing. I was taken completely by surprise and shocked. I was also "analytically" speechless and not able to think in terms of exhibitionism, homosexuality, and the other implications of his behavior. All I could do was react to his provocativeness, and I refused to go on with the interview. I told him he was making a travesty of his treatment and that I could not work with him under these circumstances. I, therefore, asked him to leave and not to return until he felt that he wanted to meet my conditions for analysis (in this case this simply meant wearing clothes). He left, but returned for his next appointment appropriately dressed. He was then able to discuss the meaning of his previous bizarre behavior.

Would it have been possible to have dealt with his

nakedness during the previous hour and not have had to send him away? Perhaps some analysts could have worked under these circumstances and have been able to view the patient's behavior in an analytic context, that is, use it as material at the time it occurred.

Are there specific kinds of behavior which are unusually disruptive of the analytic situation? Different analysts can tolerate different types of responses. Behavior cannot be classified as disruptive on an absolute basis, but only in terms of the interaction between the patient and the analyst, which includes the analyst's unique responses. Some therapists have a particular tolerance for certain types of behavior. This does not necessarily mean that they are more tolerant of all types of acting out. On the contrary, they may find it difficult to relate to patients whom most other analysts would not find troublesome. The analyst's reaction is, to a large measure, idiosyncratic. At this point the analyst has to evaluate the extent of his personal contribution to the unmanageable therapeutic situation. If it is significant, it may be best that the patient be sent to another analyst who has either greater tolerance, or, at least, different kinds of idiosyncracies.

The ultimate resolution of any kind of acting out is achieved when the patient is able to view it as a phenomenon which has an intrapsychic origin, as will be detailed in the next section. This optimal situation requires the ego to be using its self-observing faculties, an ego function that the analyst augments. In acting out and in extreme regression the patient's self-observing capacities are presumably minimal and not available for insight formation.

THE SELF-OBSERVING FUNCTION

The ego's self-observing function, like any psychic formation, may be considered in terms of a hierarchical continuum (see Chapter Six for discussion of the hierarchical continuum of analytic help), and its qualities described in terms of phases of psychosexual development. As the ego achieves greater structure throughout the course of spontaneous maturation or analytic integration, all the ego functions become more efficient, including the ability for self-observation. In the primitive ego state characterized by gross disturbances in reality-testing or profound withdrawal, which is often found in psychotic patients, one wonders whether there is sufficient capacity for self-observation to make the patient analytically accessible.

Regression and fixation do not reproduce ego states identical to the phase of psychosexual development to which they correspond. The regressed ego state contains pathological distortions and defensive superstructures. The phase of specific capacity for self-observation will undergo considerable distortion while being incorporated into the ego's defensive and distorted operations during regression. On the other hand, there are many acquired adaptive techniques that are not completely lost in the regressed state. These skills are, in some way, involved in relating to both the outer world and inner needs. A gross example is the ability of most psychotic patients to talk and make observations considerably beyond the level of sophistication of the neonate. These skills, although they may be subjected to considerable distortion, will still enable the patient to make observations compatible with analysis. Although the general level of ego structure may be extremely primitive and the chief adjustive modalities may operate with a preponderance of primary process, there still may be self-observing elements that have survived the regression and include later acquired secondary process factors.

What the patient observes about himself is determined, in part, by his psychopathology. However, insofar as the regressive path is an uneven one and the ego consists of various parts operating at different developmental levels, some aspects of the patient's self-awareness is enhanced. If all ego systems are operating at approximately the same developmental level, then the perceptual system is relatively unaware of the internal psychic state in the same way that one is not ordinarily aware of a bodily appendage. Where there is a somatic dysfunction which leads to pain, then one is very much aware of the soma. Similarly, insofar as the perceptual system does not undergo the same degree of regression of some other ego systems, the patient's self-awareness, although very much distorted, may be accentuated. Such distortions are not necessarily contraindications to analysis since they are dealt with in the context of the transference.

The analytic setting, by stimulating regression, also enhances self-awareness. Most patients even before treatment show considerable self-preoccupation. Whether this self-preoccupation, which may be a pathologically distorted self-awareness, can be made analytically useful is a crucial question, but can this be determined at the onset by making a diagnostic evaluation? Some regressed states may be characterized by a defensive turning away from any kind of introspection. Analytic flexibility, however, is preferable to a priori judgments, and the analytic regression and the introjective-projective aspects of this regression often lead to the development of a useful self-observing function that would not have been predictable during the first few interviews.

If the patient refuses to relate to the analyst, then analytic regression can not take place and the capacity for self-observation will not be enhanced. The inaccessible patient has been briefly discussed (see Chapter Six), but now I am emphasizing the factors that might determine whether a patient becomes engaged in analysis to the point where he regresses as described above, or whether he remains rigidly fixated and withdrawn from the analytic setting. In order to involve himself in the analytic process, the patient has to feel, to some extent, that he has made an autonomous choice. To feel that treatment is imposed equates the analytic situation with the threatening external world in general, and the patient's ability to make discriminations about what's occurring within and outside of the psyche is impaired. Insofar, however, as he had made a choice, therapy becomes a situation which he believes will gratify desires. Because of the constant reliability of the analytic setting, one which is different from the projected external world, the patient becomes able to look inside himself. Therefore, according to this thesis, the patient has to have some autonomy in order to develop the capacity for analytic self-observation.

There are different degrees of autonomy, and patients suffering from characterological defects have only a minimum amount. One of the purposes of analysis, however, is to foster autonomy. One cannot expect or demand that a patient have a considerable degree of a function, the absence of which is a manifestation of psychopathology. If the patient can walk voluntarily from the waiting room into my consulting room, I consider him to have sufficient autonomy to consider analysis. A colleague told me of various experiences in which a resistive patient was able to choose to walk through the door into the consulting room and thereby isolate the analytic situation from the imposing external world that forcibly brought him to the waiting room. Such patients are able to discriminate between two frames of reference, the painful environment and the analytic setting. Such a discrimination makes the development of further self-observation possible.

In primitive ego states the boundaries between the self and the outer world are blurred. It is generally believed that in the phase of infantile omnipotence the neonate does not recognize the existence of an external reality, one apart from himself. His universe is presumably a homogeneous one, but in disrupted ego states, characterized by tension resulting from psychic trauma, it is one that is homogeneously bad, consisting of a hostile, attacking persecuting outer world and a hateful, unlovable self. The distinction between the self and the outer world is still blurred, but the perceptual system is, nevertheless, functioning and everything is felt as hateful and associated with disruptive rage. This is not an unusual outcome of the fixation and regression seen in so many character disorders and psychoses.

Since the patient perceives everything as bad, he indiscriminately attacks external objects and himself. This occurs because of faulty ego structure and introjective-projective mechanisms. In view of such blurring of ego boundaries, one may question whether there is sufficient therapeutically useful self-observing ego function available to conduct analysis.

The manifestations of such an ego state as it occurs in an adult patient are presented to the analyst, sometimes quite vociferously. This ability to communicate, however, is evidence of sensory awareness and some secondary process. What the patient expresses (hatred, rage, self-disgust, etc.) are qualities he perceived about himself, even though he may have projected many of them onto others. This type of awareness has rudimentary features which can develop into an analytically operational self-observing function.

Describing something hateful about the self indicates the acceptance of the existence of a self and the capacity to make an evaluation. In a sense, he is scrutinizing and describing destructive and disruptive introjects. This constitutes a self-observation of internal pathological factors. Similarly, his ability to blame the external world indicates he has the capacity to blame the analyst, perhaps a necessary step for the formation of a workable transference state. To be able to recognize that he is projecting is necessary for the resolution of the transference, and patients suffering from characterological defects often find it difficult to make such a distinction. Insofar as his universe is a homogeneous one, the analyst is often not distinguished from the self either, and an inoperable transference psychosis may occur. Nevertheless, the patient's ability to feel hatred and rage signifies that he can feel and has the capacity to experience other feelings. Whether he hates himself or the projected outer world, there are some object-directed qualities to such an affect. Consequently, he has the further capacity of making more than one kind of observation about himself.

The ego progresses from operating primarily on the basis of the pleasure-pain principle to a state where ego boundaries are established, and through gradations of identifications with various external objects, object and self-discrimination develops. The ego identifications contain relative amounts of pain and pleasure, and such identifications are responsible for the formation of the superego, a psychic agency that has self-observing qualities. If the superego introjects are cathected with intense hostile feelings, they may be projected during an ego regression so that the self-observing function is externalized, resulting in the belief of being watched by a hating persecutor. This belief may be precariously masked by its opposite; the patient insists that he feels only sentimental love for the exclusively benign persons by whom he feels surrounded. These are familiar manifestations of the transference regression of many patients who have a psychotic core and, insofar as the analyst is kept externalized, there is only a minimum of identification and a moderate degree of ego splitting. However, although with hostility, the patient is at one level relating to an external object, the analyst. This cathexis of an external object signifies that the patient has the potential to distinguish between the self and the outer world, that is, he is able to make assessments about himself in regard to an external object (even though delusional).

The capacity to experience diverse feelings about the self and projected and disowned parts of the self is associated with the ability to discriminate between the self and the outer world. Such patients can also value what they hate. Hostile, destructive introjects which have been impediments to psychic development are projected onto the analyst. The analyst is then valued specifically because he has lessened the tension the patient experiences in hating himself. This leads to a dual perception of the analyst. The patient, by being able to relate to the analyst from two different perspectives, a hating one and one that is valued because he has adaptive significance, is beginning to involve himself in an operable transference. The value of projecting is that it can eventuate into analytic self-observation, and in the therapeutic setting can be thought of as the *anlage* of the self-observing function. By being capable of experiencing another type of feeling, he is developing an ability to compare different percepts of the analyst. Eventually, he may be able to distinguish the analyst from what he has had to project onto him—to experience the positive side of the ambivalence. When this occurs, the patient has progressed and his ego has gained structure.

The ability to be aware of the self begins early in the course of ego development and can be considered the *anlage* of the self-observing function which is indispensable for analysis. Obviously, to observe the self one has to be able to make some discrimination between self and object representations. Just as there is a continuum between early recognition of part objects and viewing objects as synthesized whole objects, the awareness of the self undergoes progressive secondary-process refinement to an optimal development for analytic work. *The self-representation, in fact, develops from the fusion of self-object representations and the awareness of objects is paralleled by the awareness of the self.* In the analysis of psychotic patients, the transference is often characterized by a symbiotic fusion with the analyst and one notes sequences of progression and regression, the analyst, at times, not being distinguished from the self and, at times, with ambivalent object differentiation, being viewed as a hating persecutor or an omnipotent savior. If the patient is able to experience object relations as ambivalent part objects, then he has sufficient ego organization to be potentially capable of developing a self-observing function which can lead to transference resolution.

The perception of different levels of tension is a perception of an internal state, and one from which self-observation can develop. With further ego structure one acquires the concept of time and the ability to distinguish between past, present, and future. The patient may feel miserable in the present, but even misery has to have some frame for a differential comparison. It cannot be experienced in a vacuum. This implies a concept of a better state which may be projected into the future. Feelings have to be compared to other feelings and it is the possibility of a better ego state that makes a patient feel so terrible in the present, especially if he believes that future happiness is unattainable. However, as long as one's unhappiness can be related to the awareness that somewhere a state of happiness exists, then the patient has the capacity to develop hope. It is this capacity that the patient uses for analytic integration and which leads to self-observation. Since the patient can feel one ego state and compare it to another, which for the moment may be unobtainable, his universe is no longer homogeneous. *This disruption of homogeneity can, on the one hand, be the outcome of psychic trauma, or, on the other, of structuralization and may lead to further development.*

As one can see, the scrutiny of the various elements involved in therapeutic interaction leads to a discussion and elaboration not only of technical factors as highlighted in both Boyer's and Hoedemaker's chapters, but also of many basic fundamental theoretical issues. Both require further exploration, a pursuit which should eventually clarify our conceptual basis of the therapeutic process.

Chapter Eight

Further Theoretical and Clinical Aspects

Peter L. Giovacchini, M.D.

At this point it becomes pertinent to examine our concepts about the psychopathology of the group of patients we have discussed. Some analysts have raised the question as to whether we are describing a homogeneous group, and Monke (1964) asked how useful a diagnosis, or rather the word *schizophrenia,* is, especially when we attempt to orient our thinking in a therapeutic frame of reference.

NOSOLOGIC DISTINCTIONS

When we examine the patient in a therapeutic context, nosologic distinctions recede into the background. A striking example of how the diagnostic classification of the patient was minimized occurred in a postgraduate clinical seminar where Dr. S. Lipton was presenting a case. He had described in detail a patient's behavioral aberrations which were definitely paranoid in quality and then went on to describe the transference interaction. At no time had he said anything about diagnosis.

Finally, one of the members of the seminar group asked, "But haven't you considered schizophrenia?" whereupon Dr. Lipton, after a short pause, replied, "Of course I have, but it didn't help," and he then went on to give further details about the unfolding of the transference neurosis. Schizophrenia was not mentioned again, and the group felt much more comfortable when it was made explicit that we were not going to burden ourselves with a constricting adherence to diagnostic issues.

Should we, therefore, discard diagnosis entirely and in its place emphasize the patient's particular intrapsychic conflicts, especially as they shape the course of the transference neurosis? The latter certainly requires emphasis, but this does not mean that we should discard all diagnostic concepts. A "therapeutic" diagnosis replaces the traditional diagnostic label. It may have elements similar to the usual nosologic categories but it is not static; the patient's response to the therapeutic setting, an ever-evolving one, is the main diagnostic criterion.

Recently it has become increasingly clear that the diagnostic category *schizophrenia* no longer refers to a group of cases that is as homogeneous as we once believed. Bleuler, many years ago, questioned homogeneity when he wrote about the "Group of Schizophrenias," and today we are impressed by the diverse types which are labeled schizophrenia. Practically everything concerning this so-called entity has been questioned: etiology, course, developmental and environmental aspects, and constitutional and hereditary factors. Immense quantities of data have been collected from many research approaches, including those conducted in biochemical and physiological laboratories. However, these studies have not added particularly to our understanding of how to relate to such patients in a therapeutic setting.

The problem becomes compounded when we broaden our vista to include cases that have been referred to by a variety of labels, such as character disorders, borderline cases, or ambulatory psychoses and pseudoneurotic schizophrenia. Again one has to inquire as to whether we are dealing with specific and distinct categories which have some value in predicting the therapeutic course or in determining the prognostic outcome. These labels are comparatively recent, although the cases to which they refer have been with us for a long time. Most likely we have become more aware of such cases because the usual formulations applying to the "classical" neurosis are not particularly helpful in understanding this group. The label "character disorder" is especially confusing because in the past it has been considered synonomous with Alexander's concept (1930) of the neurotic character, which refers to a patient whose intolerance of tension leads to externalization and acting out. The types of patients described here may resort to primitive functioning and acting-out behavior, but this has not been considered a distinguishing feature. Instead, we have referred to a characterological defect as a common denominator.

In seminar discussions the question of "definition" of the cases being studied always comes up, especially when we compare "schizophrenia" with character disorders. How do these cases, which are identified by the existence of a characterological defect, differ from those cases which are phenomenologically identified as schizophrenia? Schizophrenics also suffer from faulty ego structure which results in a variety of characterological defects. Both groups show narcissistic fixation and difficulties in relating to the external world. On the other hand, many investigators believe that there is an advantage in distinguishing patients with characterological defects from overt psychoses, and, within the former group, believe there is a further advantage in separating the character disorders from the so-called borderline cases.

The character disorders are distinguished chiefly by an ego defect which leads to distortions in the perception of various areas of the external world. The defect, to some extent, involves all ego systems and, consequently, the patient's interactions with the external world are also affected. One sees adjustment problems accompanied by dissatisfaction with the self and a poorly integrated identity sense. However, one does not see well-systematized delusional systems or hallucinations as are sometimes found in the psychoses. In a sense, the latter seem to have more structure than we encounter in the character disorders, even though the psychotic is further removed from reality. Furthermore, the character disorders, according to some analysts, do not readily become psychotic. Gitelson (1958) believed that certain ego systems become "hypertrophied" as part of their defect and enable the patient to deal with the traumatic features of his reality. Even though this leads to a pathological adjustment it is still adaptive and not easily disrupted. In other words, the ego defect may have defensive elements or a defensive superstructure which prevents the ego from undergoing a psychotic dissolution. These defensive elements, unlike the defenses erected against unacceptable id impulses, are ego mechanisms that are involved in relating to the vicissitudes and the demands of both internal needs and the restrictions of the outer world and external objects. Insofar as they are ego mechanisms which deal with a traumatic reality,[1] they have become part of the character structure and are characterological defenses and adaptations.

When studying the borderline patient, one also finds a defective ego, but not as well defended as that of the character disorders. His defenses rarely involve the development of a "hypertrophied" ego segment that can be used adaptively. He is more apt to use primitive mechanisms of defense, such as denial and projection, although to a lesser degree than the clinically psychotic patient. His projections tend to be more diffuse than those seen in the classical paranoid, who frequently demonstrates systematized focalized delusions in addition to generalized projection. The borderline patient tends to project with less intensity and organization. Nevertheless, his reality-testing is tenuous; trauma can cause him to "strengthen" his defenses to the point where he becomes clinically psychotic. In some instances a psychosis occurs after a decompensation, one that is fixed by the formation of a systematized delusional system instead of a return to the previous shaky defenses.

The behavior of the borderline patient reflects the influence of the primary process more obviously than that of the person who suffers from a character disorder. He is often referred to as schizoid, a term which indicates withdrawal of cathexis from external objects. The

[1] The traumatic reality of early childhood has become incorporated into the ego as destructive constricting introjects which later are projected onto the outer world and then defended against.

borderline patient does not appear to attempt to involve himself with some facet of the external world in order to "pull himself up by the boot straps." His orientation is more autistic. He finds it difficult to even fantasize the possibility of receiving gratification from an external object. He deals with objects in terms of megalomanic manipulation or withdrawal. Those who have character disorders also manipulate and have megalomanic expectations, but there are still more qualities to their object relationships which indicate there is recognition of the object as separate from the self.

Hard and fast distinctions are impossible to make. These conditions constitute a continuum and there may be little value in distinguishing two diagnostic categories. In this book we have been prone to consider our cases as belonging to a single general category. Our belief is that our theoretical and therapeutic formulations apply to a large group of cases, including character disorders, borderline cases, and some psychotics. The common denominator is that there has been a profound disturbance of emotional development reflected in manifestations of defective structuralization of the adult's ego. This discussion attempts to scrutinize small differences in ego operations and defensive readjustments of this group of patients. These may assume some importance in the therapeutic interaction, and our alertness to subtle variations may broaden our comprehension of the specific vicissitudes which enter into the formation of the transference relationship. Understanding the various ego systems in terms of defensive "hypertrophies" or lacks of adjustive techniques helps the therapist to focus on what is most relevant in determining our therapeutic response.

Precocious Development of Ego Systems and Characterological Defenses

Very often such patients give the impression of particular efficiency and talent in some area which is then exploited to the fullest as an adjustive modality. This is frequently seen in the intellectual area and one finds a history of intellectual precocity. It also becomes apparent that the only way they can relate to the world is "through their mind" and this method compensates for an inability to feel and to become affectively involved in meaningful object relationships. These patients are too frightened of the latter, and are, therefore, unable to give or receive love. Intellect becomes a defense against the fear of becoming emotionally involved. At first the display of intellect may resemble strength, but one becomes aware of its desperate and constricting qualities.

Closer examination also reveals that even in the intellectual area there is considerable fragmentation and, at times, not much accomplishment. There is often a hollow, empty quality to their pursuits and little is achieved. Projects are started but the patient lacks the organization or the drive to bring them to successful completion. In other instances there is an obsessional rigidity which never enables the patient to go beyond the preliminary stage, or, if he can be productive, he lacks the mobility and flexibility which are characteristic of creative accomplishment. Since the patient has so few resources available to him, he cannot enjoy his intellectual pursuits for their own sake; instead, he clings to them for psychic survival so he is unable to relax and has to maintain rigid control over them, which results in vast expenditures of energy and psychic constrictions similar in their manifestations to those caused by countercathexis.

Patients with character disorders suffer from intense feelings of worthlessness, a self-appraisal that is commonly found in psychopathological states where the ego is poorly structured and primitively fixated. Characterological defenses such as "hypertrophied" intellectualism often do not work, for several reasons. As has been mentioned, because of a general lack of integration, the ego is impaired in its executive capacity. This leads to a tremendous discrepancy between what the patient feels he needs and what he can accomplish, for, in many instances, the patient hopes to "save" himself through his intellectual efforts. The patient has to be rescued from his inner "badness." In order to achieve this he needs an omnipotent "goodness," a savior of omnipotent and godlike proportions to elevate him from a state of helpless vulnerability to one where he can feel worthy. To feel worthy, however, requires cosmic acceptance so the patient has to produce something of universal significance. A patient in a professional field feels he has to make a great discovery which will win him international acclaim. Since he is always in pursuit of omnipotence, he is always disappointed. His preconscious or unconscious preoccupation is focused exclusively upon the acclaim he hopes to gain rather than on the work itself, so projects are seldom completed.

These patients often find that life consists of a repetitive and continual pursuit of tasks which always leads to the same blind alley. What is most impressive is the dull monotonous quality they find to be pervasive in all of their activities. Basically, they are constantly frustrated in trying to prove that they are worthwhile, that is, in attempting to establish a structured identity. Their behavior varies. It may range from a direct acknowledgment of worthlessness and impotence in the management of their daily lives to attempts at restitution and overcompensation which may be manifested by intellectualism, paranoidlike projection, or a defensive arrogance.

Ego Psychological Aspects of Therapeutic Activity

The specific defenses which characterize patients with ego defects are, of course, prominent in the therapeutic interaction as well as in daily life. The analyst's responses to unusual and sometimes bizarre elements in the patient's behavior have to be understood and can be viewed from the frame of reference of ego psychology.

The analyst's reactions have been scrutinized as "countertransference phenomena" and this has been valuable. As previously discussed (see Chapter Seven), the limits of analyzability cannot be separated from certain conditions required by the analyst so he can relax sufficiently in order to conduct analysis. In some instances, these are conditions based upon countertransference attitudes.

Countertransference has received much attention in the recent literature but has not been consistently defined. Here I would like to distinguish it from other responses which occur within the analyst. Countertransference for our purpose is simply the analyst's reactions as they are primarily determined by unconscious factors. These tend, to a large measure, to be irrational and idiosyncratic reactions based upon conflictful intrapsychic elements within the analyst. If he becomes aware of such reactions or if they are limited in scope, they need not seriously interfere with analysis. In fact, it is conceivable that they may even augment analytic progress if the analyst is able to recognize the irrational response and then use his newly found insight to empathize with the patient because he is now aware of a similar or complementary problem. The interplay of the analyst's unconscious with the patient's free associations is a fascinating topic which also has received little attention in the literature.

In order to elaborate upon the psychological processes occurring within the analyst, it is useful to distinguish between other reactions occurring during therapy from countertransference. The analyst responds to the patient from many different levels and some of his responses are not founded exclusively on the basis of irrational or conflictful elements characteristic of deeper layers. Of course, every mental construct has its unconscious substrata, but there are some reactions which are primarily determined by secondary process factors and are the outcome of experience and training. The unconscious (see Chapter Seven) contributes to the process that eventually leads to understanding of what is occurring within the patient, but the ego is still operating with synthetic and integrative systems simultaneously. Still the distinction between a countertransference response and other responses is relative and every presumably autonomous response has some countertransference element in it. It is the degree of countertransference involvement that is important.

The ego psychology of therapeutic activity cannot be

explored without considering the stimuli the patient provides. Unlike the discussion in Chapter Seven, we are not now concerned with the analyst's idiosyncratic (countertransference) responses to unique features within the patient's personality that are perhaps characteristic of severe psychopathology. The emphasis now is on how different kinds of material stimulate specific types of mental operations within the analyst, operations that involve a variety of structures such as memory traces, integrative and synthetic systems, as well as activities such as fantasy formation and reality testing.

Our therapeutic response is dependent upon many factors and influenced by the combination of various levels of stimuli. Insofar as patients with characterological defects have considerable trauma during infancy, it becomes relevant to inquire what effects specific knowledge and documentation of the past have upon the analyst.

It has been emphasized that understanding of both the current and past realities is important. An ego defect causes perceptual and cognitive distortion of current reality. In such cases a major part of the therapeutic activity consists of pulling together fragmented percepts, in order that they may become synthesized into a gestalt that is an accurate appraisal of the external world. One can raise the question as to whether the analyst's synthetic functions are able to construct fragmented reality elements into a whole. Implicit in this question is a division of analytic activity into two types, one dealing with phenomena which are chiefly conscious and preconscious, and the other with phenomena mainly unconscious. Does such a division occur in the analyst's psyche, causing him to make such a dichotomy?

Again one has to acknowledge that everything the patient presents has its unconscious determinants. However, to speak of helping the patient by strengthening reality testing is to emphasize the relationship between his ego and the outer world, and to minimize the relevance of unconscious drives and mental operations. The analyst views the patient's percepts of reality and compares them with his own as they are determined primarily by secondary process factors. When the patient and analyst are able to look at the same segments of reality, it is easy to make comparisons and one can assume that the analyst's perceptions are more objective and correspond better to the actual situation. Then the analyst is able to recognize how the patient has distorted and fragmented percepts. Presumably, the analyst's more realistic perceptions are communicated to the patient and cause him to function with better reality-testing than previously. This transaction supposedly meets one of the most basic requirements of cases with ego defects since their reality distortions are fundamental to their pathology, and are the consequence of early developmental disturbances and faulty object relationships.

Can reality testing be achieved by virtue of the analyst's superior ability to be objective?

First, one has to consider whether the analyst's ability to be objective is really superior and, if it is, whether it is relevant to the therapeutic process. Relevance would be determined by the analyst's ability to communicate his synthesizing elements to the patient and the patient's capacity for integrating this synthesis within his psychic framework. Even in the frame of reference of the transference neurosis, the question still remains whether the patient can gain an ego function, so to speak, when one's attention is exclusively directed toward the development of such a function. This is an educative role in spite of the fact that it occurs within the context of the transference neurosis. One would also have to make the dubious assumption that the contamination of the transference neurosis is minimal and that it can be handled analytically.

From the viewpoint of the analyst's psychic operations, one has to inquire from what primary process foundations his secondary process stems. He perceives the external world objectively, but there is no such phenomenon as total objectivity. Secondary process cannot exist without an underlying primary process. As discussed in Chapter Six, the work of interpretation consists of superimposing primary process responses within the analyst upon the patient's primary process, but with the additional factor that the analyst's secondary processes are added onto this congruence. The secondary process accretion is organized, coherent, and verbal, and constitutes the interpretation. Still what has happened is essentially a response to the patient's primary process, at least initially. This is an entirely different situation from what has been described as strengthening of reality-testing by educational measures.

The analyst's secondary process evaluation of the external world is now determined on the basis of his primary process and not the patient's when he assumes an educative role. So, the reality conveyed to the patient is one founded upon the analyst's personal orientation. He is, in effect, attempting to correct the patient's secondary process distortions and to synthesize fragmented elements by responding only to the patient's secondary-process lacunae and not to their primary-process basis, adaptive value, or meaning of these distortions. If he attempted to do the latter, he would be relating to the patient in an analytic and interpretive fashion and this would not be considered primarily a reconstructive, educative experience aimed specifically at improving the patient's reality-testing.

It becomes understandable that the patient may find it difficult to accept the analyst's personal percepts as his own. He has to incorporate the analyst's reality into his own ego, but it becomes difficult to amalgamate within his psyche because, in a sense, it is a foreign body. It is not an upward, hierarchically structured extension of the primary process and, as with any foreign body, it is not functional. Unless one can deal with the patient's primary process too, that is, deal with primitive introjects which have impeded and distorted the upward extension of the secondary process, it becomes difficult to understand how these distortions can be corrected. It becomes especially difficult to see how a "frontal assault," a direct confrontation of the analyst's secondary process with the patient's secondary process, can be effective, even temporarily.

Many analysts agree that this type of confrontation does not lead to a significant character change, but, nevertheless, it has a supportive value, one which is essential for such cases so analysis can follow. This activity is considered preparatory to analysis, since the patient is so out of touch with reality that he cannot even perceive the reality of his treatment. The patient is in need of auxiliary secondary process in order to be able to function in the therapeutic setting.

How effective such a maneuver might be and its possible drawbacks has been discussed (see Chapter Six), but it can be pursued further. It must be granted, however, that there are some patients who need someone to manage some facets of their chaotic situation to effect sufficient stabilization so therapy can proceed. Whether this can be done by the analyst while preserving the necessary conditions for therapy already discussed (see Chapter Six), is still an unsettled question.

Our interest now is to emphasize the analyst's psychic operations. What are his reactions if he assumes the role of an alter ego? Is he achieving his purpose of creating a setting that is stable for analysis, or is he perhaps unconsciously defeating this aim? This may be only a temporary defeat, and, as with any parameter, a deviation from analysis is relinquished as quickly as possible. But still this question must be pursued not only in terms of the effects strengthening of reality has upon the patient, but also in terms of what changes this type of relationship has upon the analyst's psyche. Does it help, as he hopes, or does it hinder his ability to relate to the patient from an analytic perspective?

I feel there are at least two factors which must be examined. The analyst is oriented toward fostering the patient's autonomy. By analyzing within the context of the transference neurosis, he hopes to create a setting that is favorable for the awakening of the patient's autonomous potential. He addresses himself to removing obstacles to the patient's spontaneous development. He demonstrates his faith in the patient's capacity for emotional development by his continued interest in understanding the intrapsychic, and by not assuming that he is helpless and has to have someone tell him what direction his emotional development should take. He does not deprive him of the opportunities for autonomous choice, so the patient can develop an identity that is truly his own, even though he may have identified with some aspects of the analytic interaction.

When the analyst becomes an adjunctive ego, he is projecting his ego operations onto the patient. If he is able to augment the patient's reality testing, then the patient has been able to introject them, but, by the same token, the analyst has had to have been able to project. I doubt that any relationship can be completely one-sided, that is, where one person relates to another with a particular psychic mechanism, and the other person is relating exclusively on an entirely different plane without reciprocity or complementarity. This one-sided interaction is even less likely to occur when the analyst's purpose is to have the patient incorporate aspects of himself. In other words, such activity by the analyst may cause him to function at a primitive level which corresponds to the patient's psychopathology. Anyone who puts himself in the role of supplying adjustive techniques and assumes the position of a teacher is always giving something of himself to the other person. This, of course, occurs to some extent in any analysis, but the analyst is conveying an attitude, one of exploration and interpretation, rather than showing the patient how to adjust or doing it for him. If the analyst "gives" the patient such techniques, how does it affect his capacity for conveying a self-observing, introspective attitude to the patient? To return to the analogy of the teacher, if he directs and sometimes actually does the work for the student, he is not allowing him the opportunity to discover for himself. The good teacher guides with the aim of helping the student to work independently. True, he supplies him with techniques, but these are all means by which he can then master problems without his help. This is often done by correcting bad habits as well as supplying new information, but never before he feels the student is able to integrate it and make it his own.

The analyst is confusing his role of fostering the patient's autonomy with that of projecting an aspect of himself onto the patient. This projection does not foster the patient's autonomy; it also hampers the analyst's autonomy. Projection, as with any other object-directed ego mechanism, does not occur in a vacuum. In other words, with every projection there is a corresponding introjection, even though it may be of a considerably lesser degree. When the analyst is confronted with a patient who has a fragmented reality sense, he has to identify with this aspect of the patient, at least partially so, in order to recognize the problem. This partial identification has to occur to some extent in every relationship whose purpose is to help another person, whether by psychoanalysis, psychotherapy, or even a student-teacher relationship. But it is the quality of the identification that differs in these various relationships.

By directing himself to that aspect of the patient's personality which has led to faulty reality conceptions, the therapist is also fragmenting his observations. Instead of relating to the patient with free-floating attention, one that might be considered a holistic type of observation, he is limiting himself to only one particular area of the patient's psyche. From time to time, the analyst may *choose* to focus upon a particular aspect of the patient's psyche, but when he has felt it necessary to limit himself to one area, this leads to a constriction of his autonomy. He feels impelled to "remain" with reality and, until some improvement is noted, he cannot deal with any other level of the patient's personality. Some analysts feel that it would be even dangerous to make such an attempt. Consequently, even though the restriction is self-imposed, his analytic mobility and autonomy are hampered.

The above assumes that analytic mobility can be equated with autonomy, and the corollary that whatever is done to hamper this mobility also has a significant effect on the analyst's autonomy. It makes the further, but perhaps more obvious, assumption that restrictions on the therapist's autonomy would also affect his attitudes toward the patient, specifically those attitudes aimed at fostering the patient's autonomy.

The first assumption would involve us in a general discussion of autonomy; one that would carry us into interesting but not relevant areas. Here I wish to confine myself to the concept of professional autonomy. Having to change one's analytic approach to a preparatory supportive one, constitutes, in my opinion, an impingement, to use Winnicott's expression (1955), upon analytic autonomy. This opinion does not ignore the fact that the analyst has assessed the clinical situation and then reached a decision, but I do not feel that it is an autonomous decision, that is, one without some coercion. The patient has been able to convince the analyst that in some vital respects he is helpless. Whereas in analysis the analyst and patient are cooperating with each other and looking at intrapsychic phenomena, in trying to supply the patient with an ego function, there is a differential between the analyst and patient. Looking at something together, even though the analyst is better able to integrate and understand than the patient, is still relating to each other in the same frame of reference, one which constitutes a therapeutic alliance. To accept the patient as needing something and then believing it can be supplied puts the analyst on a "higher" level, helping someone who has fewer or less-structured ego mechanisms. When one is confronted with such a situation, he is, in a sense, forced to respond. To some extent, the need to respond to someone's helplessness is always experienced as an imposition. There is not the same degree of reciprocity in such an object relationship as there is when the participants are operating on an approximately similar level. There may be immense satisfaction in giving a person help that is appropriate to early developmental phases, but there is always some resentment. There are maneuvers by which the resentment is minimized, ranging from the fee to the "end of the hour," as Winnicott describes (1949), but to feel resentment implies that to some extent one's autonomy feels threatened and one has to compensate for this loss. These compensations can, in themselves, be satisfying, but they are of a different order from those experienced in a reciprocal relationship where one does not feel imposed upon.

Why does one have to feel imposed upon in offering a patient a concrete form of help? Benedek (1959) pertinently points out that the mother's successful motherliness in helping her child develop is a developmental experience for her too, although Winnicott, who does not disagree with this thesis, points out that the mother also feels imposed upon. Benedek emphasizes that the mother's ego reaches higher levels of development which are associated with higher levels of autonomy. To nurture her child and to create conditions for ego structuralization by her nurturing is a task that is intrinsic to a structured, well-integrated developmental level. Such nurturing is one of the functions (operational aspects) of this advanced developmental phase. To give help, that is, the type of help associated with early developmental stages, need not be an imposition and hamper autonomy, but can instead lead to the attainment of higher levels of autonomy.

The analyst, however, does not operate in the same frame of reference as the mother-child dyad. Harris (1960) has pointed out similarities, but there are significant differences. Reference has already been made to ways in which the adult patient's fixations are not replicas of the corresponding stages of childhood. Another significant difference is that the analyst does not wish to be a mother; he is not aspiring to reach a developmental level which has the same quality as motherliness.

His analytic work furthers his development, but this occurs because, as he is discovering new intrapsychic relationships, he is adding segments to his own ego. This is an ego expansion and constitutes psychic development, an expansion that occurs because all levels of his personality are involved. To restrict himself only to a secondary process appraisal and response is not a creative accomplishment. It is not an operational aspect of a higher level of psychic integration. Therefore, the gratifications the analyst receives from helping the patient in this exclusively secondary process fashion are not felt as deeply, nor are they as rewarding as analytic activity. It is this distinction, this differential of satisfaction, which determines whether one feels imposed upon or whether the therapeutic relationship is characterized by mutuality and reciprocity, that is, where both participants can continue their emotional development despite the fact that they begin from different starting points. Without such mutuality the analyst is not an autonomous agent if, for no other reason, than that he does not feel free to pursue "higher" levels of autonomy, but must remain fixated to the one particular function of secondary process elaboration.

The analyst responds to the primary process elements of a patient's associations and subjects them to secondary process synthesis and refinement as discussed in Chapter Six. One cannot analyze and give form to material that is at the same level of psychic operations. Secondary process cannot add new integration to other secondary process material; it can correct distortions, but it does so within the same frame of reference. There is no further structuralization. The difference is similar to maintenance and repair as contrasted with creating something new. A patient expressed this situation in an apt fashion. Crab grass ruins lawns, and one can spend much time and energy, even ingenuity, in getting rid of it. This is, however, not the same as beginning with black dirt, grass seed, and shrubbery and creating an original landscape arrangement. The analogy breaks down when discussing a patient, since inherent in the raw material of the primary process is an arrangement, but the analyst makes it possible for the patient to give it form. But the point remains that one cannot analyze when there is not a differential in the material. If one is dealing with the end product, so to speak, then there is nothing to analyze. Filling in lacunae, repair, correcting distortions, and the like, do not constitute an activity where something is "added" to the patient's or the analyst's psyche.

The same comments can be made about an ego defect as were made about resistance and motivation (see Chapter Seven). The behavioral manifestations of the defect are brought into the treatment and influence the course and development of the transference neurosis. Consequently, it behooves the analyst to use this material for analytic purposes rather than doing away with it by correcting distortions. Such material can be disruptive to analysis, but this involves the analyst's reaction and, at times, his idiosyncrasies, as has been discussed (see Chapter Seven).

The "Objective" Past

There are situations, as Serota (1964) reminds us, where the patient attempts to give objective information about his background in order to help us correct his distortions. They sometimes bring the analyst photographs from the family album, home movies, or, in one case, a tape recording of the patient's father trying to teach him mathematics when he was a young child. There are many points of view from which one can discuss this interesting topic. Our focus here is again to inquire how such material can be used analytically and how it influences the analyst's psychic operations and his ability to analyze. Patients with characterological defects have had an especially traumatic past, so one wonders how an objective appraisal of it is relevant to analysis.

Material such as photographs and movies is considered to be objective evidence of the patient's past, but just how objective is it? Relatively speaking, since it refers to a past that can be seen or heard, it is less prone to be distorted than free associations, which have more unconscious determinants. Still, is the photograph unbiased? One has to consider the photograph from two viewpoints, the subject and the photographer. When an artist is painting a picture, he is putting a good part of himself into the painting. Photography, although much more objective, still has artistic elements and even the rankest of amateurs projects some features of his personality into the picture. Our viewpoint is much too psychically deterministic to believe that the clicking of a shutter is a purely mechanical phenomenon. From the subject's or patient's viewpoint, the particular period of his past or the setting he chooses to present to the analyst may be so designed as to becloud a variety of reality features. This, too, is revealing, but then it is material which resides in the same frame of reference as the patient's associational material and not particularly representative of an unbiased reality.

The analyst has signaled, directly or otherwise, that he is interested in such material, or the patient is being manipulative and acting out some facet of the transference relationship. The motivation behind bringing the analyst some memento, as with everything else, is multidetermined. One determinant may be a response to the analyst's interest, or it may constitute a resistance against further exploration of the transference relationship. Frequently patients tend to defend themselves against disruptive and frightening currently experienced transference feelings by returning to their genetic antecedents. It is a commonly encountered situation with some female patients to talk about their sexual feeling toward their father, rather than having to face disturbing erotic feelings toward the analyst. Similarly, by exposing the past, or even better, a synthetic externalization of the past, it can be used in the service of resistance against exposing himself in the present to the analyst.

As previously emphasized, resistance can be valuable and need not be avoided. What one has to caution against is that the analyst does not contribute to the resistance. An analyst can often directly respond to the patient without augmenting his resistance or allowing himself or the patient to lose sight of the fact that one is dealing with some defensive or manipulative activity. In this instance, the analyst might respond with curiosity or have the response that the patient wanted to provoke, and still discuss the situation analytically. It is not always necessary to frustrate the patient in order to preserve the analytic interaction. One could, for example, answer a personal question or look at a photograph and still maintain an analytic decorum. He can still weave the interaction into an interpretive framework.

Whether analysis can be preserved if one still responds to some aspect of the patient's resistance depends upon how the analyst responds. He can respond to content and, at the same time, maintain himself in another frame of reference. In other words, he can relate to the patient at one level and still be an observer appraising how he and the patient are relating to each other. If he can maintain this dual frame of reference, then he can preserve his analytic demeanor. However, it must be recognized that there are certain types of interaction where it is no longer possible to be both participant and observer. The analyst, because he becomes involved in some way with the patient or because his percepts of the patient have been channeled into specific areas, may find it difficult to maintain his role of observer. Are there certain types of stimuli which either enhance the therapist's ability to analyze or, on the negative side, impede him? Are there optimal conditions which enhance the analyst's ability to analyze? Such a favorable condition is a well-developed transference neurosis. How does learning about a "concrete" reality affect analytic activity?

The ever-hovering attention which characterizes analytic receptivity involves an interplay of secondary process synthesis and fantasy activity. The latter brings into focus a number of mnemic images, reconstructions the analyst makes about present and past events that encompass the significant figures in the patient's life, imagos that have been projected into the transference setting. To better understand dreams, for example, one often attempts to visualize the dream as the patient reports it and then fix an image of both the action and the various dream elements in our mind. This activity is possible because of the analyst's ability to construct visual images which are, in part, determined by free-floating fantasy activity.

Analytic activity requires mobility and one must be able to tolerate, as has been frequently stressed for creative activity, considerable ambiguity and lack of closure. The analyst must be able to combine the visual image he has constructed in response to the patient's free associations with a variety of his own memory traces. Some are derived from his past, and some are reflections of material he has collected since he started treatment with the present or other similar patients. This combination and juxtaposition of memory traces and recent constructs need not be entirely conscious (preconscious) and its operations can be predominantly primary process. Simultaneously, integrative and synthetic ego systems are operating with considerable quantities of psychic energy. Once this free-floating fantasy activity has undergone sufficient secondary process elaboration, it eventuates into an insight which, when communicated to the patient, constitutes an interpretation.

The analyst's responses may also include the auditory modality. Individual personality styles or other factors inherent in the therapist's psychic structure determine whether auditory or visual factors are predominant in his response to the patient's material. However, I would conjecture that the visual modality is most frequent and reports from creative scientists indicate their creative activity is primarily visual. Visual activity, as Freud (1900) frequently stated, is closer to the primary process and, therefore, more mobile.

Since what is subjected to secondary process activity involves many visual elements which are reflections of fantasy material, and, since the transference is characterized by projections of imagos that have no corresponding objects in either the past or the present, one wonders how knowledge about a concrete reality affects analytic activity. Freud's early papers on technique (1910, 1914) stressed a mirrorlike anonymity, a concept which has in recent years frequently been misunderstood and criticized. Freud felt that if the patient knew too much about the analyst's personal life he would be hampered in his ability to make transference projections and later to recognize them as transference manifestations. The same recommendation applies to the analyst also. Although, on the surface, it may seem paradoxical, there may be a disadvantage in the analyst's knowing too much about the patient.

Consequently, one has to determine which types of information are pertinent. The acquisition of exact knowledge of the patient's past does not impress me as being particularly useful. The concrete reality of past situations and object relationships is not directly relevant to the analysis, in contrast to the reality of the object relationship with the analyst, which determines the form and content of the transference neurosis. The patient never relives an exact replica of his past in the transference. The early imagos associated with the infantile ego differ from the external object. The patient reenacts relationships which are the result of a combination of early introjects with subsequent experiences. These later experiences, as well as developmental and maturational factors, cause revisions of infantile imagos. The objective past has undergone considerable elaboration and distortion by the time it is projected in the transference. The patient's distorted perceptions of past reality have led to constrictions and fixations, and it is precisely these percepts that have to be distinguished from the *present* reality. The analyst's judgment as to how they distorted the past is not meaningful or useful in the context of analysis, although in other studies this may be crucial.

The attempt to gather objective data about the patient's past, as in extensive history-taking or the use of ancillary methods such as casework studies with relatives, can become impediments to analysis, since it may hamper the analyst's capacity for free-floating fantasy. A confrontation with objective reality introduces a secondary process element. As such, it cannot be subjected to the mobility of the primary process; if it is, then it is no longer objective or real, and it is representative of the analyst's intrapsychic structure rather than the patient's. In some instances, such a percept may interfere with the juxtaposition of the patient's archaic imagos with corresponding primary process organized memory traces of the analyst. For example, I saw a patient walking down the street with his mother, who was small, thin, and frail. She impressed me as being weak, and her demeanor seemed kind and gentle. It was hard to reconcile this image with that of a hostile, devouring ogre, the patient's childhood and current impression of her. Undoubtedly, she had changed considerably, and the mother the patient spoke of no longer existed. Perhaps she had never existed as the witch he had described, his version being the result of considerable elaboration. Nevertheless, she stood for something very important in his psychic economy. The witch role he had assigned to her had to be dealt with, and the fact his mother is not a witch and never really was didn't make much difference from a therapeutic viewpoint.

Having a picture of a crucial person in the patient's life, one different from the one he presents, could introduce a complication. Whenever he spoke of his mother it became difficult to go along with his associations and to maintain the primary-process mobility mentioned above. The image of the sweet old lady intruded itself when he began describing processes that indicated he was able to encapsulate considerable amounts of rage in the mother imago. This "objective" percept tended to minimize my recognition of the constricting and damaging effect of what the patient experienced as a disruptive introject.

However, the introduction of external reality, whether past or present, need not hamper analytic activity and freedom. The analyst may be able to dissociate himself from such percepts just as the patient is able to view the analyst, to some extent, from two different viewpoints. The analyst can never and should never aim to be a total mirror; the patient always knows something about him in addition to his role as analyst and this knowledge will not be harmful as long as the analysis does not contribute to a potential confusion of roles. Similarly, the analyst can keep the two realities separate; as long as he is involved in and dedicated to analytic activity, other items of information will not matter. What is important is to recognize in terms of analysis that this kind of information is not helpful and is addressed to a layer of the personality associated with secondary process activities and corresponds to later developmental aspects of the psychic hierarchy.

Further Theoretical Considerations

All of these clinical considerations are consistent with the model of the psychic apparatus that stresses a hierarchical organization. It is not essentially different from the one Freud constructed, although he frequently introduced modifications. However, this model tends to emphasize the ego and its operations. Freud was cognizant of the importance of the ego and the works of modern ego psychologists are extensions of Freud's metapsychology. These extensions emphasize autonomous ego operations, adaptation, and a variety of energic factors.

All of the above topics are sufficiently important to deserve detailed consideration, but insofar as this chapter deals primarily with clinical phenomena and technical and theoretical aspects of treatment, only one aspect of the psychic model will be scrutinized, that is, its organization from the viewpoint of a continuum.

Viewing the psyche as a multiplicity of levels highlights the importance of ego functions which are closer to the uppermost layers. These functions are of special significance for the study of cases with characterological defects, since they are characterized by disturbances of such functions.

Ego functions imply structure and are included in Freud's first model, a stimulus-response one. Ego systems are designed to be aware of and to respond to stimuli that have their origin both in the external world and within the organism. Both the technique and methods of response, and what has been responded to, have to be placed in their proper perspective. Psychopathology as well as normal development involves these aspects of the psychic apparatus.

Every aspect of the psychic apparatus, structure, and function can be included in an hierarchical continuum. When studying functions, one is dealing with the products of the ego's executive systems which, when directed to the external world, determine the patient's behavior.

Whatever a person does, or, in the case of verbal behavior, says (as when free-associating), can be placed in a definite spot on the hierarchical continuum. In other words, both the content and the form of the patient's productions can be considered first in general terms, whether it is primitive, corresponding to early developmental states, or adaptive, coherent, and reality oriented, qualities that are associated with later highly integrated well-structured developmental stages. Then, more specifically, one can roughly assess the relative amounts of primary and secondary process and which of these two modes of operation is predominant. When one makes such evaluative judgments about behavior, one is simultaneously assessing the structure of the ego systems that have initiated the behavior. Consequently, one can associate a response with a particular ego state. The latter can be described in the same terms of relative amounts of primary and secondary process and the stage of psychosexual development to which it predominantly corresponds. It has become increasingly apparent, especially since the formulation of the structural hypothesis, that structure and function cannot be separated. Freud (1923) formulated the concepts of id, ego, and superego in operational terms.

Needs can be placed in a similar continuum (see Chapter Six). One can adopt a frame of reference of progressive structuralization without having to deal with a specific instinct theory or to bring in concepts of epigenesis as Spitz (1959) has done, nor is it necessary to distinguish whether the stimulus is internal or external, since every need passes through all layers of the psychophysiological apparatus, beginning with the most primitive. An internal need may be stimulated by an external situation, or may primarily arise because of physiological requirements which have a periodic rhythmicity, although even needs arising primarily "within" the organism frequently have an external component, too, as in sexual stimulation. In any case, as the need, which in the stimulus-response model can be equated with the stimulus, impinges on sensory systems and traverses the various layers of the psyche, it undergoes a hierarchical elaboration. What began as a result of a disruption of a homeostatic equilibrium due, for example, to metabolic cyclical physiological requirements, normally becomes progressively elaborated. At first the response to such a disruption is at a biochemical physiological level. But before it can be experienced as a definitive need, it has to be felt, that is, reach sensory awareness. This can be achieved only when this initial homeostatic imbalance attains mental representation. The latter is a structured, sophisticated elaboration of what can be conceptualized as having been an elemental somatically bound stimulus, and, in terms of total organization, represents the advanced end of a hierarchical spectrum.

The process of becoming aware of what initially is a physiological requirement involves a hierarchical elaboration of this inner need, which, when having reached the highest levels of ego organization, is experienced in socially adaptive terms and cathects appropriate executive systems that respond with reality-attuned behavior designed to gratify the need. If there are defects in the ego organization, then the need is experienced in a distorted fashion and correspondingly the executive systems, insofar as they, too, are defective, and because they are responding to a pathological, distorted stimulus, respond in an inept fashion that is essentially frustrating to the organism. The executive apparatus may achieve sufficiently for survival, but this does not usually involve pleasurable satisfaction.

If the range of development of the psychic apparatus is a narrow and constricted one, then the hierarchical elaboration of the need (similar to the hierarchical elaboration of help; see Chapter Six) is also narrow and constricted and closer to what has been defined as the primitive end of our spectrum, the physiological, biochemical level. This constriction of the hierarchical development of needs has many manifestations that are clinically important and are indicators of the faulty development of various ego systems.

The above indicates there is a parallel between the ultimate elaboration of a traumatically induced need and emotional development. This emphasizes that all of the patient's productions, what he feels as well as what he does, recapitulate the course of his development, and in the therapeutic interaction the analyst is in a particularly favorable position to determine the relative participation of different developmental levels. What the patient brings to analysis is, in a sense, a miniature replica of the balance between the primitive and the more highly structured that is characteristic of the psychic organization of the moment. The nature of this balance determines the functional adequacy of the ego.

A psychic model which is based primarily on the concept of a structural and functional hierarchy is especially useful in evaluating the clinical phenomena that one encounters most often in cases of severe psychopathology. Clinical interaction and theoretical elaboration are dependent upon one another; neither is meaningful without the other. Theoretical understanding causes us to study our rationale and to bring into focus problems which would have been unnoticed if one did not conceptualize beyond the simple level of observation. Regarding the therapeutic process in the context of a logically consistent theoretical system, one founded on the principle of structural hierarchies, causes us to reexamine our ideas about the necessity of modifying the therapeutic approach to patients suffering from characterological defects. Such theoretical considerations sharpen our concepts about the processes underlying the psychoanalytic method, and, as this chapter stresses, the more we learn about the psychoanalytic method, the wider is its range of application, one which includes a variety of clinical conditions at one time considered analytically inaccessible.

CHAPTER 9

Epilogue

Peter L. Giovacchini, M.D.

The examination of clinical phenomena leads to many interesting ramifications which, when viewed from an historical perspective, enables the investigator to form a dim awareness of future developments. Here we hope to indicate a direction that will extend our concepts of what is considered psychoanalytically treatable. The usual clichés of fragile ego, shaky defenses, psychotic core, among others, need to be seen in another perspective, primarily an ego-psychological one. What have been considered contraindications could be the most important factors that, in some instances, make analysis mandatory.

What is being proposed may, at first, seem to upset and contradict well-established principles. This is certainly not our purpose; the fundamental tenets of psychoanalysis, I believe, are strengthened rather than modified or undermined by our study of characterological problems. In fact, the thesis of this book emphasizes the use of the classical approach instead of introducing changes that are purportedly necessary because this group of patients may "decompensate" if analysis is attempted. Here, the theoretical basis of the psychoanalytic process has to be understood in the context of an ego-psychological focus.

In the classroom, the student may complain that principles, as those discussed here, are the antithesis of everything they have been taught. Even though this is an overstatement, the fact that they are confused is obvious. They feel the same way I once did when at a psychoanalytic meeting the author presented his thesis in a logically sound, convincing fashion. The formal discussant then proceeded to present an opposite hypothesis in an equally coherent rational fashion, so at the end of the evening I had the feeling they were both correct.

Returning to our hypotheses, we can understand that a person who has been taught the distinctions between the transference and narcissistic neuroses and the therapeutic limitations of the latter might feel that we are being iconoclastic, at least from a theoretical perspective. Our residents show their discomfort when faced with a dilemma that overstrains their tolerance for ambiguity.

Such ambiguities, however, are not uncommon as scientific investigation progresses. Sometimes, antithetic concepts are the outcome of the particular observational frame. Classical Newtonian concepts have been "contradicted" by both relativity physics and quantum mechanics. Physicists, especially in the earlier part of this century, found these theoretical disagreements exciting as well as perplexing. The scientific atmosphere was highly charged and characterized by enthusiasm. Ambiguity had its advantages and became an incentive for scientific progress.

The new concepts and the older physics are not mutually exclusive. It depends upon what part of the field is being examined, where in the spectrum between the infinitesmal and the infinite our attention is directed. Certain experiments indicate that light is corpuscular (matter) and others that it is a wave. Absolute time and space are concepts that are relevant to ordinary movement, whereas they do not apply to speeds that approach that of light. In spite of such incompatibilities, theoretical integrations follow which are able to include these seemingly disparate constructs and phenomena.

Here, we are proposing an extension of the psychoanalytic method to patients who, according to psychoanalytic theory, cannot be so treated. Rather than being iconoclastic, as discussed above, such a proposal may cause one to feel that we are being more Catholic than the Pope, or it has been thought of as representing a reactionary position opposed to innovation and experimentation with new treatment approaches. But to use the psychoanalytic method where it has been previously believed to be inapplicable, in itself represents an advance. Since this procedure would be in conflict with the existing theory, then theoretical modifications and integrations are required. Ego psychology furnishes us with an observational approach that is particularly pertinent to the study of patients with characterological problems, whereas concentration upon the id and psychodynamic factors has greater explanatory significance for the psychoneuroses. Each approach complements the other, and the inclusion of character structure and ego mechanisms as well as conflictful forces between the ego and the id adds dimensions to our concepts of psychopathology that cause us to extend our concepts about the applicability, as well as the theoretical basis, of the psychoanalytic process.

Psychoanalysis is ready for an examination of its theoretical edifice. There is no danger that basic foundations will have to be rebuilt. Freud was too deterministically minded and too skillful a scientist to rest his system on flimsy assumptions based upon ad hoc reasoning. Revisions of later accretions, however, have been formulated gradually during the last fifty years, the main revisionist being Freud himself.

If students can be faced with contradictory statements which seem to have considerable merit, then we should recognize that we are living in exciting times. There is no harm in being confused as long as we are not dismayed. The interest that has been shown in the ideas in this book indicates that there are many analysts who share our enthusiasm, not necessarily accepting our ideas in toto, but agreeing that there are questions to be asked and problems to be delved into. The subject of the treatment of characterological and schizophrenic disorders is far from closed.

As Boyer and I have emphasized, a phenomenological approach to clinical problems limits one's appraisal of therapeutic possibilities. When Freud concentrated on intrapsychic processes rather than upon nosological classifications, he was more optimistic about the efficacy of the psychoanalytic procedure. General psychiatry had erected diagnostic categories, systems of classification, that were based almost exclusively on observable behavior and the patient's mental status. Freud's unique contribution was to understand the purpose of the patient's behavior in terms of unconscious motivation rather than simply categorizing. As a consequence, he was able logically to extend his formulations to a theoretically plausible treatment method. Although diagnosis was only of minor importance, Freud later believed that his method was especially suited for the psychoneuroses, the transference neuroses, which he distinguished from the narcissistic neuroses, a group that included the psychoses and patients that today have been referred to as character disorders.

If the difference between the transference neuroses and the narcissistic neuroses is that the latter do not form transferences either when psychoanalytic treatment is attempted or in their mode of relating to objects in general then such a distinction is not valid. Many analysts have reported and documented intense transferences in psychotic and borderline states, patients that would be definitely considered to be examples of narcissistic neuroses. If the existence of transference is to be the criterion that separates these two groups, then there is no advantage in designating one group the narcissistic neuroses. These patients may have unique types of transferences, but this does not vitiate against the possibility that their transference neuroses or psychoses can eventually be resolved. The concept of transference also has to be clarified (see below).

The contributors to this book have found that most of their patients have had characterological problems and did not fit the psychodynamic mold of the psychoneuroses as described in the early literature. True, their problems could be viewed from a psychodynamic perspective but, as reviewed in previous chapters, their difficulties could best be understood in terms of ego defects involving the identity sense and perceptual and executive ego systems. Insofar as we seldom saw a patient who could be formulated in terms similar to those outlined by Freud, the question as to whether the "classical" psychoneurotic patient existed or just how frequently one encountered such a patient had to be asked. Frequently, the course of therapy reveals that what seems to be a psychoneurosis primarily based upon an oedipal conflict masks underlying primitive pregenital problems and ego defects. One cannot come to any definite conclusions but this book raises the question as to whether psychopathology has been modified, perhaps because of cultural changes, or whether our further understanding of transference phenomena, because of insights gained from the structural theory and ego psychology, has enabled us to see aspects of psychopathology that were not previously apparent.

Our initial chapters (Boyer) are clinical, but the interplay of a structural theoretical approach, an ego-psychological perspective, and the patient's behavior is constantly stressed. The model that is worked out later is one that emphasizes a hierarchically ordered psychic apparatus.

In order to stress structural differentiation, I have constructed a model, purely for classroom exposition, called the "cylinder" model. The geometric figure of the cylinder is apt because it is three dimensional and one can view a psychic state in terms of both breadth and depth.

As many others have stressed, the organism can be conceptualized as consisting of numerous levels beginning roughly with the molecular and after traversing through various physiological systems of increasing complexity (biochemical, cellular, hormonal, organ,

organ system, etc.) finally merging with psychological systems. The latter are our primary interest and can also be arranged in an order of increasing complexity, one end of the spectrum consisting of a relatively undifferentiated id and the other end containing various ego systems that are involved in reality-attuned, secondary-process appraisal and behavior, which may include consciousness. The bottom part of the cylinder represents the undifferentiated (psychologically) end of our spectrum whereas the uppermost part refers to integrative and synthetic ego functions, both perceptual and motor. The only reason for viewing what is essentially a serial hierarchy as a cylinder is that one can vary its height and width, emphasizing that any psychic element has varying degrees of primary- and secondary-process elements. For example, a psychic state may be characterized by a preponderance of primary process, the upper part of the cylinder being relatively small. This would, of course, represent psychopathology, whereas a cylinder where there is a minimum of primary-process elements may represent a well-functioning ego but possibly a constricted one. Defenses also have relative amounts of primary- and secondary-process operations.

In Figure II one might be describing a person who has a rigid hold on reality but no flexibility. He has strong restrictions that are the outcome of intense repression and a lack of primary-process mobility. Figure I might depict a schizophrenic patient or a person who has regressed and decompensated. A well-functioning, expansive, flexible psyche is characterized by a balance of primary-process and secondary-process forces. In terms of the cylinder, it would be longer and wider and

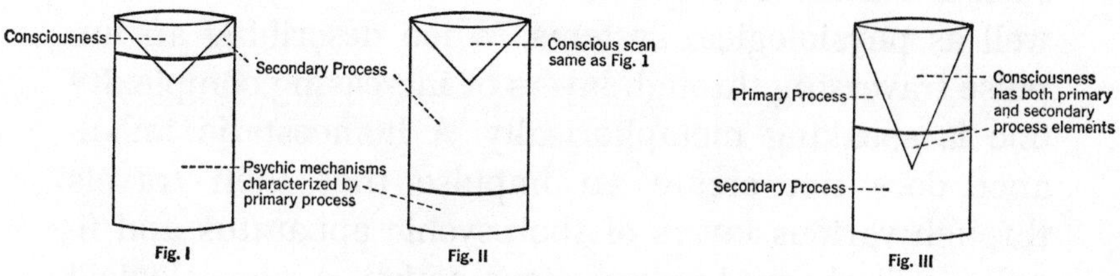

the span of consciousness would plunge deeper (Figure III).

Any psychic element can be considered in terms of such a structural and functional hierarchy. Ego states, drives, as well as the patient's behavior and associations, can be examined from the viewpoint of this model.

By stressing a structural hierarchy, the hydrodynamic energy theory and the concept of discharge are not needed when describing the satisfaction of an instinctual need. Needs traverse the psyche from the bottom of the cylinder to the uppermost layers. In so doing they acquire greater structure as they gain further psychological components and mental representation. Needs, therefore, can also be thought of in terms of a structural hierarchy and containing varying degrees of development. Chapter Six discussed the development spectrum of dependent needs and how a particular ego state requires a characteristic mode of gratification.

The organism, because of an anabolic-metabolic rythymicity, as well as external stimuli, becomes aware of a homeostatic disturbance which affects various physiological systems. The cylinder model, which adapts itself to a stimulus-response sequence, can depict such a homeostatic disturbance as affecting psychic as well as physiological systems. When describing an impulse traversing through layers of increasing complexity one is speaking metaphorically. A homeostatic imbalance does not create an impulse that then travels through various layers of the psychic apparatus and finally is discharged in conscious action. A physiological imbalance sets off a variety of responses that also impinge on sensory systems, causing conscious awareness and responses by the ego's integrative, synthetic, and executive systems. In other words, such a need makes itself felt at all levels from the physiological to the psychological. Any psychic construct can be looked upon from different frames of reference from the molecular, so to speak, to psychological approaches. The latter can be further subdivided and a person's behavior, free associations, symptoms, general adaptation, and the like, can be considered in terms of its id component or its ego factor. Within the ego sphere, defensive, integrative, and adaptive mechanisms might be stressed. None of these approaches are mutually exclusive; the clinician may choose to focus upon one particular level because he believes it will lead to therapeutic benefit. On another occasion he may find it necessary to focus upon a different level as there are shifts in the transference neurosis and the ego state.

With severe psychopathology, as the cylinder model depicts, a psychic element may have led primarily to the activation of the primitive aspects of the mental apparatus and not have involved the so-called higher ego systems. In characterological disorders and schizophrenic states these systems are only minimally developed and the range of development of any psychic element, including instinctual needs, is narrow and constricted. There are limitations of structural and functional differentiation in these clinical entities.

Terms such as "primitive and advanced" or "higher and lower" are imprecise and used loosely. There are, nevertheless, some advantages in considering the psychic apparatus as containing primitive elements that are contrasted to reality-attuned secondary-process mechanisms. The former refer to structures and function that are characteristic of early developmental phases although in the neuroses and psychoses they have become pathologically distorted. Similarly, in the somatic sphere some systems, based on embryological development and function, are considered as being less differentiated from certain highly specialized groups of cells, for example, such as found in the central nervous system. However, the observational frame, the molecular, biochemical, physiological or psychological, does not, in itself, imply a hierarchy. There is nothing more primitive in viewing the organism's reactions in terms of cellular changes than in terms of the ego's adaptive mechanisms. What is being observed may, on the other hand, be at a different level (higher or lower) from content scrutinized in another observational frame.

Returning to clinical problems, the patient's maladaptations reflect characterological problems when the psychic apparatus is seen in terms of the above model, insofar as it stresses a structural and functional hierarchy. Boyer (Chapter Three) quotes various authors who have reviewed Freud's cases and other patients who have been considered from a psychodynamic viewpoint and who, as discussed above, have been found to be narcissistically fixated and, at times, phenomenologically psychotic. In fact, some British analysts believe that most if not all psychopathology has to be explained in terms of a basic psychotic core, neurotic defenses being only a surface superstructure.

The above may be an overstatement but overstatements tempered with moderation can sometimes have merit. Rather than making sweeping generalizations about clinical entities, it might be prudent to study our patients without preconceived judgments about psychopathology. This also means that we must not take for granted that the patient's problem is a regression from a primarily oedipal conflict. The psychodynamic approach continues to be valuable but the ego apparatus has to be also included in our appraisal (a characterological approach).

Regardless of our ultimate conclusions about psychopathology the pragmatic question about treatability inevitably arises. Can we reconcile our theoretical formulations about characterological defects with metapsychological aspects of the treatment process? Several chapters in this book express the opinion that we can and this question is discussed from various perspectives.

Any discussion of treatability must review the concept of transference. Freud's recognition of transference phenomena was undoubtedly one of the most significant and valuable discoveries about the psychotherapeutic interaction. Transference occurs in many object relationships but in psychoanalysis it is our point of greatest resistance and yet our most powerful therapeutic tool. Therefore, the transference reaction has to be examined further in patients suffering from characterological and schizophrenic disorders over and above the question as to whether it does or does not occur.

If the transference neurosis is defined as the projection of impulses characteristic of the oedipal phase onto the analyst, then the cases discussed here obviously do not form transference neuroses. Similarly, if the concept of transference requires that intrapsychic elements are exclusively projected onto the analyst, our patients do not fulfill this condition either.

Freud and his early followers considered transference as the projection of an infantile imago. Granted that it may be advisable to distinguish between transference, transference neurosis, and transference reaction, our concern now is whether some relationship toward the analyst exists and whether it can become therapeutically useful.

The patient's early object relationships are important determinants regarding the establishment and the course of the relationship with the analyst. The study of object relations are an aspect of ego psychology that has led to valuable insights about psychopathology as well as emotional development.

Since the formulation of the structural theory there has been a tendency to put the external nurturing source in its proper place, developmentally and defensively. The external object and its internal representation is not in early stages of emotional development perceived in its totality, that is, as a whole object. Most psychoanalysts accept the thesis that there is a gradual progression from viewing objects as part objects to whole objects.

If transference is defined as the projection of an

archaic imago then one is referring to the projection of a part object. Freud also drew a continuum of object relations from autoerotic preobject states to narcissistic object choices and finally to relationships with external objects.

The schizophrenic patient is narcissistically fixated. Consequently one would expect him, in treatment or with persons in general, to relate to objects on the basis of a narcissistic object choice. Can a narcissistic object choice lead to a therapeutically useful transference relationship?

Some analysts believe that a patient who relates to the outer world primarily on a narcissistic basis does not form transference relationships. But, the concept of the archaic imago does not restrict how archaic the imago might be. If the patient relates to the analyst as if the latter were an extension of himself this still represents the projection of a primitive self-representation, which consists of introjects of early objects, usually destructive, assaultive part objects. In addition to the projection of these early self-object fusions there have been innumerable revisions of these introjects due to later experiences and relationships that are also projected.

The narcissistic transference relationship involves a fusion of the patient with the analyst which can strengthen delusions of omnipotence or, if the patient is able to differentiate himself from what he has projected onto the analyst, he may be able to synthesize fragmented parts of the self, parts that had not achieved cohesiveness and unity because of nonfunctional, destructive introjects. The latter are impediments to psychic development which when projected onto the analyst may permit the release of a previously submerged developmental potential. Of course, there are many factors that contribute to therapeutic integration. For the moment, the point is being stressed that the projection of archaic part objects may lead to a therapeutically useful transference relationship.

Some analysts believe that transference reactions have to be directed exclusively toward the analyst. If the patient projects elsewhere, then one does not have an analytic relationship. The neurotic conflicts with the outer world are replaced by a transference neurosis where the analyst becomes the recipient of infantile impulses. Other persons become less important and the patient's problems are fairly well contained in the consulting room. If he expresses his conflicts in his everyday life, he is acting out and being resistant to analysis.

The exclusive projection of infantile impulses onto the analyst represents an ideal therapeutic situation, one that never occurs initially in patients suffering from characterological defects. I doubt that it occurs spontaneously with any patient. Insofar as transference for patients suffering from severe psychopathology consists of the reliving of part-object relationships, it is plausible that they fragment their object relationships. Different feelings are not directed toward one object since the regression that is further stimulated by analysis leads to an ego state that has not fully attained the capacity to experience diverse feelings toward the same object. The patient's psychopathology is manifested in object relationships which are, in some instances, not sufficiently structured to achieve the synthesis that is the outcome of ambivalence. When the patient is able to project both sides of the conflict onto the same person he has made considerable progress. However, one cannot expect the patient to behave in a fashion that is beyond his emotional capacity. Such behavior is a goal of treatment and not a precondition.

The inability to relate to persons as whole objects and the fragmentation of the transference has been considered a contraindication to analysis. Therapy is designed to support defenses and is supposed to have an educative influence. Frequently, however, the therapist moralizes against symptoms, exhorting the patient to give them up. The fact that they have adaptive significance and are of value to the patient seems to be ignored. Similarly, transference is not allowed to unfold spontaneously. The therapist encourages the patient to repress the negative transference. The projection of destructive introjects onto the therapist is implicitly discouraged.

We have stressed the complications that often occur when the therapist's desire to support defenses is misconstrued as omnipotence by the patient. Unimpeded transference often assigns omnipotence to the analyst; to attempt to support the patient may reinforce this spontaneous tendency and lead to ego disruption. The negative transference, on the other hand, can also cause considerable discomfort and provoke unpleasant countertransference attitudes.

Manipulation by the therapist distorts the transference insofar as deliberate role-playing cathects infantile imagos that would probably not have been projected without the analyst's intervention. Mirrorlike anonymity, for the patients as sensitive as those described here, can be misconstrued as rejection and coldness and create a tense and inhibited atmosphere. Where does one draw the line? Can the analyst be comfortable and natural and still not intrude his personality so that the transference can spontaneously develop?

There is no clear-cut answer to this question. The individual style and personality of the analyst is important and years of experience with patients as well as other factors "teach" the analyst to be comfortable with his patients. The analyst, of course, has to be comfortable in his role as analyst. He is dedicated to analysis and all of his conduct is guided by an analytic intent which is conveyed to the patient from the first interview. Eventually, a situation of nonanxious calm occurs, one which fosters introspection and understanding.

Again one can not outline precisely how this self-observational attitude is fostered. The patient's regressed ego often reverts to primitive modes of adaptation. Introjection as well as projection are characteristic techniques of early developmental phases, phases that are relived in the transference relationship. Insofar as destructive introjects can be projected onto the therapist, the ego becomes relatively unimpeded in the introjection of new imagos. During the course of analysis (usually very early) the patient perceives the analyst's nonanxious observational attitude. Even though regressed, he is able to some extent to incorporate this attitude and establish what I have referred to as the *analytic introject.* This is similar to such recent concepts as the therapeutic or working alliance, but I prefer emphasizing the structural and object relationship qualities of the analytic interaction. An alliance also refers to object relationships, but besides interpersonal factors, the concept of an introject has advantages. The formation of such an introject is a continuing process and its "absorption" (internalization) into perceptual, integrative, and even executive systems is the outcome of successful analysis. There is an analytic progression from superficial imitation of the analytic attitude to the discrete formation of an analytic introject and finally to the amalgamation of an introspective, self-observing, understanding attitude into all ego systems. The latter extends the patient's perceptual sensitivities and his object relationships may become warmer and empathic.

Analytic intent is conveyed to the patient, and a person suffering from characterological problems gains considerable reassurance to have someone whose exclusive interest is focused upon him. As long as the analyst maintains his analytic intent, the fact that he is a human being in other respects, too, will not interfere with the course of analysis. The question of mirrorlike anonymity is not relevant. The analyst can reveal many aspects of his personality because not to do so would create an artificially strained atmosphere. From the analyst's viewpoint mirrorlike anonymity would be role-playing and would constrict his analytic mobility. As long as his "analytic personality" is dominant, other aspects of his emotional makeup will not interfere with his availability for transference projection.

Freud provides us with an excellent example of where he related to his patient (Rat Man) in a nonanalytic fashion, and yet this did not seriously interfere with the course of analysis. Dr. Jerome Beigler, at a seminar, called our attention to Freud's therapy notes on the Rat Man. On one occasion his patient began his session by telling Freud that he was hungry, whereupon Freud gave him something to eat. The ensuing discussion was lively and opinions were divided. Some believed that Freud introduced a parameter, stepping out of the analytic role by attempting to gratify his patient's wishes. The next few treatment hours were characterized by omnipotence; some of the group maintained this was an artifact stimulated by Freud's response, which caused the patient to believe in the omnipotence of his wishes. Even though the patient had such an omnipotent attitude about himself anyway, Freud's response supposedly brought it to the surface prematurely, before it could be subjected to analytic integration.

Other members of the group had different ideas. For Freud not to feed a hungry man would have been out of character. Those of the group more familiar with the middle-European attitude about eating pointed out that it is quite natural to offer food, a small courtesy that is not particularly meaningful. Their final conclusion was that as long as Freud had no therapeutic purpose in feeding his patient then it would not interfere with the course of analysis. He was not role-playing and, therefore, he could keep separate one aspect of his personality from his analytic intent.

I do not know which of the points made at this seminar is more correct. However, the latter principle is apt and applicable especially to the treatment of patients suffering from severe psychopathology. Insofar as their egos are not well structured and their sense of discrimination poorly developed, they have difficulty in that they confuse the multiple facets of the analyst's personality with each other. A well-developed ego, because of its better ability to differentiate, would be less apt to confuse the analyst as analyst with other levels of his personality. This leads us to formulate one of the antithetical conclusions mentioned at the beginning of this chapter. Patients suffering from characterological and schizophrenic disorders, if in any way therapeutically accessible, cannot tolerate a *nonanalytic* approach. To deviate from analysis may cause complications that vitiate against the possibility of progressive character change. This does not mean that there are not many nonanalytic therapeutic interactions where the patient has benefited considerably. In these instances, there may be symptomatic improvement and the patient, to a large measure, may become socially rehabilitated. However, there is seldom much character change and the patient-therapist relationship sometimes is maintained on the basis of a delusional belief in the therapist's omnipotence. Such a relationship may be stabilizing but it is also precarious. Stepping outside of the analytic role in this group of patients is a frequent source of decompensation. Many suicides have occurred because the analyst in his eagerness (and anxiety) to save and rescue the patient has unwittingly promised the patient omnipotence, a promise which eventually led to bitter disappointment, a repetition of innumerable childhood traumas.

The traumatic aspects of the past are reflected in the transference and, as they become the dominant transference theme, the therapist may lose sight of the fact that he is dealing with transference phenomena. Some patients need to construct a personal universe that is similar to the frustrating, traumatic one of childhood. This need is defensive and may contain masochistic elements but it is also vital for the total equilibrium. All defensives, to some extent, require some aspect of the environment that supports their defenses. There has to be some ego–outer world syntonicity to maintain the defense. What is being described is different in that the need for general psychic equilibrium goes beyond being congruent with a relatively structured defense such as masochism. The patient externalizes adaptive mechanisms and requires an outer world that he has learned to cope with. He does not have adjustive techniques that can deal with a relatively benign nonfrustrating world. All he has known is a depriving assaultive environment and he has learned to survive at a primitive level that is in resonance with such surroundings.

This constellation has to be recognized especially because of its implications for the transference. The patient attempts to convert the analyst into the same frustrating environment he knew in childhood. Can this be considered transference? Anna Freud distinguishes between this process, which is called externalization, and transference.

I believe two points have to be briefly clarified: (1) the relationship between externalization and the defensive mechanism of projection, and (2) the above question regarding the distinction between this process and transference. Concerning projection, one usually limits this mechanism to attributing impulses, affects, and some aspects of psychic structure such as self and object representations to some external objects. Externalization is distinguished in that it is considered to be the projection of psychic mechanisms such as the controlling aspects of the superego, the patient constructing a critical prohibitive environment. Similarly, if an important adjustive mode is repression the patient may attempt to relate to repressive segments of his environment. These distinctions become important as we examine the concept of transference. If the environment has to be constructed in a particular fashion so the ego can maintain itself, it is not surprising that the patient would attempt to convert the analytic situation into a familiar one with which he can cope. Making the analyst into a replica of the early environment and the projection of archaic imagos are related activities. An object, whether part or whole, internal or external, is never an isolated entity; it is always in an environmental context. When the child introjects he not only internalizes a person but he also incorporates the setting that is characteristic of the object. Conversely, when later in life the object is projected onto the analyst, the setting is an important aspect of this projection. There is no advantage in designating the projection of the object artificially separated from its setting as transference. The internal object in its adaptive or disruptive setting is a fundamental mechanism that determines the ego's adjustment. The object *plus* the setting constitutes a gestalt that is projected onto the therapist. In the character disorders the fact that the assaultive setting is emphasized rather than a discrete object does not require that we modify our views about transference. Somewhere in the setting one will eventually find an archaic imago, which in schizophrenic patients is often represented as an environmental element, such as water, sun, the wind, storms, and the like. In any case, as long as we view all of the patient's reactions as transference, the therapist continues the analytic interaction.

The above implies that, among other factors, *transference is a point of view.* All of the patient's productions contain transference elements or defenses against these elements. Any relationship as previously discussed can be understood in terms of a structural hierarchy. The perceptual system, as well as other ego systems, functions on the basis of a broad spectrum with admixtures of primary- and secondary-process types of operation. Its range of perception includes viewing external objects in a reality-oriented coherent fashion with an accurate appraisal of their role in a contemporary setting, to distorted impressions based upon a confusion with objects of the infantile past. These distortions are the essence of transference. Insofar as introjects affect the functioning of all ego systems, including perception, some aspect of our impressions about contemporary persons will be determined by these early introjects. The archaic imago will cause distortions of what we perceive and then will also contribute to our reactions to the external world. The contribution, both perceptual and motor, may be minimal. It may also apply to other persons beside the analyst. Nevertheless, in all behavior, there is a transference element.

The analyst orients himself around these transference elements no matter how minimal or diffuse they may be. By constantly relating to how the patient's mind works, by being dedicated to understanding what is going on inside the patient, the analyst is fostering the development of transference. The analytic situation, because of its constant reliability, is conducive to regression. The regressed ego is less structured and infantile introjects become highly cathected. Consequently, in a sense, the analyst has helped create the transference. Minimal transference elements receive impetus from regression and the analyst's fostering of introspection. The patient's relationship to the therapist may at first contain only a small "percentage" of transference but the analyst's integrative interpretations lead to the further cathexis of archaic imagos. Insofar as the analyst becomes partially identified with the primitive the patient tends to displace feelings directed toward these imagos onto him. If the analyst, for the purpose of the treatment, chooses to see some transference in all of the patient's productions, he becomes representative of an approach that attempts to understand transference implications of behavior. The analysand eventually identifies with this attitude and examines his distorted feelings toward the analyst. What was previously a minimal transference element, by shifting one's focus and identifying with the analyst's attitude, now becomes the predominant theme.

Of course, the analyst has not "caused" transference but he has created a setting where it can develop. The spontaneous unfolding of the transference is not necessarily spontaneous; the analyst has to foster its development by not doing anything to interfere. This sounds like a tautology, but there are many subtle interactions between patient and therapist where the analyst unwittingly has shifted his interest from understanding how the patient's mind works to telling him how to run his life, that is, shifting from exploring the expectations of and conflicts about the analyst-introject fusion to the assumption of a role that is identical to the introject's. Not to interfere by trying to manage the patient's life is hard work and demands analytic skill.

In the final chapters of this book, there is considerable discussion about the therapeutic benefits derived from the recognition of the intrapsychic origin of behavior and its adaptive qualities. How does the analytic interaction lead to ego development? How does the projection of archaic imagos onto the therapist benefit the patient?

To some extent these questions were considered when the therapeutic process underlying interpretation was discussed (Chapter Six). The superimposition of the analyst's secondary process onto the patient's primary process leads to structure and ego expansion. There are, however, many subtle factors to the analytic interaction that make this topic inexhaustible.

The aim of analytic treatment is achieved by interpreting the transference. Once the patient recognizes how intrapsychic forces have led him to distort his perception of the analyst he is in a better position to evaluate and respond to the tasks that are imposed upon him by the external world and inner needs.

The patient, in the process of transference resolution, develops the capacity to recognize that he has projected archaic imagos. Since these imagos and the conflicts attached to them are now, in a sense, outside of himself, he is better able to examine them. The transference projection creates distance and, as the patient recognizes that he has constructed his picture of the analyst on the basis of feelings within himself, his capacity for objectivity increases. It is much more difficult to perceive and appraise feelings and situations when one is close to them. Putting psychic elements into the analyst furnishes the patient with a repository for his feelings and in a sense he has "stepped outside of himself." This is not the same situation as a frightening dissociation but instead represents an integrative experience.

Objectivity is enhanced by the analyst's participation. An ego that has projected destructive introjects is partially relieved of some pressures. Early traumatic object relationships cause ego fixation. The traumatized ego introjects disruptive and depriving experiences and is unable to incorporate subsequent experiences that have an adaptive potential. With the projection of nonadaptive constricting introjects, the ego gains some ability to incorporate aspects of the analyst's secondary process. The archaic imagos within himself interfere with acquiring what is essentially a learning experience; attributing the disruptive qualities of these early experiences to the analyst lessen their effect upon the patient since their projection causes a partial decathexis of their representation within the patient. Consequently, the recognition that he has projected and the fact that he is able to examine the content of his projection allows the patient to integrate the analyst's secondary process and to use it, in a positive feedback sequence, for further evaluation of the projected introjects. The progressive decathexis of the archaic imagos that follows releases the previously repressed developmental drive and further synthesis and integration is achieved.

There are other reasons why it is adaptive to project inner disturbing forces onto the analyst. Since these early relationships were experienced as assaultive and destructive their internal representations are considered dangerous, and the ego has to expend enormous quantities of energy to defend itself against them. The ego's balance is precarious because it is the victim of self-destructive forces. To project these feelings onto the analyst gives the patient some protection and some of the energy used for countercathexis becomes available for integration and the incorporation of positive experiences.

Patients with characterological and schizophrenic

disorders frequently look around to see if the analyst is still alive. They are often very sensitive to what seems to be a rejection and abandonment by the analyst, but analysis reveals they are also concerned about having killed the analyst. They are frightened that the analyst will not be able to survive their projection.

Insofar as the analyst is able to survive the projection, he is "stronger" than the dangerous introjects. What had previously been self-destructive impulses, because of the transference projection, are now destructive impulses toward the analyst. They are manifested as negative transference. The patient gains considerable security in that he no longer feels as threatened and, since the analyst is not destroyed, the patient no longer believes that his hostility is overwhelming and uncontrollable. The analysis of the negative transference for patients suffering from severe psychopathology is invaluable and gives the patient considerable support.

The thesis stressed throughout this book is that support is an intrinsic aspect of the psychoanalytic process and one need not introduce extra-analytic procedures in order to give the patient sufficient stability so that therapy can proceed. The unfolding of the transference and the analyst's observing orientation can become very important stabilizing experiences.

The process of projecting and externalizing and then discussing the adaptive value of projecting as well as identifying the conflicts attached to the archaic imagos shift the patient's orientation from one of experiencing and suffering to observation. The analyst makes himself available for the patient's projections and finds them fascinating instead of dangerous and repulsive. For example, a young schizophrenic patient constantly talked about killing himself. From a superficial viewpoint such a preoccupation was ununderstandable. Realistically, he has everything to live for; he is personable, bright, and wealthy, so there is no rational reason why he should want to commit suicide. The fact that he wanted to and the further puzzling feeling that he was somehow going to please me by killing himself presented me with an extremely interesting enigma. Rather than responding directly to the content of the material, I found myself absorbed by it. I saw it as a phenomenon which demanded understanding which could be supplied only by learning about the unconscious intrapsychic factors underlying this impulse. Its adaptational value was also kept in mind. The patient soon realized that I was not dismayed but interested in examining valuable material and he gradually developed the same attitude about his feelings that I had. He also became very curious as to why he felt the way he did and together we were able to examine his impulses. He had succeeded in shifting from the position of being a helpless victim of his feelings to an observational frame of reference. He now shared my enthusiasm for examination and the transference projection became the central focus of our attention. That I should be pleased by his death became the riddle that required explanation, and soon the projected introjects underlying this feeling became apparent.

The development of the self-observing attitude parallels the decathexis of internal disruptive forces. These processes are the essence of working through which results in an ego that has gained greater structure and has considerable free energy in store to master the problems of everyday living. The decathected internal representations of the projected imagos become fragmented and cease to exist as discrete entities that provoke defensive reactions and energy expenditure. Instead they become relatively harmless and less painful memories that are no longer pathologically operational (at least much less so). It is as if the introjects were "dissolved" into the ego, being able to maintain their destructiveness only when they have discrete boundaries. A depressed patient graphically illustrated this process in a dream. Throughout the years he would be plagued by many dreams where his dead father appeared, always in a threatening frightening context. After several years of analysis, he dreamed of the resolution of this conflict. As usual, his father appeared in the dream looking very much as he did during the patient's childhood. He did not, in contrast to earlier dreams, appear threatening. Instead he had a shadowy filmy quality which when viewed from a certain angle reminded him of my "shadelike" presence. Then his father literally broke up into innumerable small fragments and as an entity disappeared. The patient, even during the dream, felt that an enormous weight pressing on him had been lifted and from the time of the dream he no longer felt depressed. He reported feeling energetic in contrast to his previous lassitude.

The energy required to maintain the introject was now available for other purposes. A nonfunctioning introject becomes an adaptive technique that is amalgamated into the ego and is incorporated by various ego systems.

In therapy, changes do not occur abruptly. Prior to reporting the above dream the patient had been working on his problem as it was relived in the transference. The dream was a manifestation of years of analytic work.

A final theme of this book focuses upon the analyst's emotional orientation. Analysis is a two-person relationship and the analyst's participation from the viewpoint of his psyche also has to be investigated. Countertransference elements have been frequently discussed in recent years but other elements of the analyst's psyche, while he is analyzing, have not received much attention. An ego psychology of the analyst's psychic operations as the transference neurosis unfolds is an essential aspect of the conceptual model underlying the therapeutic process. As the analyst "dips" into his primary process, the effects of both current and past reality have to be weighed. The mobility required for free-floating fantasy is often hampered by a concentration on secondary-process factors, as when assuming an educational role.

Patients are more or less educable. The analyst may point out and correct distortions. In some instances, he may provide the patient with information he did not previously possess. Possibly what the analyst has "taught" the patient may be useful.

Some analysts are not content with the role of educator per se. This may be a question of different styles which reflects the therapist's personal orientation. Nevertheless, many analysts feel more comfortable if the analytic role is confined to correcting distortions by interpreting their inner source. This can be educative insofar as the patient is then able to synthesize previously unavailable psychic elements and has expanded his armamentarium of adjustive techniques. To learn directly from the therapist may cause the patient to correct bad habits in a parrotlike fashion but his ego has not gained new structure.

There are parallel reactions in the analyst's psyche.

Analytic activity is fulfilling when it is a creative experience. The patient gains accretions to his ego but the analyst's ego also gains. Every creative endeavor leads to an ego expansion, although the psychic levels that are further structuralized in the patient are different from the levels of the analyst's psychic apparatus that undergo expansion. The former involve the acquisition of basic adjustive techniques whereas hopefully the analyst effects an aesthetic synthesis as he attains the standards of his ego ideal.

The analytic experience is beneficial to both the patient and the analyst. The patient, if analysis is successful, achieves autonomy. Relatively speaking, he is better able to choose how he will relate to both inner and outer pressures, whereas previously he had no choice because of constrictive introjects. The analyst gains an increasing respect for the fascinating and subtle operations of the unconscious. He learns with each case that the patient is a human being worthy of study, a scientific but not cold and detached attitude. He does not feel hopeless even though the patient may at first. Underneath the chaos and turmoil, the analyst discovers a developmental core that must not be impinged upon. Every patient increases the analyst's confidence in the psychoanalytic process, which is reflected in his therapeutic attitude of calm optimism. By not reacting to the patient with sorrow and pity, he is not degrading him; rather his interest and desire to analyze enhances the patient's dignity. The analyst by not interfering with the development of the patient's autonomy is also enhancing his own. The analysis of cases suffering from characterological and schizophrenic disorders is a profound and moving experience for both participants.

Bibliography

Abadi, Mauricio 1954. "Consideraciones psicoanalíticas acerca de algunos aspectos de una psicosis con amaurosis congénita," *Revista de Psicoanálisis*, 13 (1956), 21–40.

Abenheimer, Karl M. 1955. "Critical Observations on Fairbairn's Theory of Object Relations," *British Medical Journal*, 28 (1955), 29–41.

Abraham, Karl 1907. "On the Significance of Sexual Trauma in Childhood for the Symptomatology of Dementia Praecox," in *Clinical Papers and Essays on Psychoanalysis*. New York: Basic Books, 1955, pp. 13–20.

——— 1908. "The Psychosexual Differences Between Hysteria and Dementia Praecox," in *Selected Papers on Psycho-Analysis*. London: Hogarth Press, 1948, pp. 64–79.

——— 1913. "Restrictions and Transformations of Scoptophilia in Psycho-Neurotics, with Remarks on Analogous Phenomena in Folk-Psychology," in *Selected Papers on Psycho-Analysis*. London: Hogarth Press, 1948, pp. 169–234.

——— 1924. "A Short History of the Development of the Libido," in *Selected Papers on Psycho-Analysis*. London: Hogarth Press, 1924, pp. 418–501.

Ackerknecht, Erwin H. 1943. "Psychopathology, Primitive Medicine and Primitive Psychiatry," *Bulletin of the History of Medicine*, 14 (1943), 30–67.

Ackerman, Nathan W. 1958. "Behavioral Trends and Disturbances of the Contemporary Family," in I. Gladston (ed.), *The Family in Contemporary Society*. New York: International Universities Press, 1958, pp. 52–69.

———, and Marjorie L. Behrens 1955. "Child and Family Psychopathology: Problems of Correction," in P. H. Hock and J. Zubin (eds.), *Psychopathology of Childhood*. New York: Grune and Stratton, 1955, pp. 177–196.

Adler, Alfred 1917. *The Neurotic Constitution*. New York: Moffat, Yard and Co., 1917.

Alanen, Yrjö 1958. *The Mothers of Schizophrenic Patients: A Study of the Personality and the Mother-Child Relationship of 100 Mothers and the Significance of These Factors in the Pathogenesis of Schizophrenia.* Copenhagen: Munksgaard, 1958.

Alexander, Franz 1929. *Psychoanalysis of the Total Personality.* New York and Washington: Nervous and Mental Disease Publishing Co., 1929.

——— 1930. *The Psychoanalysis of the Total Personality.* New York and Washington: Nervous and Mental Disease Publishing Co., 1930.

——— 1930a. *The Neurotic Character in the Scope of Psychoanalysis: Selected Papers of Franz Alexander.* New York: Basic Books, 1961.

——— 1931. "Schizophrenic Psychosis: Critical Considerations of Psychoanalytic Treatment," *Archives of Neurology and Psychiatry,* 26 (1931), 815–826.

——— 1933. Book Review: "Die Psychoanalyse des Kindes," by Melanie Klein. *Psychoanalytic Quarterly,* 2 (1933), 141–152.

——— 1954. "Psychoanalysis and Psychotherapy," *Journal of the American Psychoanalytic Association,* 2 (1954), 722–733.

———, and Thomas M. French (eds.) 1948. *Studies in Psychosomatic Medicine.* New York: Ronald Press, 1948.

Alikakos, Louis C., Emanuel Starer, and William Winnich 1956. "Observations on the Meaning of Behavior of Group of Chronic Schizophrenics," *International Journal of Group Psychotherapy,* 6 (1956), 180–192.

Amendola, E., and C. Garzillo 1955. "Psichoanalisi delle Schizofrenie," *Rassegna di Neuropsichiatria,* 9 (1955), 479–496.

Arieti, Silvano 1955. *Interpretation of Schizophrenia.* New York: Brunner, 1955.

——— 1964. "Schizophrenia," *Encyclopaedia Britannica.* Chicago: Encyclopaedia Britannica, Inc., 1964, vol. 20, pp. 69–71.

Arlow, Jacob A. 1952. Discussion of Dr. Fromm-Reichmann's paper, in E. B. Brody and F. C. Redlich (eds.), *Psychotherapy with Schizophrenics: A Symposium.* New York: International Universities Press, 1952.

———, and Charles Brenner 1964. *Psychoanalytic Concepts and the Structural Theory.* New York: International Universities Press, 1964, pp. 144–178.

Astrup, Christian, Arne Fossum, and Rolf Holmboe 1962. *Prognosis in Functional Psychoses: Clinical, Social and Genetic Aspects.* Springfield, Ill.: Charles C Thomas, 1962.

Avenburg, Ricardo 1962. "Modificaciones estructurales en un paciente esquizofrénico a traves del primer mes de análisis," *Revista de Psichoanálisis,* 19 (1962), 351–365.

Azima, Haasan, and Eric D. Wittkower 1956. "Gratifications of Basic Needs in Schizophrenia," *Psychiatry,* 19 (1956), 121–129.

Bak, Robert C. 1939. "Regression of Ego-Orientation and Libido in Schizophrenia," *International Journal of Psycho-Analysis,* 20 (1939), 64–71.

——— 1941. "Temperatur-Orientierung und Überfliessen der Ichgrenzen in der Schizophrenie," *Schweizer Archiv für Neurologie, Neurochirurgie und Psychiatrie,* 46 (1941), 158–177.

——— 1943. "Dissolution of the Ego: Mannerism and Delusion of

Grandeur," *Journal of Nervous and Mental Disease*, 98 (1943), 457–464.

——— 1954. "The Schizophrenic Defense Against Aggression," *International Journal of Psycho-Analysis*, 35 (1954), 129–134.

Balint, Michael 1957. *Problems of Human Pleasure and Behavior*. London: Hogarth Press, 1957.

——— 1959. *Thrills and Regressions*. London: Hogarth Press, 1959.

Barkas, Mary 1925. "The Treatment of Psychotic Patients in Institutions in the Light of Psychoanalysis," *Journal of Neurology and Psychopathology*, 5 (1925), 333–340.

Bash, Kenower W. 1957. "Descensus ad infernos. Aus der Analyse eines Falles von Schizophrenic mit katamnestischen Angaben," *Psyche* (Heidelberg), 11 (1957), 505–525.

Bateson, Gregory 1960. "Minimal Requirements for a Theory of Schizophrenia," *Archives of General Psychology*, 2 (1960), 477–491.

———, and Margaret Mead 1942. *Balinese Character: A Photographic Analysis*. New York: Special Publications of the New York Academy of Science, 1942.

Bateson, Gregory, Don D. Jackson, Jay Haley, and John Weakland 1956. "Towards a Theory of Schizophrenia," *Behavioral Science*, 1 (1956), 251–264.

Beaglehole, Ernest 1940. "Cultural Complexity and Psychological Problems," *Psychiatry*, 3 (1940), 330–332.

Bellak, Leopold 1948. *Dementia Praecox, The Past Decade's Work and Present Status. A Review and Evaluation*. New York: Grune and Stratton, 1948.

Belo, Jane 1960. *Trance in Bali*. New York: Columbia University Press, 1960.

Benedek, T. 1959. "Parenthood as a Developmental Phase," *Journal of the American Psychoanalytic Association*, 7 (1959), 3.

Benedetti, Gaetano 1955. "Il problema della conscienza nelle allucinazione degli schizoprenici," *Archivio di Psicolgia, Neurologia e Psichiatria*, 16 (1955), 287–312.

——— 1955a. "A propos de l'acces psychotherapeutique au monde du schizophrene," *Evolution psychiatrique*, 1 (1955), 145–157.

——— 1955b. "Möglichkeiten und Grenzen der Psychotherapie Schizophrener," *Bulletin der Schweizerischen Akademie der Medizinischen wissenschaften*, 11 (1955), 142–159.

Bergman, Paul 1962. "The 'Dissident Schools,'" *Psychiatry*, 25 (1962), 83–95.

———, and Sibylle K. Escalona 1949. "Unusual Sensitivities in Very Young Children," *Psychoanalytic Study of the Child*, 3–4 (1949), 333–352.

Bernfeld, Siegfried 1944. "Freud's Earliest Theories and the School of Helmholtz," *Psychoanalytic Quarterly*, 13 (1944), 341–362.

Bertshinger, H. 1911. "Process of Recovery in Schizophrenia," *Psychoanalytic Review*, 3 (1916), 176–188.

Betz, Barbara 1950. "Strategic Conditions in the Psychotherapy of Persons with Schizophrenia," *American Journal of Psychiatry*, 107 (1950), 203–215.

Bibring, Edward 1937. "On the Theory of the Results of Psycho-Analysis," *International Journal of Psycho-Analysis*, 18 (1937), 170–189.

——— 1947. "The So-Called English School of Psychoanalysis," *Psycho-Analytic Quarterly*, 16 (1947), 69–93.

Binswanger, Herbert 1954–1955. "Zur Theorie und Praxis der Psychotherapie Schizophrener." *Zeitschrift für Psycho-Somatische Medizin*, 1 (1955), 253–260.

——— 1956. "Freud's Psychosentherapie," *Psyche* (Heidelberg), 10 (1956), 357–366.

——— 1957–1958. "Die Psychiatrie und der Psychiater. "Rückblick auf der Internationalen Kongress für Psychiatrie in Zurick und Ausblick zur Psychotherapie der Schizophrenen." *Zeitschrift für Psycho-Somatische Medizin*, 4 (1958), 268–275.

Binswanger, Ludwig 1910. "Über Neuropsychosen," *Deutsche medizinische Wochenschrift*, No. 50, and *Zentralblatt für Psychoanalyse*, 1 (1911), 250.

——— 1917. "Über Commotionpsychosen und Verwandtes," *Korrespondenzblatt für schweizer Ärzte*, 42 (1917), 1–12.

——— 1945. "Zur Frage des Häufigkeit der Schizophrenie im Kindesalter," *Zeitschrift für Kinderpsychiatrie*, 12 (1945), 33–50.

——— 1947. "Studien zum Schizophrenieproblem," *Schweizer Archiv für Neurologie und Psychiatrie* (1956, 1958, 1959).

——— 1949. "Studien zum Schizophrenieproblem: der Fall Lola Voss," *Schweizer Archiv für Neurologie und Psychiatrie*, 63 (1949), 23–97.

——— 1952. "Studien zum Schizophrenieproblem: der Fall Suzanne Urban; der Fall Jean Jacques Rousseau," *Schweizer Archiv für Neurologie und Psychiatrie*, 70 (1952), 1–32.

——— 1957. *Schizophrenie*. Pfulligen, Germany: Neske, 1957.

——— 1958. "Daseinsanalyse, Psychiatrie, Schizophrenie," *Schweizer Archiv für Neurologie und Psychiatrie*, 81 (1958), 1–8.

Bion, W. R. 1954. "Note on the Theory of Schizophrenia," *International Journal of Psycho-Analysis*, 35 (1954), 113–118.

——— 1955. "Language and the Schizophrenic," in M. Klein, P. Heimann, and R. M. Money-Kyrle (eds.), *New Directions in Psycho-Analysis*. New York: Basic Books, pp. 221–239.

——— 1956. "Development of Schizophrenic Thought," *International Journal of Psycho-Analysis*, 37 (1956), 344–346.

——— 1957. "Differentiation of the Psychotic from the Non-Psychotic Personalities," *International Journal of Psycho-Analysis*, 38 (1957), 266–275.

——— 1961. *Experience in Groups*. London: Tavistock, 1961.

Birnbaum, Karl 1909. "Dementia Praecox und Wahnpsychosen der Degenerativen," *Zentralblatt für Nervenheilkunde und Psychologie*, 20 (1909), 429–433.

Bjerre, Poul C. 1911. "Zur Radikalbehandlung der Chronischen Paranoia," *Jahrbuch Psychoanalytische und Psychopathische Forschung*, 3 (1911), 795–847.

Bleuler, Eugen 1906. *Affectivity, Suggestibility, Paranoia*. Utica, N.Y.: State Hospitals Press, 1912.

——— 1911. *Dementia Praecox, or the Group of Schizophrenias*. New York: International Universities Press, 1950.

——— 1920. "Schizophrenie und psychologische Auffassungen. Zugleich ein Beispiel, wie wir in psychologischen Dingen ananeinder vorberieden," *Allgemeine Zeitschrift für Psychiatrie*, 76 (1920), 135–162.

Blum, Gerald S. 1953. *Psychoanalytic Theories of Personality*. New York: McGraw-Hill Book Co., 1953.

Boroffka, Frieda L. 1958–1959. "Bericht über die Behandlung einer schizophrenen Patientin mit psychoanalytisch orientierter Psychotherapie," *Zeitschrift für Psycho-Somatische Medizin*, 5 (1959), 182–188.

Boss, Medard 1958. "The Role of Psychotherapy in Schizophrenia," *Indian Journal of Psychiatry*, Second Series (1959), 1–12.

Böszörmenyi-Nagy, Ivan 1962. "The Concept of Schizophrenia from the Perspective of Family Treatment," *Family Process*, 1 (1962), 103–113.

Boven, William 1921. "Études sur les conditions du developpement au sein des familles, de la schizophrénie et de la folie maniaques," *Archives Suisses de Neurologie et Psychologie*, 8 (1921), 89–116.

Bowlby, John 1958. "The Nature of the Child's Tie to Its Mother," *International Journal of Psycho-Analysis*, 39 (1958), 350–373.

Boyer, L. Bryce 1955. "Christmas 'Neurosis,'" *Journal of the American Psychoanalytical Association*, 3 (1955), 467–488.

——— 1956. "On Maternal Overstimulation and Ego Defects," *Psychoanalytical Study of the Child*, 11 (1956), 236–256.

——— 1956a. "Ambulatory Schizophrenia. "Some Remarks Concerning the Diagnosis," *Kaiser Foundation Medical Bulletin*, 4 (1956), 457–459.

——— 1960. "A Hypothesis Regarding the Time of Appearance of the Dream Screen," *International Journal of Psycho-Analysis*, 41, (1960), 114–122.

——— 1961. "Provisional Evaluation of Psycho-Analysis with Few Parameters Employed in the Treatment of Schizophrenia," *International Journal of Psycho-Analysis*, 42 (1961), 389–403.

——— 1964. "Folk Psychiatry of the Apaches of the Mescalero Indian Reservation," in Ari Kiev (ed.), *Magic, Faith and Healing: Studies in Primitive Psychiatry Today*. New York: The Free Press, 1964, pp. 384–419.

——— 1964a. "Further Remarks Concerning Shamans and Shamanism," *The Israel Annals of Psychiatry and Related Disciplines*, 2 (1964), 235–257.

——— 1964b. "Psychological Problems of a Group of Apaches; Alcoholic Hallucinosis and Latent Homosexuality Among Typical Men," in W. Muensterberger and S. Axelrad (eds.), *Psycho-Analytic Study of Society*. New York: International Universities Press, 1964, vol. 3, pp. 203–277.

——— 1964c. "Office Treatment of Schizophrenic Patients: The Use of Psychoanalytic Therapy with Few Parameters," panel on Schizophrenia, West Coast Psychoanalytic Societies, September 26, 1964.

——— 1965. "Tratamiento ambulatorio de pacientes esquizofrénicos. Terapia psicoanalítica con un mínimo de parametros," *Acta Psicquiátrica y Psicologica America Latina*, 11 (1965), 147–154.

Braaty, Trygve 1954. *Fundamentals of Psychoanalytic Technique*. New York: John Wiley & Sons, 1954.

Brandschaft, Bernard 1964. "Remarks on the Psychoanalytic Treatment of Schizophrenia," paper presented before the West Coast Psychoanalytic Societies, San Diego, Calif., October, 1964.

Breuer, Joseph, and Freud, Sigmund 1895. *Studies in Hysteria.* New York: Nervous and Mental Disease Monographs, 1937.

——— 1895a. *Studies on Hysteria.* Standard Edition, Vol. II. London: Hogarth Press, 1955.

Brierley, Marjorie 1942. "'Internal Objects' and Theory," *International Journal of Psycho-Analysis,* 23 (1942), 107–112.

Brill, Abraham A. 1908. "Psychological Factors in Dementia Praecox, an Analysis," *Journal of Abnormal Psychology,* 3 (1908), 219–239.

——— 1909–1910. "A Case of Schizophrenia (Dementia Praecox)," *American Journal of Insanity,* 66 (1910), 53–70.

——— 1911. "Psychological Mechanisms of Paranoia," *New York Medical Journal,* 94 (1911), 1209–1213.

——— 1919. "Studies in Paraphrenia," *New York Medical Journal,* 110 (1919), 792–798.

——— 1925. "Schizoid and Syntonic Factors in Neuroses and Psychoses," *American Journal of Psychiatry,* 4 (1925), 589–598.

——— 1929. "Schizophrenia and Psychotherapy," *American Journal of Psychiatry,* 9 (1929), 519–542.

——— 1934. "Homoerotism and Paranoia," *American Journal of Psychiatry,* 13 (1934), 957–974.

——— 1941. "The Etiological Relationship of Trauma to Schizophrenia," *Medical Record,* 153 (1941), 159–162.

Brodey, Warren M. 1959. "Some Family Observations and Schizophrenia," *Archives of General Psychology,* 1 (1959), 379–402.

Brody, Eugene G. 1952. "The Treatment of Schizophrenia: A Review," in E. G. Brody and F. C. Redlich (eds.), *Psychotherapy With Schizophrenics.* New York: International Universities Press, 1952.

Bromberg, Walter 1954. *Man Above Humanity.* New York: Lippincott, 1954.

Brown, G. W. 1960. "Length of Hospital Stay and Schizophrenia: Review of Statistical Studies," *Acta Psychiatrica et neurologica Scandinavica,* 35 (1960), 414–430.

Brunswick, Ruth Mack 1928. "A Supplement to Freud's: *A History Of An Infantile Neurosis,*" *International Journal of Psycho-Analysis,* 9 (1928), 439–476.

Bumke, Oswals 1924. "Die Auflösung der Dementia Praecox," *Klinische Wochenschrift,* 3 (1924), 437–440.

Burnham, Donald L. 1955. "Some Problems in Communication with Schizophrenic Patients," *Journal of American Psychoanalytic Association,* 3 (1955), 67–81.

Bychowski, Gustav 1923. *Metaphysik und Schizophrenie: Eine Vergleichendpsychologische Studie.* Berlin: Karger, 1923.

——— 1928. "Über Psychotherapie der Schizophrenie," *Nervenarzt,* 1 (1928), 478–487.

——— 1932. "Über Schizophrenie mit neurologische Symptomen," *Zeitschrift für die gesamte Neurologie und Psychiatrie,* 140 (1932), 798–807.

——— 1943. "Physiology of Schizophrenic Thinking," *Journal of Nervous and Mental Disease,* 98 (1943), 368–386.

——— 1945. "Some Aspects of Shock Therapy: The Structure of Psychosis," *Journal of Nervous and Mental Disease*, 102 (1945), 338–356.

——— 1947. "The Preschizophrenic Ego," *Psychoanalytic Quarterly*, 16 (1947), 225–233.

——— 1951. "Remarks on Some Defense Mechanisms and Reaction Patterns of the Schizophrenic Ego," *Bulletin of the American Psychoanalytic Association*, 7 (1951), 141–143.

——— 1952. "Schizophrenia in the Period of Evolution," *Diseases of the Nervous System*, 13 (1952), 150–153.

——— 1952a. *Psychotherapy of Psychosis*. New York: Grune and Stratton, 1952.

——— 1953. "The Problem of Latent Psychosis," *Journal of the American Psychoanalytic Association*, 1 (1953), 484–503.

——— 1954. "On the Handling of Some Schizophrenic Mechanisms and Reaction Patterns," *International Journal of Psycho-Analysis*, 35 (1954), 147–153.

——— 1957. "From Latent to Manifest Schizophrenia," *Congress Report of the Second International Congress for Psychiatry* (Zurich), 3 (1957), 128–134.

——— 1963. "Schizophrenic Partners," in V. Eisenstein (ed.), *Neurotic Interaction in Marriage*. New York: Basic Books, 1963, pp. 135–147.

——— 1965. "Obsessive Compulsive Façade in Schizophrenia," paper presented before the 24th International Psychoanalytic Congress, Amsterdam, 1965.

Cameron, Norman 1961. "Introjection, Reprojection, and Hallucination in the Interaction between Schizophrenic Patient and Therapist," *International Journal of Psycho-Analysis*, 42 (1961).

——— 1964. "Abnormal Psychology," *Encyclopaedia Britannica*. Chicago: Encyclopaedia Britannica, Inc., 1964, vol. 18, p. 690A.

Campbell, C. Macfie 1909. "A Modern Conception of Dementia Praecox, With Five Illustrative Cases," *Review of Neurology and Psychiatry*, 7 (1909), 623–641.

——— 1912. "The Application of Psychoanalysis to Insanity," *New York Medical Journal*, 95 (1912), 1079–1081.

——— 1933. *Towards Mental Health; The Schizophrenic Problem*. Cambridge, Mass.: Harvard University Press, 1933.

——— 1935. *Destiny and Disease in Mental Disorders with Special Reference to the Schizophrenic Psychoses*. New York: Norton, 1935.

Caravedo, Baltazar 1924. "Actides regresivas en los esquizofrénicos," *Revista de psicologia* (Lima), 1924.

Cargnello, Danilo 1947. "La schizofrenia com turba della personalità," *Archivio di psicologia, neurologia e psichiatria*, 8 (1947), 333–393.

Carothers, J. C. 1948. "A Study of Mental Derangement and an Attempt to Explain Its Peculiarities," *Psychiatry*, 11 (1948), 47–86.

——— 1953. *The African Mind in Health and Disease*. Geneva: World Health Organization, 1953.

Cassity, John H. 1925. "Comments on Schizophrenia," *Journal of Nervous and Mental Disease*, 62 (1925), 477–484.

——— 1927. "The Functional Psychoses as an Evolution of Psychic Impotency," *Journal of Nervous and Mental Disease*, 66 (1927), 105–130.

Cawte, J. E. 1964. "Tjimi and Tjagolo: Ethnopsychiatry in the Kalumburu People of North-Western Australia," *Oceania*, 34 (1964), 170–190.

——— 1964a. "Australian Ethnopsychiatry in the Field: A Sampling in North Kimberly," *Medical Journal of Australia*, 1 (1964), 467–472.

——— and M. A. Kidson 1964. "Australian Ethnopsychiatry: The Walbiri Doctor," *Medical Journal of Australia*, 2 (1964), 977–983.

Chijs, A. van der 1919. "Über Halluzinationen und Psychoanalyse," *Internationale Zeitschrift für Psychoanalyse*, 5 (1919), 274–284.

Clark, L. Pierce 1919. "Some Practical Remarks Upon the Use of Modified Psychoanalysis in the Treatment of Borderline Neurosis and Psychoses," *Psychoanalytic Review*, 6 (1919), 306–308.

——— 1926. "The Phantasy Method of Analyzing Narcissistic Neuroses," *Medical Journal Record*, 123 (1926), 154–158.

——— 1933. "Narcissism as a Factor in Neuroses and Psychoses," *Medical Journal Record*, 137 (1933), 59–64.

——— 1933a. "The Question of Prognosis in Narcissistic Neuroses and Psychoses," *International Journal of Psycho-Analysis*, 14 (1933), 71–86.

——— 1933b. "Treatment of Narcissistic Neuroses and Psychoses," *Psychoanalytic Review*, 20 (1933), 304–326.

Cohen, Mabel B. 1953. "Introduction," in Harry Stack Sullivan, *The Interpersonal Theory of Psychiatry*, ed. H. S. Perry and M. K. Gawel. New York: Norton, 1953.

Cohen, Robert A. 1947. "Management of Anxiety in a Case of Schizophrenia," *Psychiatry*, 10 (1947), 143–157.

Coriat, Isadore H. 1913–1914. "Recent Trends in the Psychopathology of Dementia Praecox," *American Journal of Insanity*, 70 (1914), 669–682.

——— 1917. "The Treatment of Dementia Praecox by Psychoanalysis," *Journal of Abnormal Psychology*, 12 (1917), 326–330.

Davie, James M., and Thomas Freeman 1961. "The Non-Psychotic Residue in Schizophrenia," *British Journal of Medical Psychology*, 34 (1961), 117–127.

——— 1961a. "Disturbances of Perception and Consciousness in Schizophrenic States," *British Journal of Medical Psychology*, 34 (1961), 33–41.

deForest, Izette 1942. "The Therapeutic Technique of Sandor Ferenczi," *International Journal of Psycho-Analysis*, 23 (1942), 120–139.

Delay, Jean P. L., P. Deniker, and R. Green 1957. "Essai de description et de definition psychopathologique des parents des schizophrenes," *Congress Report: Second International Congress on Psychiatry*, 4 (1957), 189–232.

Delgado, Honorio F. 1919. "La psicologia de la Locura," *El Siglo Medico* (Madrid). Rev. by K. Abraham, "Literatur in spanischer Sprache," in *Bericht über die Fortschritte der Psychoanalyse 1914–1919*. Vienna: Int. P. V., 1921.

——— 1922. "Lex negación de la paternidad como sintoma psicótico," *Revista de Psyquiatría y Disciplinas Conexas* (Lima), vol. 4. Reviewed by K. Abraham in *Internationale Zeitschrift für Ärztliche Psychoanalyse*, 8 (1922), 384.

——— 1937. *Psicopathologia y Delimitación Clinica de la Esquizofrenia*, Lima, 1937.

———, and Hermilio Valdigan 1923. "Factores Psicológicos de la Demencia Precoz," *Revista de Psyquiatría y Disciplinas Conexas* (Lima), vol. 4. Reviewed by K. Abraham in *Internationale Zeitschrift für Ärztliche Psychoanalyse*, 10 (1924), 308.

Deutsch, Albert 1949. *The Mentally Ill in America.* New York: Columbia University Press, 1949.

Deutsch, Felix, and William F. Murphy 1955. *The Clinical Interview.* New York: International Universities Press, 1949.

Devereaux, George 1939. "A Sociological Theory of Schizophrenia," *Psychoanalytic Review*, 26 (1939), 315–342.

——— 1956. "Normal and Abnormal: The Key Problem of Psychiatric Anthropology," in *Some Uses of Anthropology: Theoretical and Applied.* Washington: Anthropological Society of Washington, pp. 23–48.

Dorcus, Roy M. 1964. "Eugen Bleuler," *Encyclopaedia Britannica*, Chicago: Encyclopaedia Britannica, Inc., 1964, vol. 3, p. 775.

Durkheim, Emile 1897. *Suicide: A Study in Sociology.* New York: The Free Press, 1951.

Eaton, J. M., and R. J. Weill 1953. "Some Epidemiological Findings in the Hutterite Mental Health Study," in *Interrelations Between the Social Environment and Psychiatric Disorders.* New York: Milbank Memorial Fund, 1953, pp. 222–234.

Eissler, Kurt R. 1943. "Limitations to the Psychotherapy of Schizophrenia," *Psychiatry*, 6 (1943), 381–391.

——— 1951. "Remarks on the Psychoanalysis of Schizophrenia," *International Journal of Psychoanalysis*, 32 (1951), 139–156.

——— 1953. "The Effect of the Structure of the Ego on Psychoanalytic Technique," *Journal of the American Psychoanalytic Association*, 1 (1943), 104–143.

——— 1953a. "Notes Upon the Emotionality of a Schizophrenic Patient, and Its Relation to Problems of Technique," *Psychoanalytic Study of the Child*, 8 (1953), 199–251.

Ekstein, Rudolph 1949. "Ideological Warfare in the Psychological Sciences," *Psychoanalytic Review*, 36 (1949), 144–151.

——— 1955. "Vicissitudes of the 'Internal Image' in the Recovery of a Borderline Schizophrenic Adolescent," *Bulletin of the Menninger Clinic*, 19 (1955), 86–92.

Elkind, Henry B., and Maurice Taylor 1935. "The Assumed Increase of Mental Illness," *American Journal of Psychiatry*, 92 (1935), 817–825.

Erikson, Erik H. 1966. Personal communication.

Ernst, K. 1957. "Praktische Problems der individuellen Psychotherapie in der Anstalt am Beispiel einer Schizophreniebehandlung," *Acta psychotherapeutica, psychosomatica et orthopaedagogica*, 5 (1957), 297–305.

Ey, Henri 1958. "Les Probleme Clinique des Schizophrenes." *Évolution Psychiatrique*, 2 (1958), 149–212.

Eyseneck, Hans J. 1965. "Critical Review: The Effects of Psychotherapy," *International Journal of Psychiatry*, 1 (1965), 97–178.

Faergeman, Paul M. 1946. "Early Differential Diagnosis Between Psychogenic Psychoses and Schizophrenias," in *The Memorial Volume to Professor H. Helweg.* Copenhagen: Ejnar Munksgaard, 1946.

Fairbairn, W. Ronald D. 1936. "The Effect of the King's Death Upon

Patients Under Analysis," *International Journal of Psycho-Analysis*, 17 (1936), 278–284.

——— 1941. "A Revised Psychopathology of the Psychoses and Psychoneuroses," *International Journal of Psycho-Analysis*, 22 (1941), 250–279.

——— 1944. "Endopsychic Structure Considered in Terms of Object Relationship," *International Journal of Psycho-Analysis*, 25 (1944), 70–93.

Faris, Ellsworth 1937. *The Nature of Human Nature*. New York: McGraw-Hill Book Co., pp. 287–288.

Faris, Robert E. L., and H. Warren Dunham 1939. *Mental Disorders in Urban Areas. An Ecological Study of Schizophrenia and Other Psychoses*. Chicago: University of Chicago Press, 1939.

Federn, Paul 1933. "The Analysis of Psychotics," *International Journal of Psycho-Analysis*, 15 (1934), 209–214.

——— 1952. *Ego Psychology and the Psychoses*. New York: Basic Books, 1952.

Feigenbaum, Dorian 1930. "Analysis of a Case of Paranoia Persecutoria, Structure and Cure," *Psychoanalytic Review*, 17 (1930), 159–182.

——— 1930a. "Paranoia and Magic," *Journal of Nervous and Mental Disease*, 72 (1930), 28–33.

Fein, Rashi 1958. *Economics and Mental Illness*. New York: Basic Books, 1958.

Fenichel, Otto 1937. "On the Theory of the Therapeutic Results of Psychoanalysis," *International Journal of Psycho-Analysis*, 18 (1937), 133–138.

——— 1945. *The Psychoanalytic Theory of Neurosis*. New York: Norton, 1945.

Ferenczi, Sandor 1911. "Stimulation of the Anal Erotic Zone as a Precipitating Factor in Paranoia, Contribution to the Subject of Homosexuality and Paranoia," in *Final Contributions to the Problems and Methods of Psychoanalysis*. New York: Basic Books, 1955, pp. 295–298.

——— 1911a. "On the Part Played by Homosexuality in the Pathogenesis of Paranoia," in *Sex in Psychoanalysis*. New York: Basic Books, 1950, pp. 154–186.

——— 1913. "Entwicklungsstufen des Wirklichkeitssinnes," *Internationale Zeitschrift für Ärztliche Psychoanalyse*, 1 (1913), 124–138.

——— 1914. "Some Clinical Observations on Paranoia and Paraphrenia," in *Sex in Psychoanalysis*. New York: Basic Books, 1950, pp. 282–295.

——— 1922. "Paranoia," in *Final Contributions to the Problems and Methods of Psychoanalysis*. New York: Basic Books, 1955, pp. 212–215.

——— 1925. "Psychoanalysis of Sexual Habits," in *Further Contributions to the Theory and Technique of Psychoanalysis*. London: Hogarth Press, 1950, pp. 259–297.

——— 1929. "The Principle of Relaxation and Neocatharsis," in *Final Contributions to the Problems and Methods of Psychoanalysis*. New York: Basic Books, 1955, pp. 108–125.

——— 1931. "Child Analysis in the Analysis of Adults," in *Final Contributions to the Problems and Methods of Psychoanalysis*. New York: Basic Books, 1955, pp. 126–142.

Fine, Reuben 1962. *Freud: A Critical Re-Evaluation of His Theories.* New York: D. McKay Co., 1962, chap. 18.

Fleiss, Robert 1953. "Countertransference and Counteridentification," *Journal of the American Psychoanalytic Association*, 1 (1953), 268–284.

Fornari, Franco 1956. "I fonamenti psicologici della psicoterapia analitica della sindromi schizofreniche," *Revista de psicoanalisis*, 2 (1956), 107–122.

Fortune, Reo F. 1932. *Sorcerers of Dobu: The Social Anthropology of the Dobu Islanders of the Western Pacific.* New York: Dutton, 1932.

Frank, Jerome D. 1964. "Foreword," in Ari Kiev (ed.), *Magic, Faith and Healing: Studies in Primitive Psychiatry Today.* New York: The Free Press, 1964.

Freeman, Thomas, Andrew McGhie, and John L. Cameron 1957. "The State of the Ego in Chronic Schizophrenia," *British Journal of Medical Psychology* 30 (1957), 9–18.

French, Thomas M. 1946. "The Transference Phenomenon," in Franz Alexander and Thomas M. French (eds.), *Psychoanalytic Therapy.* New York: Norton, 1946, pp. 71–95.

———, and Jacob Kasanin 1941. "A Psychodynamic Study of the Recovery of Two Schizophrenic Cases," *Psychoanalytic Quarterly*, 10 (1941), 1–22.

Freud, Anna 1936. *The Ego and the Mechanisms of Defense.* New York: International Universities Press, 1946.

——— 1943. Discussion before the British Psychoanalytic Society, January, 1943.

——— 1954. "The Widening Scope of Indications for Psychoanalysis: Discussion," *Journal of the American Psychoanalytic Association*, 2 (1954), 607–620.

Freud, Sigmund 1886. "Beobachtung einer hochgradigen Hemianasthesie bei einem hysterischen Manne (Beiträge zur Kasuistic der Hysterie I)," *Wiener klinische Wochenschrift*, 36, No. 49 (1886), 1633.

——— 1887–1902. *The Origins of Psychoanalysis. Letters, Drafts, and Notes to Wilhelm Fliess.* New York: Basic Books, 1954.

——— 1894. "The Neuro-Psychoses of Defence: An Attempt at a Psychological Theory of Acquired Hysteria and Obsessions and of Certain Hallucinatory Psychoses," *Standard Edition.* London: Hogarth Press, 1962, vol. 3, pp. 45–61.

——— 1894a. "Obsessions and Phobias: "Their Psychical Mechanism and Their Aetiology," *Standard Edition*, 1962, vol. 3, pp. 69–82.

——— 1895. "On the Grounds for Detaching a Particular Syndrome from Neurasthenia under the Description Anxiety Neurosis," *Standard Edition*, 1962, vol. 3, pp. 87–117.

——— 1896. Further Remarks on the Neuro-Psychosis of Defence," *Standard Edition*, 1962, vol. 3, pp. 159–188.

——— 1896a. "Heredity and the Aetiology of the Neuroses," *Standard Edition*, 1962, vol. 3, pp. 141–156.

——— 1898. "Sexuality in the Aetiology of the Neuroses," *Standard Edition*, 1962, vol. 3, pp. 259–285.

——— 1898a. "The Psychical Mechanism of Forgetfulness," *Standard Edition*, 1962, vol. 3, pp. 287–297.

——— 1900. "The Interpretation of Dreams," *Standard Edition*, 1953, vols. 4 and 5.

——— 1904. "On Psychotherapy," *Standard Edition*, 1953, vol. 7, pp. 255–268.

——— 1904a. "Freud's Psychoanalytic Procedure," *Standard Edition*, 1953, vol. 7, pp. 247–254.

——— 1905. "Three Essays on the Theory of Sexuality," *Standard Edition*, 1953, vol. 7, pp. 122–243.

——— 1908. "Hysterical Phantasies and Their Relation to Bisexuality," *Standard Edition*, 1959, vol. 9, pp. 155–166.

——— 1909. "Analysis of a Phobia in a Five-Year-Old Boy," *Standard Edition*, 1953, vol. 10, pp. 3–149.

——— 1909a. "General Remarks on Hysterical Attacks," *Collected Papers* (Fifth Impression). London: Hogarth Press, 1948, vol. 2, pp. 100–104.

——— 1909b. "Notes Upon a Case of Obsessional Neurosis," *Standard Edition*, 1953, vol. 10, pp. 151–249. *See also* "El Caso del 'Hombre de las Ratas,'" *Revista de Psicoanálisis*, 22 (1965), 159–199.

——— 1909c. "Preface to Sandor Ferenczi's *Psychoanalysis: Essays in the Field of Psychoanalysis*," *Standard Edition*, 1959, vol. 9, p. 252.

——— 1910. "The Future of Psychoanalytic Therapy," in *Collected Papers*. London: Hogarth Press, vol. 2, pp. 285–296.

——— 1910a. "'Wild' Psychoanalysis," *Standard Edition*. London: Hogarth Press, 1957, vol. 11.

——— 1911. "Psychoanalytic Notes On an Autobiographical Account of a Case of Paranoia (Dementia Paranoides)," *Standard Edition*, 1958, vol. 14, pp. 1–82.

——— 1911–1915. "Papers On Technique," *Standard Edition*. London: Hogarth Press, 1958, vol. 12.

——— 1912. "The Dynamics of Transference," *Standard Edition*. London: Hogarth Press, 1958, vol. 12.

——— 1913. "The Disposition to Obsessional Neurosis," *Standard Edition*, 1958, vol. 12, pp. 311–336.

——— 1914. "On the History of the Psychoanalytic Movement," *Standard Edition*, 1957, vol. 14, pp. 3–66.

——— 1914a. "On Narcissism: An Introduction," *Standard Edition*, 1957, vol. 14, pp. 67–102.

——— 1914b. "Remembering, Repeating and Working-through (Further Recommendations on the Technique of Psychoanalysis)," *Standard Edition*. London: Hogarth Press, 1958, vol. 12.

——— 1915. "The Unconscious," *Standard Edition*, 1957, vol. 14, pp. 159–215.

——— 1915a. "Instincts and Their Vicissitudes," *Standard Edition*, 1957, vol. 14, pp. 103–140.

——— 1915b. "Observations on Transference-Love," *Standard Edition*. London: Hogarth Press, 1958, vol. 12.

——— 1917. "On Transformations of Instinct as Exemplified in Anal Erotism," *Standard Edition*, 1955, vol. 17, pp. 126–133.

——— 1917a. "Mourning and Melancholia," *Standard Edition*, 1957, vol. 14, pp. 237–258.

——— 1918. "From the History of an Infantile Neurosis," *Standard Edition*, 1955, vol. 17, pp. 1–122.

——— 1920. "Beyond the Pleasure Principle," *Standard Edition*, 1955, vol. 18, pp. 3–66.

——— 1923. *The Ego and the Id* (Fifth Impression). London: Hogarth Press, 1949.

——— 1924. "The Loss of Reality in Neurosis and Psychosis," *Standard Edition*, 1961, vol. 19, pp. 183–190.

——— 1924a. "Neurosis and Psychosis," *Standard Edition*, 1961, vol. 19, pp. 147–153.

——— 1924b. "A Short Account of Psychoanalysis," *Standard Edition*, 1961, vol. 19, pp. 191–212.

——— 1926. "Inhibitions, Symptoms and Anxiety," *Standard Edition*, 1959, vol. 20, pp. 75–174.

——— 1927. "Fetishism," *Standard Edition*, 1961, vol. 21, pp. 147–157.

——— 1932. *New Introductory Lectures*. New York: Norton, 1933.

——— 1940. *An Outline of Psychoanalysis*. New York: Norton, 1949.

Fromm-Reichmann, Frieda 1947. "Problems of Therapeutic Management in a Psychoanalytic Hospital," *Psychoanalytic Quarterly*, 16 (1947), 325–356.

——— 1948. "Notes on the Development of Schizophrenia," *Psychiatry*, 11 (1948), 263–273.

——— 1949. "Notes on the Personal and Professional Requirements of a Psychotherapist," *Psychiatry*, 12 (1949), 361–378.

——— 1950. *Principles of Intensive Psychotherapy*. Chicago: University of Chicago Press, 1950.

——— 1952. "Some Aspects of Psychoanalytic Psychotherapy with Schizophrenics," in E. B. Brody and F. C. Redlich (eds.), *Psychotherapy with Schizophrenics: A Symposium*. New York: International Universities Press, 1952, pp. 89–111.

——— 1954. "Psychoanalytic and General Dynamic Conceptions of Theory and Therapy: Differences and Similarities," *Journal of the American Psychoanalytic Association*, 2 (1954), 711–721.

Fruhle, Hans W. 1932. "Schizophrenie," *Neue Deutsche Klinik*, 9 (1932), 611–635.

Galant, Johann S. 1933. "The Occurrence of Rare Phenomena in Dementia Praecox," *Journal of Nervous and Mental Disease*, 77 (1933), 163–166.

——— 1933a. "A Study of Neuropsychiatric Rudimentary Functions in Man and Schizophrenia," *Journal of Nervous and Mental Disease*, 78 (1933), 128–130.

Gardiner, Muriel 1953. "Meetings with the Wolf Man," *Bulletin of the Menninger Clinic*, 17 (1953), 41–48.

Garma, Angel 1931. "La Realidad Exterior y los Instintos en la Esquizofrenia," *Revista de Psicoanálisis*, 2 (1945), 56–82.

——— 1935. "Paranoia y Homosexualidad," *Revista de Psicoanálisis*, 1 (1944), 555–578.

——— 1945. "The Genesis of Reality Testing: A General Theory of Hallucination," *Psychoanalytic Quarterly*, 15 (1946), 161–174.

——— 1962. "La Esquizofrenia," in *El Psicoanálysis: Teoría, Clínica y Técnica*. Buenos Aires: Paidos, 1962, pp. 161–184.

——— 1965. Personal communication.

Geleerd, Elizabeth 1963. "Review of Melanie Klein's Last Book: *Narrative* of a Child Analysis," *Bulletin of the Philadelphia Association of Psychoanalysis*, 13 (1963), 39–41.

Gerö, George 1933. Review of T. Dembo, "Der Arger als dynamisches Problem," *Imago*, 19 (1933), 414–418.

Gill, Merton M., and Margaret Brenman 1959. *Hypnosis and Related States*. New York: International Universities Press, 1959.

Gioia, Gina, and David Liberman 1953. "Una Sesión Psicoanalítica de un Paciente Esquixofrénico," *Revista de Psicoanálisis*, 10 (1953), 372–378.

Giovacchini, Peter L. 1961. "Ego Adaptation and Cultural Variables," *Archives of General Psychiatry*, 5 (1961), 36–45.

——— 1963. "Integrative Aspects of Objective Relationships," *Psychoanalytic Quarterly*, 32 (1963), 393–407.

——— 1964. "Comments on Leo Stone's *The Psychoanalytic Situation*," manuscript.

——— 1965. "Some Aspects of the Development of the Ego Ideal of a Creative Scientist," *Psychoanalytic Quarterly*, 34 (1965), 79–101.

——— 1965a. "Transference, Incorporation and Synthesis," *International Journal of Psycho-Analysis*, 46 (1965), 287–296.

Gitelson, M. 1958. "On Ego Distortion," *International Journal of Psycho-Analysis*, 39 (1958), 245–258.

——— 1962. "The Curative Factors in Psychoanalysis," *International Journal of Psycho-Analysis*, 43 (1962), 194–206.

Glover, Edward 1930. "Grades of Ego-Differentiation," *International Journal of Psycho-Analysis*, 11 (1930), 1–11.

——— 1945. "Examination of the Klein System of Child Psychology," *Psychoanalytic Study of the Child*, 1 (1945), 75–118.

——— 1950. *Freud or Jung*. New York: Norton, 1950.

——— 1955. *The Technique of Psychoanalysis*. New York: International Universities Press, 1955.

Goldhammer, Herbert, and Andrew H. Marshall 1949. *The Frequency of Mental Disease. Long-Term Trends and Present Status*. Santa Monica, Calif.: The Rand Corporation, 1949.

Goldsmith, Margaret 1964. "Franz Anton Mesmer," *Encyclopaedia Britannica*. Chicago: Encyclopaedia Britannica, Inc., 1964, vol. 15, p. 287.

Gordon, Alfred 1912. "Differential Diagnosis Between Manic-Depressive Psychosis and Dementia Praecox," *Journal of Nervous and Mental Disease*, 39 (1912), 24–41.

——— 1917. "Obsessive Hallucinations and Psychoanalysis," *Journal of Abnormal Psychology*, 12 (1917), 423–430.

——— 1924–1925. "Prolonged Confusional States Simulating Dementia Praecox," *American Journal of Psychiatry*, 4 (1925), 757–776.

——— 1933. "Obsessional Phenomena in Schizoid Individuals in Relation to Eventual Schizophrenia," *Psychiatric Quarterly*, 7 (1933), 203–210.

——— 1934. "Coexistence of Psychoses of Different Types in the Same Individual," *Psychiatric Quarterly*, 8 (1934), 300–305.

——— 1951. "Transition of Obsessions into Delusions. Evaluation of Obsessional Phenomena from the Prognostic Standpoint," *American Journal of Psychiatry*, 107 (1951), 455–458.

Gorman, Mike 1956. *Every Other Bed*. Cleveland and New York: World Publishing Company, 1956.

Grebelskaya, Sch. 1912. "Psychologische Analyse eines Paranoiden," *Jahresbericht über psychologische und psychopathologische Forschung*, 4 (1912), 116–140.

Green, Maurice R. 1962. "The Roots of Sullivan's Concept of Self," *Psychiatric Quarterly*, 36 (1962), 271–282.

Greenacre, Phyllis 1918. "Content of the Schizophrenic Characteristics Occurring in Affective Disorders," *American Journal of Insanity*, 75 (1918), 197–202.

Greenson, Ralph R. 1949. "The Psychology of Apathy," *Psychoanalytic Quarterly*, 18 (1919), 290–302.

——— 1951. "Apathetic and Agitated Boredom," *Psychoanalytic Quarterly*, 20 (1951), 346–347.

——— 1965. "The Working Alliance and the Transference Neurosis," *Psychoanalytic Quarterly*, 34 (1965), 155–181.

Gregory, Ian 1960. "Genetic Factors in Schizophrenia," *American Journal of Psychiatry*, 116 (1960), 961–972.

Grinberg, Leon 1959. "Aspectos Magicos en la Transferencia y en la Contratransferencia. Sus Implicaciones Técnicas," *Revista de Psicoanálisis*, 15 (1959), 347–368.

——— 1959a. "Aspectos Magicos en las Ansiedades Paranoides y Depresivas," *Revista de Psicoanálisis*, 16 (1959), 15–26.

——— 1965. "The Relationship Between Obsessive Mechanism and a State of Self Disturbance: Depersonalization," paper read before the 24th International Psychoanalytic Congress, Amsterdam, 1965.

Grotjahn, Martin 1938. "Psychiatric Observations of Schizophrenic Patients During Metrazol Treatment," *Bulletin of the Menninger Clinic*, 2 (1938), 142–150.

Guntrip, Henry J. S. 1961. *Personality Structure and Human Interaction: The Development Synthesis of Psychodynamic Theory.* New York: International Universities Press, 1961, pp. 192–245.

Häfner, Heinz 1954. "Zur Psychopatholgie der Halluzinationischen Schizophrenie," *Archives of Neurology and Psychiatry*, 192 (154), 241–258.

Hallgren, Bertil, and Sjögren, Torsten 1959. "A Clinical and Genitico-Statistical Study of Schizophrenia and Low-Grade Mental Deficiency in a Large Swedish Rural Population," *Acta Psychiatrica et Neurologica Scandinavica*, Suppl. 140, vol. 35 (1959).

Ham, George C. 1963. "Genes and the Psyche: Perspectives in Human Development and Behavior," *American Journal of Psychiatry*, 119 (1963), 28–34.

Handlon, Joseph H. 1960. "A Metatheoretical View of Assumptions Regarding the Etiology of Schizophrenia," *American Archives of General Psychiatry*, 2 (1960), 43–60.

Harper, Robert A. 1959. *Psychoanalysis and Psychotherapy.* Englewood Cliffs, N.J.: Prentice-Hall, 1959.

Harris, F. Gentry 1963–1964. "First, Second and Third Progress Reports on the Therapy Project for Schizophrenia," mimeographed Reports of the National Institute of Mental Health.

Harris, Irving D. 1960. "Unconscious Factors Common to Parents and Analysts," 41 (1960).

Hartmann, Heinz 1925. "Ein Beitrag zur Lehre von den reaktiven Psychosen," *Monatsschrift für Psychiatrie und Neurologie*, 57 (1925), 89–108.

——— 1933. "An Experimental Contribution to the Psychology of Obsessive-Compulsive Neurosis: On Remembering Completed and Uncompleted Tasks," in *Essays of Ego Psychology*. New York: International Universities Press, 1964, pp. 404–418.

——— 1951. "Technical Implications of Ego Psychology," *Psychoanalytic Quarterly*, 20 (1951), 31–43.

——— 1953. "Contributions to the Meta-Psychology of Schizophrenia," *Psychoanalytic Study of the Child*, 8 (1953), 177–198.

——— and Ernst Kris 1945. "The Genetic Approach in Psychoanalysis," *Psychoanalytic Study of the Child*, 1 (1945), 11–30.

——— 1945a. "The Genetic Approach in Psychoanalysis," *Psychological Issues*, Monograph 14, 4 (1964), 7–26.

———, and Rudolph M. Loewenstein 1946. "Comments on the Formation of Psychic Structure," *Psychological Issues*, Monograph 14, 4 (1964), 27–55.

——— 1949. "Notes on the Theory of Aggression," *Psychological Issues*, Monograph 14, 4 (1964), 56–85.

Hartmann, Heinz, and F. Stumpfl 1930. "Psychosen bei eineiigen Zwillingen," *Zeitschrift für die gesamte Neurologie und Psychiatrie*, 123 (1930), 251–298.

Hassall, James C. 1915. "The Role of the Sexual Complex in Dementia Praecox," *Psychoanalytic Review*, 2 (1915), 260–276.

Hesnard, A. 1960. *L'oeuvre de Freud et son Importance pour le Monde Moderne*. Paris: Payot, 1960.

Hess, Eckhard H. 1964. "Imprinting in Birds," *Science*, 146 (1964), 1128–1139.

Hill, Lewis B. 1955. *Psychotherapeutic Intervention in Schizophrenia*. London: Cambridge University Press, 1955.

Hinde, R. A. 1954. "Changes in Responsiveness to a Constant Stimulus," *British Journal of Animal Behavior*, 2 (1954), 41–45.

Hinsie, Leland E. 1927. "The Psychoanalytic Treatment of Schizophrenia," *Psychiatric Quarterly*, 1 (1927), 313–327.

——— 1930. *The Treatment of Schizophrenia*. Baltimore: Williams and Wilkins, 1930.

——— 1932. "The Catatonic Syndrome in Dementia Praecox," *Psychiatric Quarterly*, 6 (1932), 457–468.

——— 1944. "Schizophrenias," in S. Lorand (ed.), *Psychoanalysis Today*. New York: International Universities Press, 1944, pp. 274–286.

———, and Jacob Shatzky 1940. *Psychiatric Dictionary: With Encyclopedic Treatment of Modern Terms*. London, New York, Toronto: Oxford University Press, 1940.

Hitschmann, Edward 1912. "Swedenborg's Paranoia," *American Imago*, 6 (1949), 45–50.

——— 1913. "Paranoia, Homosexualität und Analerotic," *Zentralblatt für Psychoanalyse und Psychotherapie*, 1 (1913), 251–254.

Hoch, Paul, and Joseph Zubin (eds.) 1961. *Comparative Epidemiology of the Mental Disorders*. New York and London: Grune and Stratton, 1961.

Hoedemaker, Edward 1955. "The Therapeutic Process in the Treatment of Schizophrenia," *Journal of American Psychoanalytic Association*, 3 (1955), 89–109.

——— 1958. "Preanalytic Preparation for the Therapeutic Process in Schizophrenia," *Psychiatry*, 21 (1958), 285–291.

——— 1960. "Psycho-Analytic Technique and Ego Modifications," *International Journal of Psycho-Analysis*, 41 (1960), 34–46.

Hollender, Marc H., and Ivan Böszörmenyi-Nagy 1958. "Hallucination as an Ego Experience," *Archives of General Psychiatry*, 80 (1958), 93–97.

Hollingshead, August B., and Frederick C. Redlich 1958. *Social Class and Mental Illness*. New York: John Wiley & Sons, 1958.

Hoop, Johannes H. Van der 1924. "Über die Projektion und Ihre Inhalte," *Internationale Zeitschrift für Psychoanalyse*, 10 (1924), 276–288.

——— 1925. "Über Autismus, Dissoziation und affektive Demenz," *Zeitschrift für die gesamte Neurologie und Psychiatrie*, 97 (1925), 129–147.

Horwitz, William A., Philip Polatin, Lawrence C. Kold, and Paul H. Hoch 1958. "A Study of Cases of Schizophrenia Treated by 'Direct Analysis,'" *American Journal of Psychiatry*, 114 (1958), 870–873.

Hoskins, R. G. 1946. *The Biology of Schizophrenia*. New York: Norton, 1946.

Hunter, Dugmore 1960. "Training in Child Psychotherapy at the Tavistock Clinic," *Journal of Child Psychology and Psychiatry*, 1 (1960), 87–93.

Isaacs, Susan 1939. "A Special Mechanism in a Schizoid Boy," *International Journal of Psycho-Analysis*, 20 (1939), 333–339.

——— 1943. "An Acute Psychotic Anxiety Occurring in a Boy of Four Years," *International Journal of Psycho-Analysis*, 24 (1943), 13–32.

Isham, Mary K. 1920. "Some Mechanisms of Paraphrenia," *American Journal of Insanity*, 77 (1920), 91–98.

——— 1920a. "The Paraphrenic's Inaccessibility," *Psychoanalytic Review*, 7 (1920), 246–256.

Israel, Robert H., and Nelson H. Johnson 1956. "Discharge and Readmission Rate in 4254 Consecutive First Admissions of Schizophrenia," *American Journal of Psychiatry*, 112 (1956), 903–909.

Jackson, Donald D. 1959. "Family Interaction, Family Homeostasis and Some Implications for Conjoint Family Psychotherapy," in J. Masserman, *Science and Psychoanalysis*. New York: Grune and Stratton, 1959, vol. 2, pp. 112–141.

——— 1961. "The Monad, the Dyad and the Family Therapy of Schizophrenics," in A. Burton (ed.), *Psychotherapy of the Psychoses*. New York: Basic Books, 1961, pp. 318–328.

Jacobson, Edith 1954. "Contribution to the Metapsychology of Psychotic Identifications," *Journal of the American Psychoanalytic Association*, 2 (1954), 239–262.

——— 1954a. "On Psychotic Identifications," *International Journal of Psycho-Analysis*, 35 (1954), 102–108.

——— 1955. "Sullivan's Interpersonal Theory of Psychiatry," *Journal of the American Psychoanalytic Association*, 3 (1955), 149–156.

——— 1959. "Depersonalization," *Journal of the American Psychoanalytic Association*, 7 (1959), 591–610.

Jelliffe, Smith Ely, undated. *Collected Papers*. Chicago: John Crerar Library.

——— 1907. "The Signs of Pre-Dementia Praecox: Their Significance and Pedagogic Prophylaxis," *American Journal of Medical Science*, 134 (1907), 157–182.

——— 1908. "Some General Reflections on the Psychology of Dementia Praecox," *Journal of American Medical Association*, 50 (1908), 202–205.

——— 1910. "Dementia Praecox. A Historical Summary," *New York Medical Journal*, 91 (1910), 521–531.

——— 1927. "The Mental Pictures in Schizophrenia and in Epidemic Encephalitis: Their Alliances, Differences and a Point of View," *American Journal of Psychiatry*, 6 (1927), 413–465.

Jones, Ernest 1909. "Psycho-Analytic Notes On a Case of Hypomania," *American Journal of Insanity*, 66 (1909), 203–218.

——— 1933. "The Phallic Phase," *International Journal of Psychoanalysis*, 14 (1933), 1–33.

——— 1938. *Papers on Psychoanalysis* (4th Ed.). Baltimore: William Wood and Co., 1938.

——— 1953. *The Life and Works of Sigmund Freud, 1856–1900. The Formative Years and the Great Discoveries*. New York: Basic Books, 1953.

——— 1955. *The Life and Works of Sigmund Freud, 1901–1919. Years of Maturity*. New York: Basic Books, 1955.

Jores, Arthur, and Hellmuth Freyberger (eds.) 1960. *Advances in Psychosomatic Medicine*. New York: Brunner, 1960.

Joseph, Betty 1959. "An Aspect of the Repetition Compulsion," *International Journal of Psycho-Analysis*, 40 (1959), 213–222.

Jung, Carl G. 1906. *Studies in Word Association: Experiments in the Diagnosis of Psychopathological Conditions Carried Out at the Psychiatric Clinic of the University of Zürich*. London: W. Heinemann, 1918.

——— 1907. *The Psychology of Dementia Praecox*. New York: Nervous and Mental Disease Monograph Series, 1944.

——— 1908. *Der Inhalt der Psychose in Freud's Schriften zur Angewandenten Seelenkunde*. Leipzig and Vienna: Deuticke, 1908.

——— 1911. "A Criticism of Bleuler's 'Theory of Schizophrenic Negativism,'" in *Collected Papers on Analytical Psychology*. London: Bailliere, Tindall and Cox, 1916, pp. 200–205.

——— 1914. "The Content of the Psychoses," in *Collected Papers on Analytical Psychology*. London: Bailliere, Tindall and Cox, 1916, pp. 312–351.

——— 1939. "On the Psychogenesis of Schizophrenia," *Journal of Mental Science*, 85 (1939), 999–1011.

Kahlbaum, Ludwig 1863. *Gruppierung der psychischen Krankheiten*. Danzig: Kafemann, 1863.

Kallmann, Franz J. 1950. "The Genetics of Psychoses," *American Journal of Human Genetics*, 2 (1950), 385–390.

Karpas, Morris J. 1915–1916. "Paraphrenia Erotica. A Contribution to the Study of Synthetic Psychiatry," *American Journal of Insanity*, 72 (1916), 291–296.

Karpman, Benjamin 1944. "Hebephrenic Phantasies, Relations to Two Basic Crime Trends: Analysis of Techniques Used in One Case," *Journal of Nervous and Mental Disease*, 100 (1944), 480–506.

Kasanin, Jacob S. (ed.) 1944. *Language and Thought in Schizophrenia.* Berkeley and Los Angeles: University of California Press, 1944.

——— 1945. "Developmental Roots of Schizophrenia," *Psychiatry,* 6 (1945), 770–776.

——— and Eugenia Hanfmann 1942. *Conceptual Thinking in Schizophrenia.* New York: Nervous and Mental Diseases Monograph Series, 1942.

Katan, Mauritz 1939. "A Contribution to the Understanding of Schizophrenic Speech," *International Journal of Psycho-Analysis,* 20 (1939), 353–362.

——— 1950. "Structural Aspects of a Case of Schizophrenia," *Psychoanalytic Study of the Child,* 5 (1950), 175–211.

——— 1954. "The Importance of the Nonpsychotic Part of the Personality in Schizophrenia," *International Journal of Psycho-Analysis,* 35 (1954), 119–128.

Kaufman, M. Ralph 1934. "Projection, Heterosexual and Homosexual," *Psychoanalytic Quarterly,* 3 (1934), 134–136.

——— 1939. "Religious Delusions in Schizophrenia," *International Journal of Psycho-Analysis,* 20 (1939), 363–376.

Kempf, Edward J. 1919. "The Psychoanalytic Treatment of a Case of Schizophrenia: Report of a Case," *Psychoanalytic Review,* 6 (1919), 15–58.

Khan, M. Masud R. 1960. "Clinical Aspects of the Schizoid Personality: Affects and Technique," *International Journal of Psycho-Analysis,* 41 (1960), 430–437.

Kielholz, Arthur 1951. "Von Zweisinn," *Schweizerische Zeitschrift für Psychologie und ihre Andwendungen,* 10 (1951), 97–116.

Klein, Melanie 1920. "Der Familienroman in statu nascendi," *Internationale Zeitschrift für Ärztliche Psychoanalyse,* 6 (1920), 151–155.

——— 1930. "The Importance of Symbol-Formation in the Development of the Ego," *International Journal of Psycho-Analysis,* 11 (1930), 24–39.

——— 1930a. "The Psychotherapy of the Psychoses," *British Journal of Medical Psychology,* 10 (1930), 242–244.

——— 1932. *The Psycho-Analysis of Children.* London: Hogarth Press, 1950.

——— 1935. "A Contribution to the Psychogenesis of Manic-Depressive States," *International Journal of Psycho-Analysis,* 16 (1935) 145–174.

——— 1946. "Notes on Some Schizoid Mechanisms," *International Journal of Psycho-Analysis,* 27 (1946), 99–110.

——— 1948. *Contributions of Psycho-Analysis.* London: HPI, 1921–45.

——— 1952. *Developments in Psychoanalysis.* London: Hogarth Press, 1952, p. 300.

——— 1955. "On Identification," in Melanie Klein, Paula Heinmann, and Roger E. Money-Kyrle (eds.), *New Directions in Psycho-Analysis.* London: Tavistock Publications, 1955, chap. 14.

Kline, Nathan S. 1957. "A Point of View as to the Nature of Schizophrenia," *American Journal of Psychiatry,* 114 (1957), 505–508.

Knight, Robert P. 1953. "Management and Psychotherapy of the Borderline Patient," *Bulletin of the Menninger Clinic,* 17 (1953), 139–150.

——— 1953a. "Borderline Patients," *Bulletin of the Menninger Clinic*, 19 (1953), 1–12.

Kolb, Lawrence C. 1956. "Psychotherapeutic Evolution and Its Implications," *Psychiatric Quarterly*, 30 (1956), 579–597.

Korner, Annaliese F. 1964. "Some Hypotheses Regarding the Significance of Individual Differences at Birth for Later Development," *Psychoanalytic Study of the Child*, 19 (1964), 58–72.

Kraepelin, Emil 1903. *Lehrbuch der Psychiatrie*. Leipzig: Barth, 1903 (7th edition).

Kris, Ernst 1950. "On Preconscious Mental Processes," *Psychoanalytic Quarterly*, 19 (1950), 540–560.

——— 1951. "Ego Psychology and Interpretation in Psychoanalytic Therapy," *Psychoanalytic Quarterly*, 20 (1951), 15–30.

——— 1954. "Introduction," in Sigmund Freud, *The Origins of Psychoanalysis, Letters, Drafts, and Notes to Wilhelm Fliess*. New York: Basic Books, 1954.

——— 1955. "Neutralization and Sublimation: Observations on Young Children," *Psychoanalytic Study of the Child*, 10 (1955), 30–46.

Laforgue, René 1926. "Scotomazation in Schizophrenia," *International Journal of Psycho-Analysis*, 8 (1927), 473–458.

——— 1926a. "Schizophrenie, Schizomanie und Schizonoia," *Zeitschrift für die gesamte Neurologie und Psychiatrie*, 105 (1926) 448–458.

——— 1929. "Absperrungsmechanismen in der Neurose und Beziehung zur Schizophrenie," *Internationale Zeitschrift für Psychoanalyse*, 15 (1929), 246–258.

——— 1935. "Contribution à l'étude de la Schizophrénie," *Evolution Psychiatrique*, 3 (1935), 81–96.

——— and Henri Claude 1925. "Sur la Schizophrénie et la Constitution Bipolaire du Caractère schizoide," *Evolution Psychiatrique*, 1 (1925), 27–36.

———, and Angelo L. M. Hesnard 1930–1931. "Les processus d'autopunition en Psychologie des Névroses et des Psychoses en Psychologie Criminelle et en Pathologie Générale," *Revue Française de Psychoanalyse*, 4 (1931), 2–84.

Landauer, Karl 1914. "Spontanheilung einer Katatonie," *Internationale Zeitschrift für Ärztliche Psychoanalyse*, 2 (1914), 441–458.

——— 1924. " 'Passive' Technik. Zur Analyse narzissisticher Erkrankungen," *Internationale Zeitschrift für Ärztliche Psychoanalyse*, 10 (1924), 415–422.

——— 1926. "Die Schizophrenie," in P. Federn and H. Heng (eds.), *Das Psychoanalytische Volksbuch*. Stuttgart: Hippocrates, 1926, pp. 381–394.

——— 1927. "Automatismen, Zwangsneurose und Paranoia," *Internationale Zeitschrift für Ärztliche Psychoanalyse*, 13 (1927), 10–19.

——— 1927–1928. "Die Onanieselbstschuldigungen in Psychosen," *Zeitschrift für Psychoanalytische Padagogik*, 2 (1928), 161–162.

——— 1928. "Die Indikationen zur psychoanalytische Behandlung," *Hippokrates*, 1 (1928), 265–279.

——— 1930. "Die Demeinschaft mit sich Selber. Über Narzissitische Charaktere, Neurosen und Psychosen," *Psychoanalytische Bewegung*, 2 (1930), 260–272.

Landis, Carney, and James P. Page 1938. *Modern Society and Mental Illness*. New York: Farrar and Rinehart, 1938.

Lebovici, Serge, René Diatkine, and H. Danon-Boileau 1956–1957. "Das Psychodrama und die Behandlung von Psychosen," *Zeitschrift für Psychosomatische Medizin*, 3 (1957), 220–231.

———, Yves Roumajon, Jacques Morin, and Bourreau 1954. "Deux Cas de Schizophrénie de l'Adolescence, Présentation de Malades," *Annales Médico-Psychologiques*, 112 (1954), 195–197.

Lehrman, Philip R. 1919. "Mental Mechanisms in the Psychoses and Neuroses," *New York State Journal of Medicine*, 110 (1919), 150–152.

Lemieux, Rogert R. 1961. "L'Aspect Changeant de la Schizophrénie," *Canadian Psychiatric Association Journal*, 6 (1961), 127–131.

Lewin, Bertram D. 1950. *The Psychoanalysis of Elation*. New York: Norton, 1950.

Lewis, Nolan D. C. 1923. *The Constitutional Factors in Dementia Praecox*. New York and Washington: Nervous and Mental Diseases Monograph Series #35, 1923.

——— 1925. "Comments on the Pathology of Dementia Praecox," *Journal of Nervous and Mental Disease*, 62 (1925), 225–260.

——— 1928. "Graphic Art Productions in Schizophrenia," *Proceedings, Association for Research in Nervous and Mental Diseases*, 5 (1925), 344–368.

——— 1929–1930. "Mechanisms in Certain Cases of Prolonged Schizophrenia," *American Journal of Psychiatry*, 9 (1930), 543–552.

——— 1936. *Research in Schizophrenia (Past Attainments, Present Trends, and Future Possibilities)*. New York: National Committee on Mental Hygiene, 1936.

——— 1937. "The Position of the Psychiatrist in a Plan of Research in Schizophrenia," *Psychiatric Quarterly*, 11 (1937), 537–543.

——— 1944. "Prognostic Significance of Certain Factors in Schizophrenia," *Journal of Nervous and Mental Disease*, 100 (1944), 414–419.

——— 1949. "Criteria for Early Differential Diagnosis of Psychoneurosis and Schizophrenia," *American Journal of Psychotherapy*, 3 (1949), 4–18.

———, and Elsie Blanchard 1931. "Clinical Findings in 'Recovered' Cases of Schizophrenia," *American Journal of Psychiatry*, 11 (1931), 481–492.

Liberman, David 1952. "Fragmento del análisis de una psicosis paranoide," *Revista de Psicoanálisis*, 9 (1952), 413–454.

——— 1957. "Interpretación correlativa entre relato y repetición: su aplicación en una paciente con personalidad esquizoide," *Revista de Psicoanálisis*, 14 (1957), 55–62.

Lidz, Theodore, Stephen Fleck, and Alice R. Cornelison 1965. *Schizophrenia and the Family*. New York: International Universities Press, 1965.

———, Sarah Schafer, Stephen Fleck, Alice Cornelison, and Dorothy Terry 1962. "Ego Differentiation and Schizophrenic Symptom Formation in Identical Twins," *Journal of the American Psychoanalytic Association*, 10 (1962), 74–90.

Little, Margaret 1958. "On Delusional Transference (Transference Psychosis)," *International Journal of Psycho-Analysis*, 39 (1958), 134–138.

Loewald, H. W. 1960. "On the Therapeutic Action of Psychoanalysis," *International Journal of Psycho-Analysis*, 41 (1960), 16–34.

Loewenstein, Rudolph M. 1951. "The Problem of Interpretation," *Psychoanalytic Quarterly*, 20 (1951), 1–14.

——— 1956. "Some Remarks on the Role of Speech in Psychoanalytic Technique," *International Journal of Psycho-Analysis*, 37 (1956), 460–468.

Lorenz, Konrad 1952. *King Solomon's Ring*. New York: Crowell, 1952.

Lundholm, Helge 1932. *Schizophrenia*. Durham, N. C.: Duke University Press, 1932.

McKnight, W. K. 1958. "Historical Landmarks in Research on Schizophrenia in the United States," *American Journal of Psychiatry*, 114 (1958), 873–881.

Maeder, Alphonse E. 1910. "Psychologische Untersuchungen an Dementia Praecox-Kranken." *Jahrbuch für Psychoanalystiche und Psychopathologische Forschung*, 2 (1910), 185–245.

——— 1911. "Zur Enstehung der Symbolik in Traum, in der Dementia Praecox, etc.," *Zentralblatt für Psychoanalyse und Psychotherapie*, 1 (1911), 383–389.

——— 1923. "A Case of Paranoia. Treated by the Psycho-Analytic and Psycho-Synthetic Methods," *Journal of Sexology and Psychoanalysis*, 1 (1923), 452–466.

Mahler, Margaret S. 1963. "Thoughts About Development and Individuation," *Psychoanalytic Study of the Child*, 18 (1963), 307–324.

———, and Manuel Furer 1960. "Observations on Research Regarding the 'Symbolic Syndrome,'" *Psychoanalytic Quarterly*, 29 (1960), 317–327.

——— 1963. "Certain Aspects of the Separation-Individuation Phase," *Psychoanalytic Quarterly*, 32 (1963), 1–14.

———, and Calvin F. Settledge 1959. "Severe Emotional Disturbances in Childhood: Psychosis," in S. Arieti (ed.), *American Handbook of Psychiatry*. New York: Basic Books, 1959, chap. 14.

———, and Ketty LePerrier 1965. "Mother-Child Interaction During Separation-Individuation," *Psychoanalytic Quarterly*, 34 (1965), 483–498.

Malamud, William 1929. "The Application of Psychoanalytic Principles in Interpreting the Psychoses," *Psychoanalytic Review*, 16 (1929), 62–68.

——— 1950. "The Present Status of Research in Dementia Praecox," *Mental Hygiene*, 34 (1950), 554–568.

———, and Winfred Overholzer 1958. "Multidisciplinary Research in Schizophrenia," *American Journal of Psychiatry*, 114 (1958), 865–872.

Malis, G. Yu 1959. *Research in the Etiology of Schizophrenia*. New York: Consultants Bureau, 1959.

Malzberger, Benjamin 1940. *Social and Biological Aspects of Mental Disease*. Utica, N. Y.: State Hospital Press, 1940.

Margat, P. 1956. "Détail d'une Psychothérapie de Schizophrène," *Evolution Psychiatrique*, 3 (1956), 717–749.

Markus, Otto 1911. Über Assoziationen bei Dementia Praecox," *Archiv für Psychiatrie und Nervengrankheiten*, 48 (1911), 344–393.

Marmor, Judd 1953. "Orality in the Hysterical Personality," *Journal of the American Psychoanalytic Association*, 1 (1953), 656–671.

Matussek, Paul 1956. "Psychotherapie bei Schizophrenen," in V. E. Frankel, V. E. von Gebsattel, and J. H. Schultz (eds.), *Handbuch der Neurosenlehre und Psychotherapie*. Munich and Berlin: Urban and Schwarzenberg, 1956, vol. 4, pp. 385–417.

Mead, Margaret 1939. *From the South Seas: Studies in Adolescence and Sex in Primitive Societies*. New York: William Morrow and Co., 1939.

Meltzer, Donald 1963. "A Contribution to the Metapsychology of Cyclothymic States," *International Journal of Psycho-Analysis*, 44 (1963), 83–96.

Menninger, Karl A. 1920. "Paranoid Psychoses," *Journal of Nervous and Mental Disease*, 51 (1920), 35–40.

——— 1921. "Dementia Praecox," *Journal of the Kansas Medical Society*, 21 (1921), 381–408.

——— 1922. "Reversible Schizophrenia," *American Journal of Psychiatry*, 1 (1922), 575–587.

——— 1924. "Paranoid Psychoses with Uremia," *Journal of Nervous and Mental Disease*, 60 (1924), 26–34.

———1925–1926. "Influenza and Schizophrenia. An Analysis of Past Influenza Dementia Praecox as of 1918 and Five Years Later," *American Journal of Psychiatry*, 5 (1926), 469–530.

———1928. "The Schizophrenic Syndrome as a Product of Acute Infectious Disease. Schizophrenia (Dementia Praecox)," *Archives of Neurology and Psychiatry*, 20 (1928), 464–481.

——— 1930. "Amelioration of Schizophrenia Following Dysentery," *Journal of Nervous and Mental Disease*, 72 (1930), 535–537.

——— 1940. "Psychoanalytic Psychiatry: Theory and Practice," *Bulletin of the Menninger Clinic*, 4 (1940), 105–123.

——— 1947. "Diagnosis and Treatment of Schizophrenia," *Bulletin of the Menninger Clinic*, 12 (1947), 96–106.

Menzer, Doris, Christopher T. Standish, and James Mann 1950. "Some Observations on Individual Psychotherapy with Psychotics," *Psychiatric Quarterly*, 24 (1950), 144–152.

Meyer, Adolf F. 1911. "The Nature and Conception of Dementia Praecox," *Journal of Abnormal Psychology*, 5 (1911), 274–285.

———1921–1922. "Constructive Formulation of Schizophrenia," *American Journal of Psychiatry*, 1 (1922), 355–364.

Minkowski, Eugene 1925. "La Genèse de la Notion de Schizophrénie et ses Caractères Essentiels," *Evolution Psychiatrique*, 1 (1925), 193–236.

——— 1927. "Sur le Rattachment des Lésions et des Processus Psychiques de la Schizophrénie à des Notions plus Générales," *Revue Française de Psychanalyse*, 1 (1927), 21–23.

——— 1929. "Kritische Analyse einiger Arbeiten über die Halluzinationen," *Nervenarzt*, 2 (1929), 406–414.

Modell, Arnold H. 1956. "Some Recent Psychoanalytic Theories of Schizophrenia," *Psychoanalytic Review*, 43 (1956), 181–194.

——— 1958. "The Theoretical Implications of Hallucinatory Experiences in Schizophrenia," *Journal of American Psychoanalitic Association*, 6 (1958), 442–480.

——— 1963. "Primitive Object Relationships and the Predisposition to Schizophrenia," *International Journal of Psycho-Analysis*, 44 (1963), 282–293.

Money, John 1963. "Cytogenic and Psychosexual Incongruities, with a Note on Space-Form Blindness," *American Journal of Psychiatry*, 119 (1963), 820–827.

Monke, J. V. 1964. Personal communication.

Montagu, Ashley 1961. "Culture and Mental Illness," *American Journal of Psychiatry*, 118 (1961), 15–23.

Montano, Guillermo 1965. "Factores Esquizoides de la Personalidad de un Escritor," paper presented before the Mexican Psychoanalytic Association, February, 1965, Mexico City, mimeographed.

Morichau-Beauchant, R. 1912. "Homosexualität und Paranoia," *Zentralblatt für Psychoanalyse und Psychotherapie*, 2 (1912), 174–176.

Morse, Robert, and Douglas Noble 1942. "Joint Endeavors of the Administrative Physician and Psychotherapist," *Psychiatric Quarterly*, 16 (1942), 578–585.

Mullahy, Patrick 1940. "A Theory of Interpersonal Relationships and the Evolution of Psychiatry," in H. S. Sullivan, *Conceptions of Modern Psychiatry*. Washington: The William A. White Psychiatric Foundation, 1947, pp. 119–147.

——— 1948. *Oedipus: Myth and Complex*. New York: Hermitage Press, 1948.

——— 1949. *A Study of Interpersonal Relations: New Contributions to Psychiatry*. New York: Hermitage Press, 1949.

Müller, Christian 1955. "Schizophrénie et Psychothérapie," *Revue Médicale de la Suisse Romande*, 85 (1955), 752–759.

——— 1955a. "Über Psychotherapie bei einem chronischen Schizophrenen," *Psyche* (Heidelberg), 9 (1955), 350–369.

——— 1958. "Psychotherapiedes Psychosen," in E. Stern (ed.), *Handbuch der klinischen Psychologie. Vol. 2: Die Psychotherapie in der Gegenwart*. Zurich: Rascher Verlag, 1958, pp. 350–367.

———, and Gaetano Bendetti 1965. *Psychotherapie der Schizophrenie*. Basel: Karger, 1965.

Myerson, Abraham 1939. "Theory and Principles of 'Total Push' Method in Chronic Schizophrenia," *American Journal of Psychiatry*, 95 (1939), 1197–1204.

Nacht, S. 1962. "The Curative Factors in Psychoanalysis," *International Journal of Psycho-Analysis*, 43 (1962), 206–212.

———, and Serge Lebovici 1955. "Indications et Contreindications de la Psychoanalyse," *Revue Française de Psychoanalyse*, 19 (1955), 135–204.

Namnum, Alfredo 1964. "Some Countertransference Problems in Psychotherapy with Schizophrenics," paper presented before the West Coast Psychoanalytic Societies, San Diego, California, October, 1964.

Nelken, Jan 1911. "Psychologische Untersuchungen an Dementia Praecox-Kranken," *Journal für Psychologie und Neurologie*, 18 (1911); reviewed by E. Hitschmann, *Zentralblatt für Psychoanalyse und Psychotherapie*, 2 (1912), 663–664.

——— 1912. "Analytische Beobachtungen über Phantasien eines Schizophrenen. *Jahrbuch für Psychoanalytische und Psychopathologische*

Forschung, 4 (1912), 504–562.
——— 1912a. Über Schizophrene Wortzerlegungen," *Zentralblatt für Psychoanalyse und Psychotherapie*, 2 (1912), 1–5.
Niederland, William G. 1959. "The 'Miracled-up' World of Schreber's Childhood," *Psychoanalytic Study of the Child*, 14 (1959), 383–413.
Nöllman, Jorge 1953. "Consideraciones Psicoanalíticas Acerca de un Enfermo Esquizofrénico con Mecanismos Hipocondriaco-Paranoideos," *Revista de Psicoanálisis*, 10 (1953), 37–74.
Nunberg, Herman 1921. "The Course of the Libidinal Conflict in a Case of Schizophrenia," in *Practice and Theory of Psychoanalysis*. New York: Nervous and Mental Disease Monographs, 1948, pp. 24–49.
——— 1932. *Principles of Psychoanalysis: Their Application to the Neuroses*. New York: International Universities Press, 1955.
——— 1937. "On the Theory of the Results of Psychoanalysis," *International Journal of Psycho-Analysis*, 18 (1937), 161–169.
O'Malley, Mary 1923. "Transference and Some of its Problems in Psychoses," *Psychoanalytic Review*, 10 (1923), 1–25.
Ophuijsen, J. H. W. van 1920. "On the Origin of the Feeling of Persecution," *International Journal of Psycho-Analysis*, 1 (1920), 235–239.
Opler, Marvin K., (ed.) 1956. *Culture, Society and Human Values*. Springfield, Ill.: Charles C Thomas, 1956.
Oppenheim, Hans 1912. "Zur Frage der Genese des Eifersuchtswahnes," *Zentralblatt für Psychoanalyse und Psychotherapie*, 2 (1912), 67–77.
Orr, Douglas W. 1954. "Transference and Countertransference," *Journal of the American Psychoanalytic Association*, 2 (1954), 621–670.
Osnato, Michael 1918. "A Critical Review of the Pathogenesis of Dementia Praecox, with a Discussion of the Relation of Psychoanalytical Principles," *American Journal of Insanity*, 75 (1918), 411–432.
Pasche, F., and M. Renard 1956. "The Reality of the Object and Economic Point of View," *International Journal of Psycho-Analysis*, 37 (1956), 282–285.
Payne, Charles R. 1913–1914. "Some Freudian Contributions to the Paranoia Problem," *Critical Digest*, 1 (1914), 76–93, 187–202, 308–321, 445–451.
——— 1915. "Some Freudian Contributions to the Paranoia Problem," *Critical Digest*, 2 (1915), 93–101, 200–202.
Paz, Carlos A. 1963. "Asciedades Psicóticas: Complejo de Édipo y Elaboración de la Posición Depresiva en un Border-line," paper read before the Argentina Psychoanalytic Association, Buenos Aires, December, 1963, mimeographed.
Penrose, Lionel S. 1931. "A Case of Schizophrenia of Long Duration," *British Journal of Medical Psychology*, 11 (1931), 1–31.
Perrier, François 1955. "Sens du Transfert dans les Psychothérapies de Schizophrènes," *Acta Psychotherapeutica, Psychosomatica et Orthopaedagogica* (Basel), 3, suppl. (1955), 266–272.
Perry, Helen S., and Mary L. Gawel (eds.) 1953. *The Interpersonal Theory of Psychiatry*. New York: Norton, 1953.
Piaget, Jean 1924. *The Language and Thought of the Child*. New York: Harcourt, Brace, 1930.
——— 1952. *The Language and Thought of the Child*. London: Routledge and Kegan Paul, Ltd., 1952.

Pichon-Rivière, Enrique 1946. "Contribución a la Teoría Psicoanalítica de la Esquizofrenia," *Revista de Psicoanálisis*, 4 (1946), 1–22.
——— 1947. "Psicoanálisis de la Esquizofrenia," *Revista de Psicoanálisis*, 5 (1947), 293–304.
——— 1952. "Quelques Observations sur le Transfert Chez des Patients Psychotiques," *Revue Française de Psychoanalyse*, 16 (1952), 254–262.
——— 1961. "Algunas Observaciones Sobre la Transferencia en los Pacientes Psicóticos," *Revisa de Psicoanálisis*, 18 (1961).
Pious, William 1949. "The Pathogenic Process in Schizophrenia. (1) Ego Psychology. (2) Relation of Super-Ego to Aggression and Ego Organization. (3) Instinct Theory," *Bulletin of the Menninger Clinic*, 13 (1949), 152–159.
———1961. "A Hypothesis About the Nature of Schizophrenic Behavior," in A. Burton (ed.), *Psychotherapy of the Psychoses*. New York: Basic Books, 1961, pp. 43–68.
Pokorny, Alex D. 1965. "Problems in Psychiatric Classification," *International Journal of Neuropsychology*, 1 (1965), 161–167.
Polatin, Philip 1948. "Schizophrenia," *Medical Clinics of North America*, 32 (1948), 623–629.
——— 1949. "Pseudoneurotic Forms of Schizophrenia," *Psychiatric Quarterly*, 23 (1949), 248–276.
Racamier, P. C. 1956. "Psychothérapie Psychanalytique des Psychoses," in S. Nacht (ed.), *La Psychanalyse d'Aujourd'hui*. Paris: P.U.F., 1956, vol. 2, 575–690.
Rangell, Leo 1954. "Similarities and Differences Between Psychoanalysis, and Dynamic Psychotherapy," *Journal of the American Psychoanalytic Association*, 2 (1954), 734–744.
Rank, Otto 1926. *Will Therapy: An Analysis of the Therapeutic Process in Terms of Relationship*. New York: Knopf, 1936.
——— 1929. *Will Therapy in Truth and Reality*. New York: Knopf, 1945.
Rascovsky, Arnaldo, Susana L. deFerrer, Angel Garma, Susana A. de Mendes, Carlos Plata Mujica, Hernando Pastrana Borrero, Matilda I. W. de Rascovsky, Jaime Tomas, and Simon Wencelblat, 1960. *El Psiquismo Fetal*. Buenos Aires: Paidos, 1960.
Reich, Wilhelm 1933. *Character Analysis*. New York: Orgone Institute Press, 1945.
Reichard, Suzanne 1956. "A Re-Examination of 'Studies in Hysteria,'" *Psychoanalytic Quarterly*, 25 (1956), 155–177.
———, and Carl G. Tillman 1952. "Patterns of Parent-Child Relationships in Schizophrenia," *Psychiatry*, 13 (1952), 247–257.
Reider, Norman 1957. "Transference Psychosis," *Journal of Hillside Hospital*, 6 (1957), 131–149.
Rickman, John 1926. "A Survey: The Development of the Psycho-Analytical Theory of the Psychoses, 1894–1926," *British Journal of Medical Psychology*, 6 (1926), 270–294.
——— 1927. "A Survey: The Development of the Psycho-Analytical Theory of the Psychoses, 1894–1926," *British Journal of Medical Psychology*, 7 (1927), 94–124, 321–374.
Riklin, Franz 1906. "Beitrag zur Psychologie des Kataleptischen Zustande bei Katatonie," *Psychiatrisch-neurologische Wochenschrift* (1906),

32–33, reviewed by C. G. Jung, *Jahrbuch für Psychoanalytische und Psychopathologische Forschung*, 2 (1910), 384–385.

——— 1907. "Über Gefängnispsychosen," *Psychiatrisch-neurologische Wochenschrift*, 9 (1907), 227–230, 269–273, 280–282, 288–289, 299–300, 315–317, 336–337.

——— 1910. Über Gefängnispsychosen," *Psychiatrisch-neurologische Wochenschrift*, 11 (1910), 30–37.

Rin, Hsion, and Tsung-yi Lin 1962. "Mental Illness Among Formosan Aborigines as Compared with the Chinese in Taiwan," *Journal of Mental Science*, 108 (1962), 134–146.

Rin, Hsion, Hung-ming Chu, and Tsung-yi Lin 1965. *Psychophysiological Reactions of a Rural and Suburban Population in Taiwan*. Manuscript.

Riviere, Joan 1936. "On the Genesis of Psychical Conflict in Earliest Infancy," *International Journal of Psycho-Analysis*, 17 (1936), 395–422.

Rolla, Edgardo 1957. "Análisis de una Esquizofrenia," *Revista de Psicoanálisis*, 14 (1957), 72–75.

——— 1958. "Notes Sobre el Psicoanálisis de Psicóticos," *Acta Neuropsiquiátrica Argentina*, 4 (1958), 179–186.

——— 1959. "Actualización, Psicoanálisis de Psicóticos," *Revista de Psicoanálisis*, 16 (1959), 72–83.

——— 1964. "La Alucinación como Pseudo-Abstracción," *Revista de Psicoanálisis*, 21 (1964), 22–37.

Rollman-Branch, Hilda 1960. "On the Question of Primary Object Need: Ethological and Psychoanalytic Considerations," *Journal of the American Psychoanalytic Association*, 8 (1960), 686–702.

Romm, May 1957. "Transient Psychotic Episodes During Psychoanalysis," *Journal of the American Psychoanalytic Association*, 5 (1957), 325–341.

Rose, Arnold M., (ed.) 1955. *Mental Health and Mental Disorder*. New York: Norton, 1955.

Rosen, John N. 1947. "The Treatment of Schizophrenic Psychosis by Direct Analytic Therapy," *Psychiatric Quarterly*, 21 (1947), 3–37.

——— 1962. *Direct Analytic Therapy*. New York: Grune and Stratton, 1962.

——— 1964. "Psychoanalysis Direct and Indirect," A Doylestown Foundation Paper. Doylestown, Pa.: The Doylestown Foundation, 1964.

Rosenfeld, Herbert A. 1947. "Analysis of a Schizophrenic State with Depersonalization," *International Journal of Psycho-Analysis*, 28 (1947), 13–19.

——— 1950. "Notes on the Psychopathology of Confusional States in Chronic Schizophrenia," 31 (1950), 132–137.

——— 1952. "Notes on the Psycho-Analysis of the Superego Conflict of an Acute Schizophrenic Patient," *International Journal of Psycho-Analysis*, 33 (1952), 111–131.

——— 1952a. "Transference-Phenomena and Transference-Analysis in an Acute Catatonic Schizophrenic Patient," *International Journal of Psycho-Analysis*, 33 (1952), 457–464.

——— 1954. "Considerations Regarding the Psycho-Analytic Approach to Acute and Chronic Schizophrenia," *International Journal of Psycho-Analysis*, 35 (1954), 135–160.

——— 1956. "Bemerkungen zur Psychopathologie der Schizophrenie," *Psyche* (Heidelberg), 10 (1956), 497–509.

——— 1959. "An Investigation into the Psycho-Analytic Theory of Depression," *International Journal of Psycho-Analysis*, 40 (1959), 105–129.

Rosenthal, David, (ed.) 1963. *The Genain Quadruplets, A Case Study and Theoretical Analysis of Heredity and Environment in Schizophrenia.* New York: Basic Books, 1963.

Ryckoff, Irving M., Juliana Day, and Lyman C. Wynne 1958. "The Maintenance of Stereotyped Roles in the Families of Schizophrenics," paper presented before the American Psychiatric Association, San Francisco, May, 1958.

Rycroft, Charles 1960. "The Analysis of a Paranoid Personality," *International Journal of Psycho-Analysis*, 41 (1960), 59–69.

Sachs, Wulf 1947. *Black Hamlet.* Boston: Little, Brown and Co., 1947.

Sagredo, Oscar 1955. "Psicoterapía de Esquizofrenia (Metodo de Rosen)," *Archivos Médicos de Cuba*, 6 (1955), 173–193.

——— 1955a. "Psychotherapy of Psychosis: A Comparative Study," *Archivos de los Hospitales Universitários* (Havana), 6 (1955); abstr. *Psychoanalytic Quarterly*, 24 (1955), 475.

Salzman, Leon 1964. "Socio-Psychological Theories in Psychoanalysis: Karen Horney and Harry Stack Sullivan," *American Journal of Psychoanalysis*, 24 (1964), 131–144.

Sandford, Beryl 1952. "An Obsessional Man's Need to Be 'Kept,'" *International Journal of Psycho-Analysis*, 33 (1952), 114–152.

Saussure, Raymond de 1924. "Diagnostic Différentiel entre la Folie Maniaque Dépressive et la Catatonie," *Encéphale*, 19 (1934), 73–82.

Savage, Charles 1958. "Problems and Countertransference of the Analyst in the Treatment of Schizophrenia," paper presented before the American Psychoanalytic Association, San Francisco, May, 1958.

Scarizza, Spartaco, (ed.) 1965. *Proceedings of the First International Congress of Direct Psychoanalysis*, September 11–12, 1964, Rome, Italy. A Doylestown Foundation Paper. Doylestown, Pa.: The Doylestown Foundation, 1965.

Schaffer, Leslie, Lyman C. Wynne, Juliana Day, Irving M. Ryckoff, and Alexander Halperin 1962. "On the Nature and Sources of the Psychiatrist's Experience with the Family of the Schizophrenic," *Psychiatry*, 25 (1962), 32–45.

Scheflen, Albert E. 1961. *A Psychotherapy of Schizophrenia. A Study of Direct Analysis.* Springfield, Ill.: Charles C Thomas, 1961.

Schindler, Raoul 1955. "Übertragungsbildung und Übertragungsführung in der Psychotherapie mit Schizophrenen," *Acta Psychotherapeutica, Psychosomatica et Orthopaedagogica* (Basel), 3, suppl. (1955), 337–344.

——— 1957. "Über die grundsatzliche Stellung der Psychotherapie bei Psychosen," *Acta Psychotherapeutica, Psychosomatica et Orthopaedagogica* (Basel), 5 (1957), 147–155.

Schultz-Henkel, Harald, 1952. *Das Problem der Schizophrenie: Analytische Psychotherapie und Psychose.* Stuttgart: Thieme, 1952.

Schumacher, Willi 1963. "Zur Methodologie der Psychatrischen Diagnostic und Forschung," *Biblioteca Psychiatrica et Neurologica*, Fasc. 121 (1963).

Schwartz, Morris S., and Alfred H. Stanton 1950. "A Social Psychological Study of Incontinence," *Psychiatry*, 13 (1950), 399–416.

Schwing, Gertrud 1940. *A Way to the Soul of the Mentally Ill*. New York: International Universities Press, 1954.

Scott, W. Clifford M. 1948. "Notes on the Psychopathology of Anorexia Nervosa," *British Journal of Medical Psychology*, 21 (1948), 241–247.

——— 1949. "Progress of Psychoanalysis in Great Britain," *British Medical Bulletin*, 6 (1949), 31–35.

Searles, Harold F. 1959. "Integration and Differentiation in Schizophrenia: An Over-All View," in *Collected Papers on Schizophrenia and Related Subjects*. New York: International Universities Press, 1965, pp. 317–348.

——— 1959a. "Integration and Differentiation in Schizophrenia," *Journal of Nervous and Mental Disease*, 29 (December, 1959).

——— 1961. "Phases of Patient-Therapist Interaction in the Psychotherapy of Chronic Schizophrenia," *British Journal of Medical Psychology*, 34 (1961), 169.

——— 1962. "The Differentiation Between Concrete and Metaphorical Thinking in the Recovering Schizophrenic Patient," in *Collected Papers on Schizophrenia and Related States*. New York: International Universities Press, 1965, pp. 560–583.

——— 1963. "Transference Psychosis in the Psychotherapy of Chronic Schizophrenia," *International Journal of Psycho-Analysis*, 44 (1963), 249–291.

——— 1963a. "Transference Psychosis in the Psychotherapy of Chronic Schizophrenia," in *Collected Papers on Schizophrenia and Related States*. New York: International Universities Press, 1965, pp. 654–716.

——— 1964. "Direct Psychoanalytic Psychiatry, by John N. Rosen," *International Journal of Psycho-Analysis*, 45 (1964), 597–602.

——— 1964a. "The Contributions of Family Treatment to the Psychotherapy of Schizophrenia," in *Collected Papers on Schizophrenia and Related States*. New York: International Universities Press, 1965, pp. 717–752.

——— 1964b. In Spartaco Serizza (ed.), "Proceedings of the First International Congress of Direct Psychoanalysis," September 11–12, 1964, Rome, Italy. A Doylestown Foundation Paper. Doylestown, Pa.: The Doylestown Foundation, 1965.

——— 1965. In *Collected Papers on Schizophrenia and Related Subjects*. New York: International Universities Press, 1965.

Sechehaye, Marguerite A. 1947. *Symbolic Realization*. New York: International Universities Press, 1951.

——— 1955. *Die symbolische Wuncsherfülling. Darstellung einer neuen psychotherapeutischen Methode und Tagebuch der Kranken*. Bern: Hans Huber, 1955.

——— 1956. "The Transference in Symbolic Realization," *International Journal of Psycho-Analysis*, 37 (1956), 270–277.

——— 1957. " 'Affects' et Besoins Frustres Vus à travers les Dessins d'une Schizophrène," *Acta Neurologica et Psychiatrica Belgica*, 57 (1957), 972–992.

——— 1957a. "La Realization Symbolique, un Catalyseur de la Structuration du Moi Schizophrénique," *Acta Psychotherapeutica, Psychosomatica et Orthopaedagogica* (Basel), 5 (1957), 274–296.

Segal, Hanna 1950. "Some Aspects of the Analysis of a Schizophrenic," *International Journal of Psycho-Analysis*, 31 (1950), 268–278.

——— 1954. "A Note on Schizoid Mechanisms Underlying Phobia Formation," *International Journal of Psycho-Analysis*, 35 (1954), 238–241.

——— 1956. "Depression in the Schizophrenic," *International Journal of Psycho-Analysis*, 37 (1956), 339–343.

Seligman, C. G. 1929. "Temperament, Conflict and Psychosis in a Stone Age Population," *British Journal of Medical Psychology*, 9 (1929), 187–202.

Serota, H. M. 1964. "Home Movies of Early Childhood: Correlative Developmental Data in the Psychoanalysis of Adults," *Science*, 143 (1964), 1195.

Sharp, Ella 1930. "The Dynamics of the Methods of the Transference," in *Collected Papers on Psycho-Analysis*. London: Hogarth Press, 1950, pp. 53–56.

Sharp, Vernon H., Saul Glasner, Ivan I. Lederman, and Sheldon Wolfe 1964. "Sociopaths and Schizophrenics: A Comparison of Family Interactions," *Psychiatry*, 27 (1964), 127–134.

Shockley, Francis M. 1914. "The Role of Homosexuality in the Genesis of Paranoid Conditions," *Psychoanalytic Review*, 1 (1914), 431–438.

Silk, S. A. 1920. "Compensatory Mechanisms of Delusions and Hallucinations," *American Journal of Insanity*, 77 (1920), 523–542.

Simmel, Ernst 1909. *Kritischer Beitrag zur Aetiologie der Dementia Praecox* (dissertation). Rostock: Rats-und Universitäts-Buchdruckerei von Adlers Erben G.M.B.H.

Smith, Arnold L. 1965. "Schizophrenia: A Synthesis," *International Journal of Neuropsychology*, 1 (1965), 199–213.

Smythies, J. R. 1963. *Schizophrenia*. Springfield, Ill.: Charles C Thomas, 1963.

Sperling, Melitta 1955. "Psychosis and Psychosomatic Illness," *International Journal of Psycho-Analysis*, 36 (1955), 320–327.

Spitz, René A. 1946. "The Smiling Response," *Genetic Psychology Monograph*, 34 (1946), 57–125.

——— 1959. *A Genetic Field Theory of Ego Formation*. New York: International Universities Press, 1959.

Sprague, George S. 1937. "The Concept of Catatonia," *Psychiatric Quarterly*, 11 (1937), 222–236.

——— 1940. "Regression in Catatonia," *Journal of Nervous and Mental Disease*, 91 (1940), 566–578.

——— 1941. "The Force Concept in Schizophrenia," *Psychiatric Quarterly*, 15 (1941), 327–335.

——— 1942. "Deeper Levels of Regression," *Psychiatric Quarterly*, 16 (1942), 272–280.

Stabbs, Gerdhild von 1954. "Die Behandlung einer Schizophrenie unter besonderer Berücksichtigung der Handhabung der Übertragung,"

Acta Psychotherapeutica, Psychosomatica et Orthopaedagogica (Basel), 2 (1954), 314–333.

Standish, Christopher T., James Mann, and Doris Menzer 1950. "Some Aspects of the Psychopathology of Schizophrenia: Implications in Treatment," *Psychiatry*, 13 (1950), 439–445.

Stärcke, August 1904. *"Psychoschyis."* Amsterdam. Staatsdrukkerij, 1904.

——— 1920. "The Reversal of the Libido-Sign in Delusions of Persecution," *International Journal of Psycho-Analysis*, 1 (1920), 231–234.

——— 1921. *Psychoanalyse und Psychiatrie*. Leipzig, Vienna: Int. P. V., 1921.

——— 1928. "Zwanzig Minuten Schizophreniediskussion," *Psychiatrische en Neurologische Bladen*, 31 (1928), 484.

Staverenen, Herbert 1947. "Suggested Specificity of Certain Dynamics in a Case of Schizophrenia," *Psychiatry*, 10 (1947), 127–135.

Stengel, Erwin 1957. "Die Rolle der Psychoanalyse in der Behandlung der Psychosen, insbesondere der Schizophrenie," in P. Federn and H. Meng (eds.), *Das Psychoanaltische Volksbuch*. Bern: Hans Huber, 1957, pp. 305–311.

——— 1957a. "Schizofrenibegrepet," *Tidsskrift for den Norske Lægeforening*, 77 (1957), 1059–1062, 1079.

Stone, Leo 1954. "The Widening Scope of Indications for Psychoanalysis," *Journal of the American Psychoanalytic Association*, 2 (1954), 567–594.

——— 1955. "Two Avenues of Approach to the Schizophrenic Patient," *Journal of the American Psychoanalytic Association*, 3 (1955), 126–148.

——— 1963. *The Psychoanalytic Situation*. New York: International Universities Press, 1963.

Storch, Alfred 1922. *The Primitive Archaic Forms of Inner Experiences and Thought in Schizophrenia*. New York: Nervous and Mental Disease Publishing Co., 1924.

——— 1923. "Bewusstseinsebene und Wirklichkeitsbereiche in der Schizophrenie," *Zeitschrift für die gesamte Neurologie und Psychiatrie*, 82 (1923), 321–341.

——— 1927. "Das primitiv-mythische Denken und seine Beziehungen zur Psychopathologie," *Proceedings of the 8th International Congress on Psychology*. Groningen: Noordhoff, 1927, pp. 209–217.

——— 1930. "Die Welt der beginnenden Schizophrenie und die archäische Welt, Ein existential-analytischer Versuch," *Zeitschrift für gesamte Neurologie und Psychiatrie*, 127 (1930), 799–810.

——— 1947. "Die Daseinsfrage der Schizophrenen," *Schweizer Archiv für Neurologie und Psychiatrie*, 59 (1947), 330–385.

——— 1948. "Tod und Erneuerung in der Schizophrenen Daseinsumwandlung." *Archiv für Psychiatrie und Nervenkrankheiten*, 181 (1948), 275–293.

——— 1951. "Dasein und Welt im 'komishen' Wahn der Schizophrenen," *Schweizer Archiv für Neurologie und Psychiatrie*, 68 (1951), 192–193.

——— 1957. "Zur Schizophrenen Abwandlung der Struktor des Menschseins, erläutert an einem psychotherapeutisch behandelten Krankheitsfall," *Acta Psychotherapeutica Psychosomatica et Orthopaedagogica*, 5 (1957), 220–231.

———, and Caspar Kulemkampf 1950. "Zum Verständnis des 'Weltuntergangs' bei den Schizophrenen," *Nervenarzt*, 21 (1950), 102–108.

Strachey, Alix 1941. "A Note on the Use of the Word 'Internal,'" *International Journal of Psycho-Analysis*, 22 (1941), 37–43.

Sullivan, Charles T. 1963. "Freud and Fairbairn: Two Theories of Ego Psychology." A Doylestown Foundation Paper. Doylestown, Pa.: The Doylestown Foundation, 1963.

Sullivan, Harry Stack 1925. "Affective Experience in Early Schizophrenia," *American Journal of Psychiatry*, 6 (1926–1927), 467–484.

——— 1927. "The Onset of Schizophrenia," *American Journal of Psychiatry*, 7 (1927), 105–134.

——— 1928. "Tentative Criteria of Malignancy in Schizophrenia," *American Journal of Psychiatry*, 7 (1928), 759–788.

——— 1929. "Research in Schizophrenia," *American Journal of Psychiatry*, 9 (1929), 553–567.

——— 1931. "Environmental Factors in Etiology and Course under Treatment of Schizophrenia," *Medical Journal Record*, 133 (1931), 19–22.

——— 1931a. "The Modified Psychoanalytic Treatment of Schizophrenia," *American Journal of Psychiatry*, 11 (1931), 519–540.

——— 1940. *Conceptions of Modern Psychiatry.* Washington: William A. White Psychiatry Foundation, 1947.

——— 1947. "Therapeutic Investigations in Schizophrenia," *Psychiatry*, 10 (1947), 121–125.

——— 1947a. "Notes on Investigation, Therapy and Education in Psychiatry and Their Relations to Schizophrenia," *Psychiatry*, 10 (1947), 271–280.

Szalita-Pemow, Alberta B. 1955. "The 'Intuitive Process' and Its Relations to Work with Schizophrenics," *Journal of the American Psychoanalytic Association*, 3 (1955), 7–18.

——— 1958. "Regression and Perception in Psychotic States," *Psychiatry*, 21 (1958), 53–63.

Szurek, Stanislaus, and Adelaide M. Johnson 1954. "Etiology of Antisocial Behavior in Delinquents and Psychopaths," *Journal of the American Medical Association*, 154 (1954), 814–817.

Tausk, Victor 1919. "On the Origin of the 'Influencing Machine' in Schizophrenia," *Psychoanalytic Quarterly*, 2 (1933), 519–556.

Ter-Ogannessien, Elizabeth 1921. "Psychoanalyse einer Katatonie," *Psychiatrische-Neurologische Wochenschrift*, 14 (1921), 299–304, 309–312.

Thompson, Clara 1943. "The Therapeutic Technique of Sandor Ferenczi: A Comment," *International Journal of Psycho-Analysis*, 24 (1943), 64–66.

——— 1950. "Introduction," in Sandor Ferenczi, *Sex and Psychoanalysis.* New York: Basic Books, 1950.

——— 1952. "Sullivan and Psychoanalysis," in P. Mullahy (ed.), *Contributions of Harry Stack Sullivan.* New York: Hermitage House, 1952, pp. 101–115.

——— 1955. "Introduction," in Sandor Ferenczi, *Final Contributions to the Problems and Methods of Psychoanalysis.* New York: Basic Books, 1955.

Tolentino, Isidor I. 1956. "Aspetti Psicogenetici della Schizofrenia. Studio Clinico," *Revista Sperimentale di Freniatria e Medicina Legale della Alienazioni Mentali*, 80 (1956), 1–10.

——— 1956a. "Azione Precipitante di Alcuni Traumi Psichici negli Episodi Schizofrenici: Contributo Clinico," *Revisa di Psicoanalisi*, 2 (1956), 123–130.

——— 1957. "Contributo Clinico al Problema Psicopatologico della Paranoia," *Rassegna di Neuropsichiatria*, 11 (1957), 1–12.

——— 1957a. "Problemi di Technica in Psicoterapia: I. Il Controtransfert," *Rassegna di Studi Psichiatrici*, 46 (1957), 681–730.

———, and B. Callieri 1957. "Contributo Clinico all'Impostazione Psicodinamica della Depersonalizazione," *Revista Sperimentale di Freniatria e Medicina Legale della Alienazioni Mentali*, 81 (1957), 615–639.

Tower, Lucia E. 1956. "Countertransference," *Journal of the American Psychoanalytic Association*, 4 (1956), 224–255.

——— 1947. "Management of Paranoid Trends in Treatment of a Post-Psychotic Obsessional Condition," *Psychiatry*, 10 (1947), 137–141.

Towne, Robert D., Sheldon L. Messinger, and Harold Sampson 1962. "Schizophrenia and the Marital Family, Accommodations to Symbiosis," *Family Process*, 1 (1962), 304–318.

Vanggaard, Thorkil 1955. "A Discussion of the Basic Principles of Psychoanalytically Oriented Psychotherapy of Schizophrenia," *Acta Psychiatrica Scandinavica*, 30 (1955), 507–527.

——— 1955a. "Om schizofrene Grænsetilfælde. Bidrag til Schizofrenidiagnosens Problematik," *Nordisk Psykiatrisk Medlemsblad*, 9 (1955), 1–16.

Van Wulfften Palthe, B.M. 1940. "Over de Bezetenheid," *Geneeskundig Tijdschrift voor Nederlansch-Indie*, Afl. 36, 80 (1940), 2123–2153.

Vowinckel, Edith 1930. "Der heutige Stand der psychiatrischen Schizophrenieforschung," *Internationale Zeitschrift für Psychoanalyse*, 16 (1930), 471–491.

Waals, H. G. van der 1954. "Therapy of Schizophrenia," *International Journal of Psycho-Analysis*, 35 (1954), 154–156.

Waelder, Robert 1924. "The Psychoses: Their Mechanisms and Accessibility to Influence," *International Journal of Psycho-Analysis*, 6 (1924), 254–281.

——— 1926. "Schizophrenic and Creative Thinking," *International Journal of Psycho-Analysis*, 7 (1926), 366–376.

——— 1937. "The Problem of the Genesis of Psychical Conflict in Earliest Infancy," *International Journal of Psycho-Analysis*, 18 (1937), 406–473.

——— 1965. Personal communication.

Wallerstein, Robert S. 1965. "Reconstruction and Mastery in the Transference Psychosis," *Journal of the American Psychoanalytic Association.*

Wanke, Georg 1919. *Uber die im gewöhnlichen Leben wichtigste Geisteskrankheit: Jugendirresein, Dementia Praecox (Kraepelin), Schizophrenie (Bleuler), Paraphrenie (Magna, Freud), Zweisinn (Bresler) für Ärtze, Juristen und Erzieher*. Halle: C. Marhold, 1919.

——— 1922. Über ambulatorische oder Anstalts (Sanatoriums) Behandlung in der Psychoanalyse," *Internationale Zeitschrift für Psychoanalyse*, 8 (1922), 494–495.

Washburn, Sherwood L. 1965. Personal communication.

Wassell, B. Bohdan 1959. *Group Psychoanalysis.* New York: Philosophical Library, 1959.

Weigert-Vowinckel, Edith 1936. "A Contribution to the Theory of Schizophrenia," *International Journal of Psycho-Analysis*, 17 (1936), 190–201.

Weiss, Edoardo 1952. "Introduction," in P. Federn, *Ego Psychology and the Psychoses.* New York: Basic Books, 1952.

Wexler, Milton 1951. "The Structural Problem in Schizophrenia: The Role of the Internal Object," *Bulletin of the Menninger Clinic*, 15 (1951), 221–234.

——— 1951a. "The Structural Problem in Schizophrenia. Therapeutic Implications," *International Journal of Psycho-Analysis*, 37 (1951), 157–166.

——— 1953. "Psychological Distance as a Factor in the Treatment of a Schizophrenia Patient," in R. M. Lindner (ed.), *Explorations in Psychoanalysis: Essays in Honor of Theodor Reik, on the Occasion of his Sixty-Fifth Birthday.* New York: Julian Press, pp. 157–172.

——— 1965. "Discussion of Gustav Bychowski's Paper, *Obsessive Compulsive Façade in Schizophrenia*," *24th International Psychoanalytic Congress*, Amsterdam, 1965.

——— 1965a. "Working Through in the Therapy of Schizophrenia," *International Journal of Psycho-Analysis*, 46 (1965), 279–286.

White, Mary Julian 1952. "Sullivan and Treatment," in P. Mullahy (ed.), *The Contributions of Harry Stack Sullivan.* New York: Hermitage House, 1952, pp. 117–150.

White, William A. 1910. "The Etiology of Dementia Praecox," *Journal of the American Medical Association*, 46 (1910), 1519–1521.

——— 1910a. "The Diagnostics of Dementia Praecox," *Journal of Nervous and Mental Disease*, 37 (1910), 139–144.

——— 1921. "Some Considerations Bearing on the Diagnosis and Treatment of Dementia Praecox," *Psychoanalytic Revue*, 8 (1921), 417–422.

——— 1926. "The Language of Schizophrenia," *Archives of Neurology and Psychiatry*, 16 (1926), 395–413.

Wholey, Cornelius C. 1916. "A Psychosis Presenting Schizophrenic and Freudian Mechanisms with Scientific Clearness," *American Journal of Insanity*, 73 (1916), 583–595.

Will, Otto Allen, Jr. 1959. "Human Relatedness and the Schizophrenic Reaction," *Psychiatry*, 22 (1959), 205–223.

——— 1961. "Process, Psychotherapy and Schizophrenia," in A. Burton (ed.), *Psychotherapy of the Psychoses.* New York: Basic Books, 1961, pp. 10–42.

——— 1964. "Treatment of Schizophrenia," presented at a Staff Meeting of the University of Illinois, Department of Psychiatry, May 1964.

Wilmanns, Karl 1922. "Die Schizophrenie," *Zeitschrift für die gesamte Neurologie und Psychiatrie*, 78 (1922), 4–5.

Winkler, W. T. 1954. "Zum Begriff der 'Ich-Anachorese' beim schizophrenen Erleben," *Archiv für Psychiatrie und Nervenkrankheiten vereinigt mit Zeitschrift für die gesamte Neurologie und Psychiatrie,* 192 (1954), 234–240.

——— 1957. "Bericht über den Verlaf einer psychotherapeutischen Behandlung bei einer an Katatonie leidenden Patientin," *Acta Psychotherapeutica et Psychosomatica et Orthopaedagogica,* 5 (1957), 162–193.

———, and H. Hafner 1954. "Kontakt und Übertragung bei der Psychotherapie Schizophrener," *Zeitschrift für Psychotherapie und Medizinische Psychologie,* 4 (1954), 179–184.

———, and S. Wieser 1959. "Die Ich-Mythisierung als Abwehrmassnahme des Ich, dargestellt am Beispiel des Wahneinfalles von der jungfräulichen Emfängnis und Geburt bei paraphrenen Episoden," *Nervenarzt,* 30 (1959), 75–81.

Winnicott, Donald W. 1949. "Hate in the Countertransference," *International Journal of Psycho-Analysis,* 30 (1949).

——— 1953. "Transitional Objects and Transitional Phenomena," *International Journal of Psycho-Analysis,* 34 (1953), 89–97.

——— 1954. "Mind and Its Relation to the Psyche Soma," *British Journal of Medical Psychology,* 37 (1954).

——— 1955. "Metapsychological and Clinical Aspects of Regression Within the Psycho-Analytical Setup," *International Journal of Psycho-Analysis,* 36 (1955).

——— 1958. "Psycho-Analysis and the Sense of Guilt," in *The Maturational Processes and the Facilitating Environment.* New York: International Universities Press, 1963, pp. 15–28.

——— 1958a. *Collected Papers. Through Pediatrics to Psycho-Analysis.* London: Tavistock, 1958.

——— 1960. "The Theory of the Parent-Infant Relationship," *International Journal of Psycho-Analysis,* 41 (1960), 585–596.

——— 1963. *The Maturational Processes and the Facilitating Environment.* New York: International Universities Press, 1963.

Winston, Ellen 1935. "The Assumed Increase of Mental Illness," *American Journal of Sociology,* 40 (1935), 427–439.

Wisdom, John O. 1962. "Comparison and Development of the Psycho-Analytical Theories of Melancholia," *International Journal of Psycho-Analysis,* 43 (1962), 113–132.

Wulff, M. 1909. "Beitrag zur Psychologie der Dementia Praecox," *Zeitschrift für die gesamte Neurologie und Psychiatrie*; reviewed by K. Abraham, *Jahrbuch für Psychoanalytische und Psychopathologische Forschung,* 1 (1909), 594.

Wynne, Lyman C., and Margaret T. Singer 1963. "Thought Disorder and Family Relationships of Schizophrenics. I. Research Strategy," *American Archives of General Psychiatry,* 9 (1963), 191–198.

——— 1963a. "Thought Disorder and Family Relationships of Schizophrenics. II. A Classification of Forms of Thinking," *American Archives of General Psychiatry,* 9 (1963), 199–206.

Zapparoli, Giovanni C. 1957. "Note Sui Meccanismi Metapsicologici della Schizofrenia," *Revista Psicoanalisi,* 3 (1957), 107–150.

Zeigarnik B. 1927. "Über das Behalten von erledigten und unerledigten Handlungen," *Psychologische Forschung. Zeitschrift für allgemeine Psychologie, Ethnologie und medizinische Psychologie,* 9 (1927), 1–5.

Zetzel, Elizabeth R. 1953. "The Depressive Position," in P. Greenacre (ed.), *Affective Disorders*. New York: International Universities Press, 1953, pp. 84–116.

——— 1956. "An Approach to the Relation Between Concept and Content in Psychoanalytic Theory (with Special Reference to the Work of Melanie Klein and Her Followers)," *Psychoanalytic Study of the Child*, 11 (1956), 99–121.

——— 1960. "Criteria for Analyzability," panel of the American Psychoanalytic Association, December 1960.

——— 1965. "Additional 'Notes upon a Case of Infantile Obsessional Neurosis': Freud 1909," paper presented at the 24th International Psychoanalytical Congress, Amsterdam, July 1965.

Zilboorg, Gregory 1931. "The Dark Ages of Psychiatric History," *Journal of Nervous and Mental Disease*, 74 (1931), 610–635.

——— 1935. *The Medical Man and the Witch During the Renaissance*. Baltimore: Johns Hopkins Press, 1935.

——— 1954. Personal communication.

———, and George W. Henry 1941. *A History of Medical Psychology*. New York: Norton, 1941.

Index

A

B